Life after Fifty

A RETIREMENT HAN

PENNY TREADWELL

1 159 6720

PENGUIN BOOKS

PENGUIN BOOKS

Published by the Penguin Group
27 Wrights Lane, London W8 5TZ, England
Penguin Books USA Inc., 375 Hudson Street, New York, New York 10014, USA
Penguin Books Australia Ltd, Ringwood, Victoria, Australia
Penguin Books Canada Ltd, 10 Alcorn Avenue, Toronto, Ontario, Canada M4V 1B4
Penguin Books (NZ) Ltd, 182–190 Wairau Road, Auckland 10, New Zealand

Penguin Books Ltd, Registered Offices: Harmondsworth, Middlesex, England

First published 1992
10 9 8 7 6 5 4 3 2 1

The moral right of the author has been asserted

Printed in England by Clays Ltd, St Ives plc
Filmset in Monophoto Plantin 10½/12½ pt

To the memory of my mother and father; if I had understood them better, I could perhaps have helped them more

Contents

Acknowledgements

When I began work on *Life After Fifty*, in January 1988, it was on the understanding that I would be working with a co-author, Frank Milward. We had each separately and simultaneously approached the publishers with outlines for a book on ageing and retirement and our editors brought us together. It seemed an ideal partnership. Frank was sixty-five years old, married, with three grown-up children, and as his age at the time indicates, he was himself on the brink of retiring from his job as Community Relations Adviser for Jaguar Cars in Coventry. I was forty-seven, married, with five teenagers. While Frank's expertise lay in planning life before and after retirement, my particular interest is centred on the psychology of ageing. A few months after the start of our collaboration and shortly after his own retirement, Frank collapsed and died while on holiday with his wife in France. It was a terrible blow, not only to me personally but to the project as a whole, because despite my efforts to focus on the practical material relating to retirement, I feel that the book would have benefited from both his professional and personal experience. I am most grateful to Frank's widow, Irene, for allowing me to reproduce her husband's 'Check-lists' at the end of some of the chapters. I hope readers will find them as useful a guide as I did.

Members of the public who have helped shape this book are many and varied, and do not conform to any particular type of social background; it would be surprising if readers were not able to relate to any of the experiences recounted here to highlight a situation in their own lives. The contributors can roughly be divided between those who have been willing to share their personal experiences and those who have so generously given up precious time to offer their professional opinion and advice. This balance between experience and expertise has created a picture of old age that is both realistic and essentially optimistic. It is true that life does not automatically improve with age, but neither need it automatically change for the worse.

My gratitude in the first instance goes to those men and women who were willing to reveal anonymously intimate aspects of their lives and feelings. Without their confidence and generosity, the book could not have been written. In retrospect, some described their interviews with a relative stranger as 'a release' or 'quite therapeutic', while others acquiesced but found the process rather painful, occasionally insisting on looking at the manuscript and re-ordering their own words. To all of them, I should like to express my most profound thanks for their cooperation.

Such a book as this requires an enormous amount of research into areas where the writer sets out knowing next to nothing. For example, just to cover one item – hormone replacement therapy in Chapter 5 – the trail led from a newspaper article to a two-day conference on aspects of gynaecology and the ageing process, and no less than five interviews with members of the medical profession, followed by discussions with several women who were either undergoing the treatment or wanted to do so. Without the help and guidance of doctors, psychiatrists, social workers, carers, counsellors and many others involved in various aspects of the retirement industry, I could not have advanced in any direction. I owe the following men and women a great debt of gratitude, especially those who were willing to talk to me, often for long periods of time which must have seemed to them somewhat unrewarding:

Professor Anthea Tinker, Dr Ian Robertson, Dr Morris Notelovitz, Dr Ignac Fogelman, Glenn Lyons, Dr David Fenton, Professor Alex Comfort, Professor D. B. Bromley, Dr James O'Brian, Dr Camille Wortman, Dr William Evans, Dr Seymour Perlin, Dr H. B. Gibson, Professor Anthony Clare, Dr Jeremy Gilkes, Alan McKinna, FRCS, Dr Alan Kingdon, Jan Stanek, FRCS, Dr Joe Kearns, Malcolm Whitehead, FRCOG, Dr Julia Montgomery, Dr John Ellerington, Dr John Kellett, Dr Jack Dominian, Dr Robin Skynner, Penny Mansfield, Evelyn Cleavely, Rosemary Kent, Roy Johnson, Shelly L. Anderson,

Carlton Nogle, staff of the Abbeyfields Society, the staff at St Joseph's Hospice, Cherry Hughes and Pamela Milson of Marks and Spencer PLC, the Greater London Association for Pre-Retirement, Teresa Gorman, MP, Karen Atkinson, Gillian Davis, Susi Madron, Rowena Paxton, Pauline Hyde, Bridget Litchfield, Dr Robert Rose, Gillian Douglas and Nigel Lowe, Morlais Price and John Moysey of the Money Management Council whose financial advice was indispensable; Sister Jennifer, the staff and residents of St Mary's Convent and Nursing Home, especially Miss Winifred Smith whose company (and coffee) I continue to value and enjoy; and my friend, Mrs Raimond 'Petey' Cerf, an octogenarian whose passionate campaign to improve the quality of life for elderly people in the mostly privately owned residential homes in the United States has taught me so much.

I should also like to acknowledge the help I received from Rosemary Brown's annual publication, *Good Retirement Guide*. It has proved a gold-mine of useful information and I would recommend it to anyone either retired or on the threshold of retirement.

The poem 'Crabbit Old Age' was found in the bedside locker of an elderly patient after her death in hospital. The nurse who found it took it home and it was passed on to me by my daughter Kati from friends of hers who knew my interest. Unfortunately I have been unable to trace the nurse and have not managed to contact the anonymous writer's family. If anyone should recognize the poem, we would be pleased to hear from them.

Laugh, and the world not only laughs with you but it also finds you more lovable. My son Ross, who has a developing interest in social work and a talent for making friends, is currently working in the day-care centre of a hospital geriatric unit. His job is to provide entertainment in whatever way he chooses. Of his clients he says, 'It's hard to make them laugh – but not impossible. It is such a pleasure to see them enjoying themselves when I really get it right.' A sense of humour is an asset at any age, but in old age it is an indispensable support. Ross's experiences have taught me how laughter and good humour manage to bridge the generation gaps and I am grateful to him for sharing them with me.

Running throughout the book, the reader will find a single thread – namely, when in doubt, adrift, unhappy, anxious or depressed, do not hesitate to seek help and advice. I have learned to have no such hesitation and should like to take this opportunity to thank Dr Michael Gormley and Dr Peter Schoenberg for their help in times of stress. I should also like to express my gratitude to my husband, Tom, who encouraged me to be a writer and who continues to support me every step of the way.

The book in its final form owes so much to the work of my editors, Karen Mitchell and Esther Sidwell. Their guidance has proved invaluable and I am deeply grateful to them both.

Note. Prices, subscriptions, and so on are subject to change and are included as an indication only.

Part I
The Way Ahead

1 Retirement and the Rewards of Early Planning

> Psychologically, we age as we have always lived. The implications, therefore, are clear. If we want to do it well, we had better start preparing right now.   Dr Anthony Clare

This chapter looks at the problems and the pleasures of living a new lifestyle and discusses the factors which can help to create a successful retirement and lay the foundations for a rewarding old age.

The Third Age: the Age of Retirement

Les Universités du Troisième Âge originated in France in the 1970s and became established in Britain with the foundation of the University of the Third Age in Cambridge in 1981. Now the term, 'the Third Age', has come to describe that time of life when retirement begins and the family is concentrated on the couple or single parent whose adult children are living independently.

Although the statutory age of retirement remains at sixty for women and sixty-five for men – and the vast majority of the British workforce continue to retire at this stage – the age differential between the sexes will be eliminated in the future to bring it into line with European Community laws relating to sexual equality.

It is becoming increasingly commonplace for people to take early retirement from the job they have had most of their adult lives, and to begin life afresh, either with a new career or by starting their own small business. In an age when the average man can expect to live beyond his seventieth birthday and the average woman can expect to approach her eightieth, a book about ageing and retirement, if it is to be of any use, must begin at a stage of life when there is plenty of time for choosing and planning ahead.

Artists are among the fortunate few who do not, during the course of their lifetime, have to undergo the changes retirement brings in its wake, but for most of us it turns up as inexorably as the next birthday – and, in middle age, is greeted by many with just about the same amount of enthusiasm. Looked at in perspective, retirement must be taken in the context of a whole life, the years before retiring being as important as the years following it. The retired person is the same individual who, two or three years previously, worked in a factory or an office or a classroom. Time and circumstance will impose their own changes, but also, in order to be well prepared for what is arguably the most challenging stage of life, certain changes will need to be very consciously self-imposed.

One of the stressful features of retirement is that it is inevitably associated with images of ageing and in particular of old age. No one likes the thought of growing old, but if we are to acquire the courage and stamina to live life to its utmost, to maximize the benefits and to minimize the losses, old age requires gradual and thoughtful preparation. A social worker specializing in the care of elderly men and women in extreme need, who come to him for help when they are alone and without means of emotional or financial support, told me: 'One of the difficulties we encounter in our dealings with the elderly is that they haven't looked at the possible problems and the realities of ageing far enough in advance.'

If ageing is deemed to be a struggle, it is in part because the feeling of youthfulness which persists right through mid-life into advanced old age does not correlate with the image we see in the mirror or the way in which we are perceived by others, nor is it easy to accept the many different ways in which time forces us to change pace.

People become aware of their advancing years through the ages and activities of their children, through the needs of their elderly parents, through changes in family relationships, through the fact that they may no longer be able to advance their careers and through awareness of their own physiological and psychological changes. For years we assume that life is too long to worry about the possibility of death; the crucial turning-point comes when we look ahead and discover that life is not limitless – it is all too short. We suddenly become overwhelmed by an awareness of our own place in the process of ageing which ends in certain death, and we are afraid.

Old age is feared too because it is associated with the loss of those experiences which have given the greatest pleasure, but this fear is irrational. It does not take into account a natural ability to change and adapt; and apart from the likelihood of parents dying before their children, who can anticipate their own personal losses or when they are likely to happen? With careful planning, it is quite likely that we will be pursuing as active and vigorous a lifestyle in the seventieth decade as we did in youth or middle age.

The edges separating the middle years from old age are not well defined. Where we may have been reluctant to enter mid-life from the years of young adulthood, there will be an even greater reluctance to leave middle age. Then comes the time to admit that we are embarking on the final phase, a phase which we would no doubt prefer to delay for as long as possible. The medical profession can point to the physiological and psychological changes from middle age onwards, but these changes may occur at a different age for each individual, with variations of a decade or more. Most people hope that fate will extend their life to the maximum and for those of us who harbour a dream of being alive, active and in good health at ninety, the age of retirement appears almost young.

Thus, one of the main stumbling-blocks to enforced retirement at sixty or sixty-five is that many people do not consider themselves to be on the threshold of old age then but see themselves as being still at the vigorous peak of middle age and feel well-matched both physically and mentally to their forty-year-old colleagues. Unlike them, however, they have the advantage of having passed through the difficult and painful adjustments of mid-life and have a strong sense of having outgrown the 'younger generation'; for the most part they are happy to relinquish their youth to their children and grandchildren. For men and women who do not dread retirement, the 'new look' sixties offer a wealth of opportunity which simply did not exist for their parents' generation, who were 'pensioned off', at best tolerated but, sadly, for the most part forgotten and neglected.

The Need for Early Planning

We spend fifteen or so years preparing for our working lives, and yet almost no time is spent in preparing for what might be thirty or so years of leisure after retirement.

After years of obeying the call of the early-morning alarm clock – when sleeping in on Sunday was the great luxury of the week – suddenly every day becomes a Sunday. Where shopping for the evening meal was once a hurried affair to be completed in the lunch hour, there are now hours to spend in super-markets. But who wants to spend their mornings in bed and their afternoons in Sainsbury's? When the novelty wears off, boredom and loneliness may set in. However, after the age of fifty, if not well before, time begins to look very precious. To fill it with pleasure and enjoyment takes careful planning and a hard look at all the options.

Retirement is not a natural process: indeed, many find it a most unnatural state. It is something that society forces indi-viduals to consider at a time when they may not feel ready for it. There has been no systematic research which would indicate exactly why early death not uncommonly follows retirement, but according to Professor Anthea Tinker, Director of Age Concern's Institute of Gerontology, 'the phenomenon can be likened to the time when people move into residential care. There is a very high death rate within the first year or two. In retirement, where people move from one way of life to another, it seems to create a great shock to the system. The hypothesis is that by retiring, men have lost their role – their status – and in a sense may well give up on living. Women, on the other hand, have always worked in the home, whether or not they've had a job as well, and their home life continues. For men, the change is so dramatic – one day they're full-time workers; the next they're at home spending the time as though every day of the week was a Sunday.'

The way to cushion the physical and mental shock of retire-ment is to make preparations well in advance of the event. Professor Tinker believes that retirement as a way of life is a notion we should all grow up with and learn to accept as children. 'From childhood, we should be encouraged to look at

the whole of our lives ... we should learn to look at the end as
well as the beginning'.

Life after Fifty

In his highly regarded book, *Human Ageing*, Professor D. B.
Bromley of Liverpool University compares the process of
ageing with the process of development and growth in childhood and youth. He describes old age as a time of

lessened vitality, vigour, speed and strength, of reduced ability to
respond to demand – in short, decline and disorderliness. Thus
ageing, in a sense, undoes the work of development. It does so not
through a systematic process of dismantling, but rather through
unsystematic processes of decay and demolition, working both intrins-
ically and extrinsically, and both normally and abnormally ... In
brief, human ageing can be conveniently defined as a complex, cumula-
tive, time-related process of psychobiological deterioration occupying
the post-developmental (adult) phase of life. At present, the most we
can hope for is to delay the onset of such deterioration, to mitigate its
effects, and consequently to extend the average expectation of life by
a few years.[2]

Professor Bromley's view is bleak indeed. He confirms all
our worst fears. Medical opinion would suggest that from mid-
life on, the mind and the body are preparing to die. Life will
get worse and not better as we become older: there is little we
can do except mark time until the end arrives. Yet 'the end'
may be delayed for another forty-odd years!

Fortunately, such stark, professional opinion does not necessarily correlate with an individual's actual experience of the
ageing process and, in the light of new research, even Professor
Bromley's approach has become more pragmatic. In a telephone interview, he told me: 'The literature on the psychology
of ageing has changed. It is moving away from measuring
declines in performance towards studying ways in which these
declines can be reduced – through exercise and diet, and by
eliminating smoking and keeping alcohol consumption to a
minimum. A very recent discovery has shown that research
into the effects of ageing has been confounded by cohort
effects: that is to say, we have not previously taken into

account the changes that happen to successive generations. For example, people are growing taller; girls menstruate earlier. Now if you compare women in their thirties with women in their seventies, the latter will on average be shorter. This may in part be caused by depression of the bone following the menopause, but it is also likely to be due to the fact that the older generation did not grow as tall in the first place. Likewise, if we attempt to measure the intelligence of mature young men, it can be seen that each successive generation will show an increase in the scores of an intelligence test, leaving those of the older generations with consistently lower scores. This does not necessarily indicate that intelligence declines with age, more that it is consistent with the average intelligence of their generation.'

The American writer Gail Sheehy maintains that the 'bad press' associated with ageing is the result of research conducted by doctors, psychoanalysts and social scientists who by definition come into contact with people already suffering from depression or psychosomatic or social disorders.[3] They therefore tend to present a particular image of old age based on their experience of their patients' problems. (A similar picture emerged while I was writing a book dealing specifically with the problems of adolescence. I had consciously to keep reminding myself that the vast majority of adolescents grow to adulthood cheerfully and without much difficulty – in fact, most actually enjoy their teenage years!) Sheehy discovered the general pattern to be a great deal more optimistic and found that only 5 per cent of all Americans over sixty-five are in institutions, the other 95 per cent remaining relatively independent in their own communities, and that two thirds of older Americans live in their own homes with paid-up mortgages while 80 per cent have children near by and see them weekly. In Great Britain, the picture is broadly similar, although a smaller percentage own their homes.

Sheehy also suggests that the doom-and-gloom picture of middle and old age may have something to do with the ages of the researchers involved. From my own work, I know how difficult it is to project oneself into a stage of life of which one has no personal experience. My mother was sixty-nine when she died, and my father seventy-five – neither particularly old by today's standards, yet life seemed to be all downhill for them from their late fifties, and they became very unhappy in quite different ways, giving me to understand that ageing was inevitably a wretched process in which one was forced to exchange a full life for a miserable existence. It took several hundred retired people in different decades and three years of research to redress the balance for me.

Women on the Threshold

One cannot turn to the subject of women in the retirement years without first setting them against the background of the decade before. It is odd that despite all indications to the contrary, women in middle age have a dubious press. They are still presented as if in decline – as ageing mothers pining for their children to return to the nest or as irrational and irascible sufferers of menopausal symptoms. As an adjective in popular literature or in conversation, the word 'menopausal' is almost always used derogatively and often – particularly by men – derisively. Few seem to draw attention to the liberating aspects of the menopause.

Medical science and high standards of living have contributed to the remarkable changes that are taking place in the lives of women. In the early part of the century, the age of forty marked the beginning of the final stage in a woman's life. Now, not only is it commonplace for women to begin a demanding career in their forties – often preceded by two or three years in higher education – but it is no longer so exceptional for them to be starting a family then. The baby born to a forty-year-old may still be living at home and dependent when the mother is sixty.

Whether they have young babies or independently minded teenagers, a new world has opened up for women in middle age. For the great majority, the exhausting years of child-rearing are behind them and they can now enjoy the independence and friendship of their older teenagers and have the freedom to explore new lifestyles of their own. Government statistics show that, either from choice or from economic necessity, many more women are returning to work, after having left to look after their children. Between 1971 and 1988, there was an increase of 2·7 million in the civilian labour force, almost entirely due to a 27 per cent rise in the numbers of working women.[4]

Biologically, women are constitutionally stronger than men: that is, they are less prone to disease, infection and accidents; they are more able to endure shock, illness and extremes of physical discomfort; they have more stamina and outlive men on average by eight years. The difference in the structure of the male and female brain gives women a higher degree of sensitivity and perception, and allows for greater flexibility. In many ways, the female of the species is better equipped to manage change, whether it be associated with retirement or with the frailties and frustrations of old age.

The current social and sexual revolution has led to the multi-faceted image of modern woman as wife, mother and working woman; it is too early for in-depth analysis of the new developments, but one thing is certain – a woman in middle age needs all the extra strengths with which she is credited. It is probable that at no stage in her life will she have more simultaneous demands made upon her by others – by a psychologically vulnerable husband, by young adult children and by ailing parents – and she may be under pressure in her own career as well.

Careful research has shown that the majority of middle-aged women attach no great psychological significance to the cessation of the menses.[5] In fact, many choose to hasten the end of painful, heavy or inconvenient periods by opting to have a hysterectomy. There is also evidence that few women are plunged into depression at the thought of their children leaving home. On the other hand, it is true that depression is fairly common amongst women in middle age. However, current studies are beginning to reveal that symptoms of the menopause can begin some years before periods cease and, since it is thought that fluctuating hormone levels can interfere with emotional balance, the picture may change if hormone replacement therapy (HRT) is used rather than tranquillizers or antidepressants.

It is obvious that women in middle age are more likely to suffer severe psychological symptoms if, as so often happens, they are forced to undergo the trauma of divorce or separation and are left to cope unaided, and with diminished financial support. But even in this respect, times are beginning to change. The 'new woman', accustomed to the idea of going out to work and of not being entirely dependent upon her husband, either financially or emotionally, will hopefully be less vulnerable and better equipped to pick up the pieces after the catastrophe of a marital break-up. According to the twentieth edition of *Social Trends*, published in February 1990,[6] in 1988 a quarter of the nation's householders lived alone (as opposed to about one eighth in 1961) and it is predicted that the number will increase by more than a million in the next ten years. Given the fact that the number of children born outside marriage has risen and in 1988 accounted for 25 per cent of the total it would appear that women, on whom the task of keeping the family unit together generally rests, may choose to raise a family on their own rather than continue an unrewarding relationship with a difficult partner.

Men in a Rut?

By way of contrast, the lives of men in middle age have remained remarkably unchanged. *Social Trends*, mentioned above, showed the average British man worked the longest hours in the European Community – 43·5 hours, while British women have the second shortest hours of paid employment, clocking up an average of 29·8 hours.

Hence it would seem that the responsibility for providing the main financial support at home still rests with men. In a family where teenagers are involved in some form of further education or training, or may be living at home but able to contribute little or nothing to the housekeeping, demands on the breadwinner can increase significantly at a time when their chances for promotion in the workplace are waning. According to a 1988 Mintel report, *Women 2000*, women earn only 65 per cent of a comparable man's weekly salary and hold only 20 per cent of the professional jobs, so in most households the man is still likely to be the main breadwinner.

It seems to me that, despite the so-called feminist revolution, it is still a man's world, but for the individual man this would seem to be a dubious privilege. Studies in America have revealed the contemporary middle-aged male as being bowed down by the weight of his responsibilities. Unhappy most of the time, men are made to feel anxious, confused, guilty and helpless by their efforts to live up to high expectations, to control their emotions and to fulfil the responsibilities which the family and society impose upon them.[7]

So often one finds that women have an energy and zest for life which men lack as they become older. It is as though the spirit within men has been worn down by the demands of their careers and the financial needs of the family, so that when they come to retirement, they are unmotivated, and as dependent upon their wives as young children are upon their mothers.

The Stage Theorists

Despite the factors which tend to blur the boundaries of the ageing process, the 'stage' theorists like the American psychiatrist Erik Erikson still make a good deal of sense and provide a useful model for discussion of the second half of life. Erikson, for example, suggests that man during his lifetime passes through various stages characterized by certain 'ego qualities', each of which is in conflict with its opposite. In the final stage – maturity – 'integrity' is set against 'disgust' and 'despair'; whether or not an individual enters old age with an 'integrated' personality depends to a large extent upon the blows life has dealt him at each of the life stages, but also, perhaps to an even greater extent, on how he or she has managed to cope with the conflicts encountered along the way.[8]

The American psychologist and media personality Dr Joyce Brothers holds that every man, whatever his job or profession, goes through five stages as an adult. She describes these in her book, *What Every Woman Should Know About Men*:

1. *Onward and Upward*: the tension-ridden years from twenty-one to about thirty-five, the age varying somewhat from man to man, when the male concentrates on establishing himself at work, marrying and starting a family.
2. *Consolidation*: the years from about thirty-five to forty or possibly forty-three or forty-four, when he pulls together the accomplishments of the previous period.

3. *The Pivotal Decade*: it may be from forty to fifty, forty-five to fifty-five or somewhere in between. It is the time when a man senses the arrival of middle age, and it is characterized by physical and psychological distress. The quality and character of the rest of a man's life are largely determined during this stage, hence its description as pivotal.

4. *Equilibrium*: the years from fifty or fifty-five until retirement. But if a man has not solved the problems of the Pivotal Decade, these years will be a bitter reprise of that stage.

5. *Retirement*: a time of satisfaction and serenity – or resentment, disappointment, and fear. It all depends on how a man emerged from the Pivotal Decade.[9]

The problem with the stage theorists is that they are inclined to create an image for personality growth which is rather too neat, too ordered, because it does not take into account the fact that individuals undergo changes, whether they be physical or psychological, at their own, often very varied, pace of development. Thus a woman may reach a particular stage, which it is suggested should occur at fifty, at the age of sixty-two, and be none the worse for arriving a little late. A man may experience a so-called 'mid-life crisis' not at thirty-five or forty-five, but at sixty, just a few years before he is due to retire, triggered less by the fear of death – which some psychiatrists see as the root cause of the 'mid-life crisis' – but more by his fear of leaving the office. When his experience of retirement proves a good deal more pleasurable than he imagined, he will be a much happier man, irrespective of how he emerged psychologically from the 'Pivotal' or any other decade.

However, the real value of studying a theory that suggests ways whereby our lives are divided into certain crucial stages which have to be negotiated before passing on to the next phase, is that it can show us the kind of person we have been, the person we have become and whether or not we would benefit by making some changes: we have the choice.

These changes can involve altering aspects of our personality and appearance or the entire structure of our lives. The choices may be limited or they may be many. The decision to change may be voluntary or it might be dictated, as in cases of enforced early retirement and redundancy.

The Personality in Retirement

Sometimes, the term 'middle-aged' is used less as a description of a period of one's life but rather more as a suggestion of a particular attitude of mind. Some people, on reaching their forties, decide that they are now 'middle-aged' and therefore they will be middle-aged. Whether the decision is conscious or unconscious, these are the people who are seen by their friends to become set in their ways and to adopt attitudes which are regarded by less complacent members of their generation as unadventurous and generally fuddy-duddy.

Yet there is greater comfort and security in early acceptance of the ageing process and those who succeed in entrenching themselves are arguably the fortunate ones for whom 'slowing down' will not cause bouts of anger and frustration. They will not become stricken with panic when they cannot instantly recall a name or an event, nor will they 'rage against the dying of the light'.

According to Professor Alex Comfort, 'only two kinds of folk are really happy conventionally retired – those who were always lazy, and those who have waited a lifetime to get around to a consuming, non-fantasy interest for which they have studied, prepared and planned, lacking only the time to do it the way they wanted'.[10]

When preparing for retirement it is necessary not only to make plans for changes in financial circumstances and increased leisure but also to plan for one's personal well-being, taking into account one's own particular strengths and weaknesses.

As retirement approaches, an honest self-appraisal is the first step towards being appropriately and adequately armed for the future. Family relationships, finance, housing, health and what to do with the hours of freedom are matters which come sharply into focus at this time. While there are those who welcome retirement and look forward to the changes of life it brings, others find it almost too dreadful to contemplate:

Mr A.P., chairman of a multinational company, aged fifty-three:

> I worked my way up this company from an office boy. I'm at the top of the ladder now and I don't

want to come off. Every day is exciting. I need very
little sleep so almost twenty hours out of twenty-four
are lived to the utmost. Life is a constant high. I just
don't want to think about life after sixty-five. I can't
imagine it will be worth living and maybe I'll just
throw in the towel.

Dr W.P., a university lecturer, divorced, aged fifty-five:

I want to excel in my job. It's a kind of insecurity, I
suppose. I can't bear for it to be thought that I am not
doing it better than anyone else could. I find the
instant feedback I receive from my colleagues for
doing a job well immensely satisfying. I've thought
about retirement: I've had to. Colleagues three years
older than me have received letters inviting them to
take early retirement. At the moment, I find the
thought of retiring very difficult. I can manage without
the love and support of a partner because I'm not
alone at work. Whatever happens, in ten years' time I
will be retired and I dread the thought of returning
alone to an empty home.

We have all met old people who are selfish, querulous,
humourless and demanding – everything that we most dislike.
The attitudes we have adopted, the people we have become in
middle age, are potentially those which are taken on into old
age. Individuals who enter retirement having been unhappy
and in a state of upheaval for most of their lives, who are
overly concerned about their health, are bigoted, self-opinion-
ated, mean-spirited and covetous, who find it hard to maintain
relationships, who manage to find fault in others but never in
themselves, or are inclined to be depressed and pessimistic,
will find themselves sliding into a more general process of
depressive decline as old age approaches. Not only will they be
unhappy themselves but they will probably make others unhappy as well.

Carl Jung was the first major analytic thinker to view middle
life as the time of maximum potential for personality growth.
Following his teaching, the developmental psychologists
Joseph and Jean Britton, in their study of men and women at

the age of sixty-five and above, concluded that changes in personality occurred naturally through the process of ageing, allowing people to adapt to new circumstances, physiological, sociological and environmental. They did not always find that people changed for the better. In fact, rather more subjects in their study changed for the worse![11] On the other hand, the authors did not doubt that man has it within his power to alter certain aspects of his personality and behaviour.

The extent to which changes in either personality or lifestyle may be desirable will depend on the effect of individual experiences and the patterns of childhood and young adulthood. Traumatic childhood experiences which may have been forgotten or repressed during early adulthood can be revived in middle age at times of great stress, and the resulting mental anguish may prove too great a burden for an individual to cope with alone. In such a case, professional help and advice should be sought so that past destructive childhood memories can be worked through and present realities more rationally assimilated.

Late Middle Age – a Renaissance?

In their 1989 special report on the over-fifties, the consumer-research company Mintel concluded: 'The popular conception of middle age as a somewhat dreary and less than glamorous time of life would appear to be profoundly misguided. The picture of late middle age that emerges from both the quantitative and qualitative research is an overwhelmingly positive one. This phase of life would appear to be a time of renaissance, of much valued freedom and rediscovery.'[12]

However, the Mintel report also found that

the degree to which the over-fifties are able to reap the benefits of these golden years is very much a function of personal circumstances, age, earnings and wealth, and, most significantly of all, whether individuals are married or have lost their spouse are the most crucial determinants of well-being and satisfaction with life. Relationships with younger family members, children and grandchildren, are far less significant. Freedom and spontaneity apart, the principal benefits of this phase of life would appear to be the restoration of peace and quiet in the home, more time to spend with a partner and friends and, above all, having the time and money to spend on oneself. Indeed the opportunity for 'selfish' spending and the chance to indulge oneself with a clean conscience would appear to be one of the features of late middle age which is most enjoyed.[13]

The report also indicated that retirement was actually more enjoyed in reality than as a prospect:

Those in their early fifties are split fairly equally between those who are looking forward to retirement and those who would prefer to go on working for as long as possible. A positive anticipation or enjoyment of retirement has a very distinct bias towards the more affluent socio-economic groups.

Retirement in the 1990s – a Changing Attitude?

With advances in medical knowledge men and women now have a greater chance of remaining in good health; many would like to be allowed to continue to benefit from the fulfilment which work brings – or they may need to earn money to pay the bills and enhance the quality of life at home. At the moment, women receive their state pension even if they keep on working after the age of sixty. Men, on the other hand, cannot claim their state pension before sixty-five.

However, in 1989 a report by MSL Advertising found that 86·6 per cent of jobs advertised carried an upper age limit of forty. Only 3·1 per cent of the employers interviewed said they would offer a job to someone over the age of forty-five.

In April of the same year, the Association of Retired Persons, an all-party pressure group lobbying for reforms to benefit older people, launched their Anti-Age Discrimination Campaign in an attempt to persuade the government to legislate against age discrimination. In response, the Prime Minister, Margaret Thatcher (then aged sixty-three), and her Secretary of State for Employment, Norman Fowler, criticized fixed-age retirement as 'anachronistic'. The Employment Committee's report on *Employment Patterns of the Over-50s* endorsed their view and stressed the need for a flexible 'decade of retirement'. The government's real fear was that the country would not be able to afford full pensions for the growing numbers of retired people.

While, as yet, little has been done to legislate against a fixed age of retirement, much has been written about the apparent enthusiasm with which employers are enticing men and women above the statutory retiring ages of sixty and sixty-five back into the workplace. On 28 September 1989, an article by the labour correspondent of the *Independent* began:

McDonalds, the fast-food chain, is to target the over-fifties – including pensioners – in a nationwide recruitment drive. The company aims to recruit at least 5 per cent of its workforce from the older age group in the early 1990s, to compensate for the sharp drop in school-leavers over the next few years ... Tesco and B & Q have made moves recently to attract older workers.

All well and good, but the question arises, will everyone be prepared, after a lifetime's experience in the workplace, to fill the gaps normally taken up by school-leavers, who have traditionally seen these jobs as time fillers and money earners while they look around for something more interesting?

The correspondent ends the article: 'A sixty-four-year-old has just been taken on as a roving litter-picker. Ivy Neild, sixty-four, is a 'dining-area hostess'. But one area appears out of bounds for older workers. 'Till work is pretty fast and furious,' said Mr Ryan (the twenty-one-year-old manager of McDonalds in Staines). 'We don't think it would be fair to put older workers on that kind of work.' One can only wonder what the 'older workers' thought about such a decision.

It is surely a step in the right direction for employers to offer work to senior citizens, but it is quite another thing to use them as a downtrodden, old fashioned labour force to be trampled upon by youth in its efforts to reach the top. Supermarkets still require executives to retire at a certain age; will managers now offer their retired executives a job stacking the shelves?

Training for Retirement

There are two ways of preparing for retirement. The first is to ask a few questions, read the available material and then just let it happen and hope for the best. The second path is to join a working group by enrolling in a retirement training course to listen to experts and learn from them. If growing up successfully depends on what can be obtained from the education system and career training, then growing old successfully depends on learning everything possible in order to enhance the quality of life in the retirement years.

The ideal time to begin training is ten years before the date of retirement. At the same time, long-term financial planning, together with a fitness and health programme, should be put into operation. (See Chapters 4, Finance, and 6, Health.)

Self-improvement training can be beneficial to everyone. Managers and workers, confused and well-organized people, can all learn new skills or experience a change of attitude. Retirement training is a growth industry. Big companies provide in-house training schemes in the years before retirement. Community colleges, the Pre-Retirement Association and private firms also run a variety of training courses. Mid-life planning, pre-retirement training or similar courses, if they are not available through the office or the firm, are available from private training organizations or the Local Education Authority; the Citizens Advice Bureau will be able to say what courses are available locally.

Choosing a Retirement Course

It seems that people as they near retirement are very willing to attend courses in order to help plan their future, but many come away disappointed. Whatever they hoped to attain from the course was somehow lacking. It may be that it was too prescriptive – it did not encourage people to make their own choices – or that it gave advice on issues bearing no relation to specific circumstances. Research has shown that the two major issues people approaching retirement choose for inclusion in a course are money and health, yet with the actual experience of being retired, they find that these concerns tend to take second place to family relationships and the effective use of time.

The Centre for Health and Retirement Education at the University of London, aware of the limitations of retirement courses, is currently involved in studies aimed at finding ways to make them more relevant to individual circumstances. In particular, the problems of women in retirement have been sadly neglected in the past and the centre is now anxious to develop courses planned with their needs and interests in mind.

It is unfortunately not possible to be sure that a retirement course will be suited to any particular individual. The programme will obviously indicate the topics, but until the prospective retiree sits down and listens to what the tutors have to say, there is no way of knowing whether or not the presentations will be helpful. Tutors are now recommended to tailor their courses to suit the groups with whom they are working, but if the group is large it will probably not be possible to take individual circumstances into account.

If there is neither time nor opportunity to join a retirement course, one alternative is to plan at home with the help of the Open University's Retirement Pack, 'Planning Retirement'. The pack is based on a book which covers more than sixty topics, including money matters, opportunities for learning, health, nutrition and diet, leisure and work, new friends, being at home, transport, partners and living arrangements. It concentrates on practical activities to help people draw up their own individual retirement plan, and there is an audio cassette which develops some of the issues through interviews and discussion. The basic study pack (Code P941S) may be purchased separately, but the full course (Code P941C), which includes the study pack, assessment pack and free loan of video cassettes, may be the better bargain although it costs more.

Further information, together with the OU retirement course planning packs, can be obtained by contacting Community Education, The Open University, Walton Hall, Milton Keynes, MK7 6AA (Tel. 0908 655047).

'Use It or Lose It'

As age advances, the old truism, 'use it or lose it', cannot be ignored. Stimulation, both physical and mental, is a vital ingredient in the quality of life at any age. The least acceptable aspect of the ageing process is stagnation. It is no mere chance that the men and women in their seventies, eighties and nineties who have provided the background to this book are living lives that are as full and rewarding as they have ever been. Rhoda, aged ninety-one, goes off on a painting expedition to Labrador in midwinter with an eighty-year-old companion, despite suffering from cancer of the jaw. Colin, aged eighty had a hip-replacement operation and a month later was preparing a buffet supper for forty people. William and Diana, both in their early seventies, think nothing of travelling forty miles on their Harley-Davidson to spend Sundays with their daughter and son-in-law and their two grandsons. Seventy-five-year-old Ellen, bound to a wheelchair for fifteen years and paralysed from the waist down, is totally reliant on her husband's care and support. Each year, they set off in their car for a holiday touring around Europe just as they used to do in the first years of their marriage.

These people are not exceptions to the rule of ageing. They are not immune to ill health or increased lack of mobility or any of the other physical problems associated with advancing years. Nor are they immune to depression or anxiety. Retirement was no more or less easy for them than anyone else; but they are all men and women who have lived life to the full. They take with them into old age an energy and vitality that has been present throughout their lives. They all have active minds alerted by interest, curiosity and involvement. Infirmity may mean that physically they sometimes have trouble keeping up with their ambitions, but it seems their minds can usually find ways to circumvent the handicaps of an ailing body.

Those who find that they are 'slowing down' and feeling 'old' or 'tired' in late middle age may be surprised to learn that energy and vitality can be acquired at any age, even in the nineties, but the physical and spiritual renewal which transforms and enhances the quality of life for its duration does not come easily. The older we become, the more difficult it is to initiate change.

Case Histories: Learning from the Experience of Others

Mr H.A. was twenty-one when war broke out. He joined the army as a private and rose to the rank of sergeant. After he was demobbed, he started work as a trainee in the National Cash Register Company; in his thirties he left to work for a publishing company. He has never married but has shared a home with the same partner for twenty-three years.

I retired when I was sixty-four. I rather looked forward to retirement but when it finally happened, the first year was odd. I missed the action, the telephone calls and being in charge of certain situations, and I missed my friends. I was determined when I left that I wasn't going to be one of those people who go back to the office all the time and for about six months I stayed away; then I couldn't resist it. One day, I picked up the phone and contacted friends and made some engagements for lunch. I still see some of them, but not as many as in the early days of my retirement. Things change. A lot of friends have themselves retired.

As retirement approaches, you have to realize that you are getting old and that there is a life cycle and that you have to face it, and that you have to do it as intelligently as you possibly can.

In the first six months of retirement, I was extremely active. One of the things I decided really early on was that as long I was physically able to do so I would continue to live in London and take full advantage of everything the city has to offer. I could not bear the idea of a life of golf and bridge.

After a while, you relax about retirement – relax into it. I've always been brought up to believe that you should be doing something constantly for other people – contributing in some way to the community. But if you spent so many years of your life at school, so many years in the army and the rest of the time working, I think in the last few years of your life, you should be allowed to do as you damn well please.

Mrs C.C. had been retired from the civil service for five years when, at the age of sixty-five, she married for the first time.

I rather enjoyed the early days of retirement. Having always worked and been on my own and entirely responsible for earning my own money and looking after myself, I found that for the first time in my life I could actually choose what I wanted to do. When I discovered what I really wanted to do was to marry Colin, it came as a bit of a surprise. He was a widower and had been married to a great friend of mine, so we had known each other for a long time. Being married has freed me of so many of the day-to-day responsibilities which looking after yourself involves. It is undoubtedly a much more comfortable life. Mind you, it took a while for us to adjust to living together. We found it irksome at first because we were both already at an age when we were set in our habits, but I think we've done a very good job.

Mr B.C. was a chemical engineer and executive director of his company before he retired. He told me:

When I retired, it took me a year to recover from the shock. I just didn't know what to do with myself. Our medical adviser on the board had warned us all a few years before retirement to think what we were going to do with our lives after the event. One of the things he said was 'For heaven's sake, get informed and don't go and retire to some tatty little seaside resort amongst people you don't know, away from your friends, relatives, children and grandchildren. I was sixty-three when he gave us this advice. I ignored it at first, but through circumstances to do with my work, the last year before retirement, I decided I would alter my position within the firm and work as a consultant, which would allow me to wind down slowly. It turned out to be a traumatic experience. All of a sudden, the challenges, the tactics, the financial wheeling and dealing were all lost to me. What we were doing had always been so exciting. It was like being on some kind of pep-up drug and then going through the withdrawal symptoms. When the moment to retire actually arrived, I found I still wasn't ready for it. Bored, frustrated and lost at home, I used to

play patience furiously hour after hour. I must have
been quite depressed for a time. There was a sense in
which the world I had always found so fascinating
had disappeared. But I had already taken steps to
become involved in a fishing project and with the
Institute of Chemical Engineering, and gradually both
of them became major interests. You can say that
after a couple of years or so, I was over the problem
of retirement and life has taken off again with really
pleasing and exciting prospects.

Redundancy

The effects of redundancy upon a family or an individual may
be quite devastating. Although it can occur at any stage in a
working life, being made redundant in middle age becomes all
the more frightening when one considers the many doors
which are closed to the job hunter after the age of thirty-five or
so. An immediate reaction is to worry about how the news
should be broken to the family:

I just didn't know how I was going to tell my wife. It
was all such a shock and I thought she would probably cope with it even less well than I could. All the
way home in the car, I was thinking, 'What the hell
am I going to say?' Then when I arrived, I found
myself saying what I always said and doing what I
always do. I kissed her and asked her how her day
went. Then I bit the bullet. I told her I'd received
some bad news. I no longer had a job. I tried to tell
her in a joky way as if it didn't matter much, and I
didn't care because I was bored, and in any case had
been thinking about moving on for some time. In
actual fact, the job meant everything to me. I couldn't
imagine life without it. I left her and went upstairs,
threw myself on the bed and sobbed and sobbed.

FOCUS, the Forum for Occupational Counselling and Unemployment Services Ltd (see Part III, Counselling), is an
organization which specializes in helping people piece together
their lives after the shattering experience of redundancy and

joblessness. According to the company's chairman and founder, Bridget Litchfield, it is easier for a shop-floor worker to find new employment following redundancy than it is for a senior executive; the more highly specialized the work, the more difficult it may be to find another job. However, the picture holds true only in cases where small numbers of men and women are made redundant: it changes dramatically in an area of high unemployment when hundreds of people are suddenly released on to the job market. Ms Litchfield deplores the fact that retraining opportunities in this country are currently so inadequate. She believes that there are not enough courses on offer and that too little thought is given to the existing courses. She said: 'They are still holding people down by not making training programmes relevant to the needs of industry in the future, neither are clients offered a guarantee of a job after retraining. What incentive do they have? If a man wants to change his work from engineering to plumbing, he needs to know that an employer will offer him a job as soon as he has his new qualifications.'

When someone is made redundant, they are most likely to worry first about what it means in financial terms and, secondly, how they can best apply for another job. A hitherto secure and long-lasting job may mean that they have neither the skills nor the experience to make the best of themselves in a competitive market. Forty per cent of jobs are not even advertised. Firms rely heavily upon agencies and speculative applications to supply their personnel, so the well-written curriculum vitae and a commanding interview technique are crucial adjuncts to success.

Pauline Hyde runs a careers advisory service, a business which she began in her forties. Many of her clients are men between the ages of forty and fifty-nine. Following redundancy, it is not unusual for them to move on to jobs with higher salaries and quite common for them to express greater satisfaction with their new positions. Not only does counselling involve helping them to find another job, but the meticulously planned assessments guide them towards a position which is particularly appropriate for their abilities and interests, strengths and weaknesses. She explained: 'We train people who may never have received any previous guidance as to which career to follow and who have never had any training on how to project themselves effectively. We teach them to job-hunt systematically and professionally, and to go off in different ways to get jobs because they don't all come through recruiters or job centres. We show them how to write a c.v. There is quite an art to this. It doesn't have to be a dull chronological document and is all-important when it comes to selling them-selves on paper and gaining an interview. Most people under-estimate their achievements, and when they take a good look at what they've done, their spirits rise. If they are in their fifties, we tend to put the age on the last page of the c.v, hoping that employers will be so interested in the first page that by the time they get to the last they will say, "Oh, he's a bit older than we thought but we'll see him anyway." In any case, it's absolutely useless to leave off the age or lie about it, because people can see when your career started, and whether or not you have done National Service.'

When it comes to the job interview, Ms Hyde's clients are counselled to 'appear as though they had vitality and to avoid obvious pitfalls like glasses with chains on them which shows employers that you have just lost your memory. An enormous amount can be done with a suntan and a bright blue shirt. People wear granny-glasses when they should consign them to their teenage children. The way you walk into a room or get out of a chair is important: be brisk!'

Redundancy counselling is a valuable investment, not just for what it can do to pave the way towards finding another job, but also in terms of its ability to provide psychological support, especially for those who are unable to discuss their feelings with a partner or with a member of the family. (Many people find they are better able to talk through their problems with one of their older, more mature children, rather than with their spouse.) If the cash is not available to buy the time and expertise of a specialist organization, the Citizens Advice Bur-eaux have counsellors – often retired people with experience in counselling and business management – who give free advice. Another source of help is the public library, which is likely to have a list of groups or individuals working locally, if not specifically in the area of redundancy, then in the related areas of stress management and pre-retirement programmes.

Although the initial blow may be heavy indeed, redundancy may produce an unexpectedly positive side. If people have been unhappy and unfulfilled in their jobs but have felt obliged to continue in them because a change might bring economic hardship to the family, it forces them to begin again; with the right kind of help and counselling they can find themselves in a new situation enjoying the happy experience of being a round peg in a round hole for the first time in their lives.

The Single Person and Retirement

Retirement, the death of a partner and divorce are different orders of experience to be sure, but they represent the three critical occasions in which people can be flung into an isolation as dramatic and frightening as imprisonment. Single men and women who have never before thought of themselves as lonely may discover loneliness for the first time in retirement. Not only are they deprived of the work which previously structured their day, but they are also denied their daily interaction with friends and acquaintances who may have formed the focus of their social world.

The difficulties women share in establishing a new social network to include male friends are well known. In the twenty-to-forty age group, there are three single men for every two single women;[14] the picture in the fifty and over age group is somewhat different. At this stage it is the single women who outnumber single men. Those who turn to 'dating' or introduction agencies may well find themselves spending a large sum of money for very little return. There are apparently just too many women on their own over fifty and not enough single men to accompany them.

How then can single women who want to meet men with a view to forming a relationship overcome the problem? The owner of an introduction agency offered the following advice and encouragement: 'If a woman is really practical and imaginative and prepared to take the risks – I don't mean personal risks but just risks about trying things – she can find a man. I do believe it's possible, but she also has to be prepared to put up with a great deal of rejection and she must first draw on the friendship of other women to support her. Women start with an enormous advantage in that they are prepared to discuss their needs more openly. It wouldn't be much use to a man if I were to suggest to him that he sit down with a friend or even a group of friends and work out a plan of action much the same as he might do at work, setting himself goals and deadlines. He would be too embarrassed and self-conscious to share this kind of "work" with another man. People have just got to be prepared to let their hair down a bit, be a little crazy and not care what anybody thinks. There are so many ways of meeting people – on the top of a bus; in shops; on the street. Shops are especially sociable because you can always get into conversation about something on display. You can turn to someone and ask their advice about wines or paints or DIY things. You can begin by writing to all your friends and asking them if they know any single men to whom they might be willing to introduce you. A couple of you might decide to throw a party for all the single people you know irrespective of age. You can also meet people through certain activities. Learn something new every year but make sure you are learning about a subject in which men are likely to be involved. Don't go to evening classes unless you are sure that there are going to be plenty of men in the right age group doing the same thing. Advertising is perhaps the most practical way of meeting the opposite sex but be careful where you advertise. Know the readership and go for a mad, really outrageous advertisement which is non-threatening, inviting and irresistible. Of course you don't want to parade your age. This is guerrilla warfare and there are no holds barred. You've got to get men out of their holes to meet you. In conjunction with another woman, all this can be fun and the cause for much laughter, but there will be a lot of rejection and at times you will hit rock bottom and that's when you will most need each other's encouragement. Make sure you mix with young people; they knock the corners off and keep you young. Don't set limits; promise yourself to meet two new men every month and be prepared to meet them even when there is only the mildest chance of attraction. Women now in their fifties and sixties were not brought up to be assertive, and in consequence, they often miss out. If they want to continue a relationship, they must be prepared to take the initiative and suggest a place and date for the next meeting.

Assertiveness courses are a very good idea – they really can do wonders for self-esteem. Don't think of men as lovers in the first instance but think of them more as potential friends. Consider their needs and be prepared to take care of their cat or help them paint the kitchen. Be sure to meet at first on a territory that is neutral and non-threatening and one which gives you something to talk about. If you've both expressed an interest in museums, meet at one; if films or concerts, make an investment and buy the ticket! Effort with appearance is important. If you look good, you'll feel good and be more confident. If all else fails, you can always start a dating agency of your own!'

An over-anxious, intense approach towards meeting members of the opposite sex is likely to act as a deterrent. I asked a man who had been divorced for some time and who went along to an introduction agency in the hopes of finding a companion, why he did not return after the first visit. 'It was just the sight of all those pages and pages of photographs of desperate-looking middle-aged women staring at me. I couldn't bear it. It wasn't their age or their looks that put me off – it was the thought of their desperation. I felt they were probably all looking for a father for their teenage children. I was suddenly afraid of the commitment their anxious faces seemed to demand.'

Making new relationships does not have to be energetic, however. Membership of the APT, Association of Retired Persons (see Part III, Retirement) gives single members the opportunity to meet others with similar interests through their Companions Club and Saga (see p. 202) offers all kinds of opportunities for increasing your circle of friends (see Chapter 5, Leisure and Working for Pleasure).

Early Retirement

At present, there is only anecdotal evidence to suggest an increase in the numbers of people in their mid-forties and fifties retiring early and perhaps beginning a new life with a different job. According to a spokesman at Age Concern it is not possible to quantify these numbers but 'it is a potentiality'. The whole field of retirement is currently very under-researched but one businesswoman to whom I spoke was in no doubt about this 'potentiality': 'Men in their mid-forties now are changing', she said. 'They are no longer conditioned to think of retirement at sixty-five as were their fathers. There are other options including, obviously, early retirement. Industries and banks are allowing early retirement. People of forty-five who are dissatisfied with their jobs are beginning to look around for new careers, perhaps going into business on their own in an entirely different field. If their partners are working and bringing in money, they are not financially so hard pressed. Therefore, maybe for the first time in their lives, they feel they have a choice of career. If making furniture is all they have ever wanted to do but did not dare to risk leaving a safe, lucrative but boring job, then what's to stop them, when a partner can take the financial strain?'

Early Retirement – Case Histories

Mr P.B. was a lecturer in higher education before he retired at fifty-five:

> I loved my job. I always used to say to people that I found it extraordinary I should be paid for doing something which I enjoyed so much. I had never thought about retirement at all until there were cutbacks in our department which led to two of my colleagues being forced to retire early. I felt great sympathy for them. The prospect of early retirement appalled me because I could not envisage a situation in which I would not be working in this marvellous job. Then something happened which made me realize I couldn't take the work for granted. Teaching jobs in higher education became scarce, and new people coming into the department were young and very high-powered. They were university graduates with doctorates, whereas my own training ground had been a school classroom for thirteen years. Perhaps I felt intellectually overwhelmed; but at the age of forty-eight I decided to make a change. At the time there was a great shortage of professional expertise and colleges of education were desperate for more lecturers with a long experience of teaching in

schools. I was warned that to go wholly on to the professional side would not be particularly fulfilling, but I didn't believe it, so I went off to do my M.Ed. and came back to specialize in professional studies, which meant I no longer taught the main subject which had given me so much pleasure in the past. I very soon found it wasn't what I wanted. I was doing the same kind of work that I had come to college to get away from. Then quite coincidentally I began to find I could no longer cooperate with a close colleague. The tensions and difficulties between us just weren't going to go away, so I thought the best thing to do was to jack it in and that's what I did.

I made the decision quite calmly and felt reasonably optimistic. I think teachers do have enough free time to work up sufficient numbers of interests so that when they are retired they've got a lot of resources – or they should have. I found myself busier than ever. In the first year of retirement, my wife was still working. I was able to do what was needed about the house and the cooking – and I've always enjoyed cooking; it was fun. Our elder daughter had just had our first grandchild so I saw a lot of her and on many occasions I was left in charge of the baby, which I enjoyed. So there was a lot to do and at first I found it very fulfilling. It was nice having my wife come home in the evening from work and telling me what she had been doing. I enjoyed being involved in her day and I listened to her more in that year than all the time I had been working.

As a result of not wanting to feel idle, I got myself involved with all sorts of little organizations; for example, I am Neighbourhood Watch coordinator and on the committee of our local gardening club; I take a lot more interest in the activities of the Labour Party. I am governor and treasurer of a school, which takes quite a bit of my time and I am on the local Arts Council Executive Committee. Together my wife and I share a passion for music and singing and we take lessons and sing in various groups and choruses.

I think the reason why I have done so many different things in retirement is a sort of need to prove to people – not necessarily to myself – that I'm not just mouldering away in slothful domesticity. When I went to have a haircut, my hairdresser would greet me and say, 'Just having an hour off work?' I'd nod my head and reply, 'yeah' – instead of saying, 'No, I'm retired now', as though there was something which was not quite pukka about taking early retirement. There seemed to be a need in me to justify not having a proper job. Now five years later, I am back at work again, albeit only for two days a week, and I take great delight in being able to say to the same hairdresser, 'I'm in rather a hurry. I've got to get up to the office and do some work.' A friend at the college offered me a part-time job just before my sixtieth birthday. It was the best present I could have had. I don't really know why it means so much to me to be in paid, official employment again. Essentially, my work is no more useful to the college than it is to the local Arts Council, the comprehensive school or the Labour Party, or even the gardening club, but the fact that I have an office to go to gives me a sense of purpose which means more to me than anything I do or could ever do in retirement.

One of the main problems associated with retirement is that of finding something to do with time which is meaningful and rewarding. It is the difference between 'filling in time' and 'living a full life'. Mr I.J.'s story is an example of achievement, fulfilment and personal growth:

When I was fifty, I reckoned I had about seven thousand days to live and I wouldn't waste any more time. I felt it just wasn't worth while making more money doing something I didn't like – which was business management – so I retired. I hadn't got any real plans. I went to America for a while, then I came back and got pretty fed up doing nothing; so I started cleaning windows and doing odd-job gardening; then a friend, knowing how much I liked being out of doors and doing heavy physical work, asked me if I would help clear a plot of land in preparation for a health club he was going to build.

Hard physical labour has always appealed to me ever since I had read a book about the siege of Malta by the Saracens. Before the siege, one of the grand admirals, Valetta, had been captured by pirates and spent a year as a galley slave. He was about fifty then. He escaped, survived all the hardships of the siege and lived to the age of eighty. It was thought that the reason he did so well was because he experienced the hard labour and frugal living at a crucial turning-point of his life. It made him tough as old leather. It seemed to me at the time that by becoming a scaffolder, hod-carrier and builder's labourer, I would have the same sort of hard, uncompromising life as a galley slave. I'm immensely proud of the work I did. All the cement mixing was done by hand. Nowadays people put up a little garden wall with a mixer. I did it with a shovel, and with just two bricklayers on the job, you had to work quite quickly.

When the club was finally built, I was offered the job of manager but I turned it down. If I went back into management it would be like going back to work. I'd have to come out of retirement. I know to most people brick-laying and hod-carrying would be work, but it wasn't to me. I loved doing it. For me it was a pleasure. My friend then persuaded me to stay on by suggesting I teach squash and tennis and do the maintenance.

The Art of Giving In Gracefully

This same interviewee – aged sixty-three when we talked – for whom physical exercise has been an essential part of life, is also a talented sportsman. Continuing our conversation, he demonstrated how 'giving in' to the effects of time does not mean 'giving up', but it is important to be realistic and not expose the body at sixty or seventy to stresses which it can no longer tolerate well:

I've always played at least two sports at a time very competitively. I was an army lightweight boxing champion as a young man and took up judo and squash to keep fit, but gradually, over the years, you begin to suffer more and more injuries with judo. Now it's squash and golf. Having played squash for thirty-odd years, it's no problem to teach. At fifty I was playing in the Veterans and my game was going downhill, so it seemed the right moment to begin coaching. I've been doing the job now for ten years, but I like to look a step or two ahead. Seven of my friends have died on the squash courts and I can see that the game might prove too much for me eventually. I don't want to end up with some serious injury which would keep me out of sport for good. I don't really like to be terribly bad at something. If I had arthritis and could not win at squash, I would give it up and try something else.

Squash is one of the most energetic of all sports and when you are younger you probably train quite hard to keep up with the game's demands but as you get older the problem is that people who continue to play think they stay fit. Perhaps they have not done much except garden for a month or so and someone rings up and they find themselves back in the game. You imagine you are as fast and cool as you were, but you are not. You put your body under a tremendous amount of stress.

I don't feel I work at keeping my body in trim. I'm a hedonist and I love it. It isn't work to me. I enjoy the gym. You get a good sweat up; you've worked hard and then have a steam and a shower and you go away feeling uplifted. I work out by weight-lifting about three times a week and usually follow this with a game of squash, which doesn't really tire me. On the days I don't weight-lift, I run locally or, if I'm in the country, I run through the woods just for the sheer pleasure.

This place closes down in five years and although I've been asked to do the same job elsewhere, I think

it will be time for a change. There is so much I still
want to do. At the moment I have a passion for
cross-country cycling on my mountain bike. I've done
the Ridgeway path and have got ambitions to go for
longer cycle rides. I've already planned a trip across
the Pyrenees from the Atlantic to the Mediterranean. I
want to walk from Land's End to John o'Groats; from
the north to south of Corsica; then I'm very keen to
fly to the States, get a motor bike and go down the
east coast – places like New Orleans and the Florida
Keys. Then I want to go across America and up the
west coast on the motor bike to visit my son who
lives in Vancouver. My wife will accompany me on
the back of the bike but she isn't keen on cycling, so
cycle tours will be carefully planned so that she can
drive and meet me at various points along the track
having seen what she wants to see along the way.

Successful retirement means looking ahead and not ignoring
the fact that physical changes associated with ageing will inevitably take place and require adaptation. In competitive sport, it
is not easy to move from the position of winner to that of also-
ran, but if anger, frustration and even death are not to follow,
it is important to accommodate the body's changing needs.

'Castles in Spain'

In retirement, the fulfilment of dreams is a real possibility but,
without detailed planning, the dream may be transformed into
a living hell, causing unimagined hardship in vulnerable old
age. The little farm in Wales, with chickens, a pig or two, a
few sheep and some cows bought for a song at a local auction
will, without knowledge or experience of animal husbandry, be
a frightening and profitless responsibility as the animals steadily eat their way through precious savings.

A bleak future can also lie in wait for people who decide to
spend their Third Age in the sun. A branch of the Association
of Retired Persons was set up in Spain in 1989 in response to
the problems encountered by many of its members who had
chosen to make the country their home in retirement. For the

most part, people are very happy with their Spanish way of life, although they seldom truly assimilate. Language is the great barrier. Many learn to communicate competently but the lack of real fluency prevents in-depth relationships with their hosts. The British have tended to weave themselves into a tight-knit expatriate community supported by a network of clubs. All goes well until there is a divorce or the death of a spouse or a serious illness. Loneliness and medical needs are the two most common problems which bring people to the ARP for help. In old age, it is quite usual for people to decide that they want to return to Britain.

Dr Robert Rose is a property developer who knows the British community in Spain very well. Recently retired, he is on the ARP's UK council of advisers. He says: 'Any move is a shock to the system – it is one of the great traumas in life. Whatever people decide to do in retirement, if it means a radical departure from their usual way of life, they must gain experience of their new world and test the water first for at least two to three years before making a final decision. Try not to think of the move in permanent terms. Moving abroad is not a one-way ticket. You can always sell your house and return home. The best advice I can offer to help prevent problems in the long run is that people should buy their property correctly through a solicitor and make absolutely sure they have adequate medical insurance. It is a prerequisite. Both BUPA and PPP offer policies especially designed for overseas residents which enable them to fly back to the UK for treatment.'

Help and Advice

People readily go to the doctor when troubled by some physical ailment, but they often find it more difficult to ask for help when there is a breakdown in their home or working life. Because they have nothing medically wrong with them, they feel they should be able to cope with the situation. Appropriate counselling in problems arising from retirement and redundancy can relieve stress and help people to achieve their goals faster. See Part III, Counselling, and also Chapter 6, Health.

Check-list: Retiring from Work; Leaving Arrangements

Twelve months before retirement

- Attend the **pre-retirement training course**; if not provided at work, see the local education authority.
- **Health check-up** – if you are in a company private health scheme, have a complete medical examination.

Six months before retirement

- Receive **confirmation of your leaving date** from the personnel department.

Three months before retirement

- **Company pension** – discussion with the pension adviser to decide on your lump-sum commutation
- **State retirement pension** – the DSS will send you notification of your accrued pension. Return the form which indicates how you want your pension to be paid.

One month before retirement

- **Social club** – obtain your membership card and make arrangements to join the company's retirement section if there is one.
- **Company car** – arrange purchase, pay road tax, insure and join a motoring organization.
- **Private health-care scheme** – get quotations from various companies; if you can afford it, make your first payment.
- **Housing benefit** – see the local housing department for rent and poll-tax rebate, and your eligibility for retirement housing in your old age.

After retirement

- **Rail Pass** and **Bus Pass** – if you have not already obtained these (they are available to anyone over sixty, whether in work or not) apply to British Rail and the Regional Transport Office.

- **Luncheon club** – join a suitable retired people's luncheon and social club or other organization which involves meeting new people and increasing your circle of friends.

2 The Family and Changing Relationships – Fears and Frustrations

> ... we cannot live the afternoon of life according to the programme of life's morning; for what was great in the morning will be little at evening, and what in the morning was true will at evening have become a lie ... The afternoon of human life must also have a significance of its own and cannot be merely a pitiful appendage to life's morning.
>
> Carl Gustav Jung, *The Stages of Life*[15]

Marriage in Retirement

While it is true that many husbands and wives look forward to retirement and being able to spend more time in each other's company, a future spent in unaccustomed togetherness is a prospect not always welcomed, particularly by those who are used to living within a framework of individual freedom and independence. Marriage is a shared experience but that sharing does not necessarily include an especially close relationship. There are many couples who actually depend upon their quite different lifestyles for happiness and marital harmony.

Retirement is a challenging time for couples who suddenly find themselves face to face with each other over the breakfast, lunch *and* supper tables seven days a week. Even in the closest relationship, such intimacy is a severe test of a couple's ability to communicate with each other and the effort involved may prove very stressful indeed; but if the past has not been closely shared, it will be much more difficult to contemplate a shared future.

Whose Future?

The changes involved in family life after retirement often
mean compromise and sacrifice but the extent to which an
individual is prepared to go to share the future with his or her
partner will depend upon the value they place upon the relationship. In the following example, the marriage becomes the first
priority.

Mrs N.B. is married to a man twenty years her senior.
When her teenage children left home to go to college, she went
back to work. Her career was very successful and very demanding. When she was forty-five, her husband retired. He soon
became jealous of the time she spent away from home and for a
while their relationship deteriorated: 'With a new career in the
forties and fifties, women find there is no space for a man in
their life. I had to make what was, for me, the only choice.'
Staying married was the most important goal, but adapting to
her husband's needs in retirement cost Mrs N.B. a full-time
job and she now works from home as a free-lance journalist.
She has also encouraged her husband to take up consultative
posts and hopes to realize her own ambition to write a novel.
She says that although she misses the extra money, the excitement and stimulation of life at the top, she feels more relaxed
and much healthier.

One of the great joys in retirement is to discover that
potential common interests can, with the extra time available,
be allowed to develop into a shared passion:

> We didn't give gardening much thought before, other
> than to say to each other that it would be nice to
> grow our own vegetables, until one day we were out
> walking and passed an allotment which is near us.
> We talked to some people who were busy gardening
> there and discovered that there were some plots avail-
> able, and the interest came from that meeting. We
> followed it up and we now have a five-rod field. It
> was a bit daunting at first, being all thistles and
> couch grass, but everybody said, 'Don't worry, just
> go on slowly and in four years, you will have what
> you want.' This is the fourth year and it is all looking

smashing. We have become totally absorbed by the garden. We plan everything together. There is such a science to it. We spent a whole four hours with a chart trying to work out just where and how the rotation should go and which seeds to use. It is very disappointing to see things not grow but marvellous to watch them coming up. We tend to produce things that are expensive to buy – mangetouts and sweet corn. We also have purple sprouting broccoli, chicory, kale, soft fruit, flowers and potatoes, which it is useful to keep moving around. We don't grow cabbages and turnips because you end up with a huge un-wanted harvest – more than you or anybody else could eat. There is so much more time for people when you no longer have the pressure of work and one of the benefits of gardening in the allotment has been the marvellous social life. Our circle of friends has become much wider.

The Rewards of Time

If mid-life and middle age are associated with change and turbulence, the years following retirement are marked by peace and harmony. A State Registered Nurse working for Marks & Spencer's is one of four welfare officers whose task it is to look after over fifteen thousand retired members of staff throughout the country. She sees personally around two thousand people a year and in the eight years since she has been doing the job, only twice have people been referred to her with problems associated with marital breakdown. The road to marital har-mony sometimes seems like an army assault course but the rewards are infinitely worth waiting for, as the following ex-ample illustrates:

I was determined to stay married until the children had left school and were on their feet, and I was fifty when I got divorced. I was quite clear in my mind that at some stage or another – perhaps when I no longer felt useful to the household – I would leave. In fact the actual circumstances of my leaving came when I was told that whenever there was any fun to be had, I always spoiled everything. I thought, this is just the sort of statement I've been waiting for, and so I left. Then I married again.

I don't think I could say, one hand on my heart, that I adopted a particularly mature or responsible attitude towards either my first or my second wife. When I was first married, I had relationships outside the marriage and while I have been with Ellie I have had relationships outside marriage. Now I'm retired, I don't see anybody else. If I am true and honest with myself, the fact that I'm at home and we are together so much means I don't have the opportunity to meet other women; but it is also because Ellie and I are the closest possible friends and we get on ever so well and I can't imagine a more comfortable and contented relationship. If one was to ask me if I had the opportunity to have some sex on the side, would I take it, of course I would. It's not that I want another relationship – what I really want is a one-night stand. I don't think that I can see the possibilities of it ever happening now though. It's easy in a work context because within that sort of routine each person can do more or less what they want.

I said to a great woman friend recently, I'm desperate to grow up and perhaps when I've grown up I won't have this desire to take every opportunity that comes along. My friend said if that's what 'growing up' meant to me I shouldn't do it – not because she wanted to encourage me to be promiscuous but because perhaps she thought I wouldn't be quite so interesting. But the truth is, since Ellie and I have both retired, things have been very stable and very profitable. I'm much less restless now than I have ever been. We have become very close. We do virtually everything together; I don't resent that, it's part of the niceness of it all. Our relationship is more rewarding than I ever expected.

Together or Apart?

If a greater togetherness in retirement draws attention to the fact that a marriage is unhappy, that the extra time in each other's company is time spent in ways which express only dislike, bitterness, regret and the unbridgeable differences between a couple, the future could be very bleak indeed. The past is a habit from which it is notoriously difficult to break, so that while in the early years of retirement a long-established relationship might seem tolerable – the fervent hope being that 'perhaps things will get better' – ahead lies the real possibility of tragic deterioration.

A marriage guidance counsellor specializing in the problems of old age is certain 'that a bad relationship between husband and wife in old age is more than anything to do with a poor relationship throughout life'. He continued: 'So often a couple can keep going because they develop outside interests which keep them out of the house, and then they start to decline; they get feeble and they are forced on to each other's company and then the problems really arise. I wish we were more ready to accept divorce in old people. I see so many elderly couples who really shouldn't be living together. When younger couples break up, it is usually because they have fallen in love with somebody else. Older people need some sort of temptation to get them out of each other's company. I have seen some dreadfully distressing relationships – they've lived in the same house for the last ten years entirely separately, making each other totally miserable. It's not so much that they fight but that they don't talk to each other; they even eat separate meals. They would be so much happier apart, but as soon as you talk about living apart, the insecurity about selling the house and wondering where they are going to live becomes an insurmountable barrier. They are afraid of being lonely – and yet how much more lonely can they be within the confines of such a marriage? They may also be afraid that something will happen and they will need their partner to care for them – but who wants to be cared for by a spouse who can't stand them? Many of my clients have a terrible fear of going into an old people's home but I think they are often unnecessarily frightened. Although it is true some homes are terrible, others provide excellent care and would certainly offer a more cheerful and fulfilling life than a wretched, loveless marriage.'

Making the Break – a Case History

> When I was in my forties and early fifties, I was just too busy. I was always working and always tired. I should have decided at that time to become a full-time professional person, instead of which I tried to run a huge house and carry on demanding work which included writing a book and teaching. It didn't matter if I was at work or at home; I felt guilty either way. My marriage was not good. I am a Roman Catholic. My husband isn't. My religion means a lot to me and it has influenced me greatly all my life. We didn't have enough time for each other and we never were able to talk about the problems. If we had been able to talk we might have been able to change things. As it was, they stayed the same way and created very deep internal stresses. My husband was always a heavy drinker, but I'd say he has a serious problem with alcohol now. Recently I discovered that he has had a mistress for a long time. I was very upset when I found out, but it provided me with the excuse I needed. When my mother died, my whole life changed. Her death seemed to set me free. At fifty-seven, I was finally able to examine my own life and the relationship I have with my husband. Now, five years later, I have decided to leave him. It's something I should have done years ago. He doesn't want change, but I'm sure it's the best thing for both of us, even at this late stage in our lives. I'm glad I have been able to come to this decision. I feel it has transformed me in every way. But it wasn't easy and took far too long for me to recognize that a change was badly needed. It's so easy to fall back on old patterns of behaviour. Personality in old age is an exaggeration of what you've always been. Looking back on the past, I realize now just how unhappy I was. Had I not decided to alter my life so radically I

could see myself in old age becoming a miserable, bitter old woman – just like my mother in fact.

Twenty years ago, I would never have thought I would be doing what I'm doing now. For the first time in my life, I have a full-time job and can concentrate upon it entirely. There are no real responsibilities any more. Just to be able to focus on one activity which I love doing is very satisfying and very fulfilling. I'm enormously relieved and happy to have made the decision to leave my husband. My daughters seem happier too. The younger one has always lacked confidence and has had difficulty in making close relationships. She and I have become much closer in the last four years. Things are really looking up for her now. She has a serious boyfriend and feels good about herself. I certainly want to remarry or at least form a long-term relationship. I feel that I'm still an attractive woman and I should love to have the opportunity to start again. This is a wonderful time for me. My only fear is my health. Apart from slight asthma, I am very fit. It would be awful not to have the chance to enjoy my new life. I take much more care of myself now and am more aware of diet and exercise. I am careful too not to put myself under any unnecessary stress.

Separation and Divorce

Currently, over two thirds of divorce petitions in the UK are filed by women,[16] and it is true that women now expect more from their partners and have higher expectations for themselves within marriage. However, a study which traced the lives of married couples over the entire period from their engagement in 1935 to 1980 suggested that the outcome of a marriage – whether it ended in divorce or continued intact, albeit unhappily – tended to depend on the personality of the *man*. Not only did the man's actions begin the marriage, they also brought it to an end. A husband who felt impelled to act out his misery might behave in such a way as to force an unsatisfactory relationship to break up. He might, for instance, flaunt an affair or become physically violent, so that his wife would be left with no choice but to break out of the marriage; or he might, without warning, walk out of the house one day and never return. If, on the other hand, he was the kind of man who did not act on his unhappiness, the couple tended to remain married.[17] Statistics which seem to suggest that women are more likely to end a modern marriage will thus include the middle-aged housewife who has been driven to initiate divorce proceedings, despite the fact that it may entail the loss of a beloved partner, home, financial security and marital status.

Women born in the 1930s and 1940s, now aged fifty and over, were often brought up to consider marriage as their prime goal in life and many would take low-paid jobs just to fill the gap before 'tying the knot'. When I pleaded with my father to let me go to university, he replied: 'Certainly not. What's the point in my paying for you to get educated when you'll end up married with children?'

The lower priority given to education and training for women in the past has meant that many wives who are left alone in their forties and fifties have only one real resource to fall back on – the force of their own personality, which may or may not be strong enough to sustain them. Will they be able to muster the confidence to start a new life, which could include basic training and further education, or will they be lost without their assumed security and the habits of a lifetime, facing a sad and lonely future? According to Relate, formerly the National Marriage Guidance Council, the vast majority of their clients are in their mid-thirties and early forties. Relatively few women older than this are counselled by the organization.

These days, according to the latest figures, 37 per cent of all marriages end in divorce, and the stable, life-long marriage can no longer be assumed to be the norm. Younger women are often prepared to take a more independent role in a relationship, taking nothing for granted, but women who married twenty or thirty years ago were still largely influenced by the attitudes of the past. The plight of the older faithful wife left by her husband for a younger woman has always tended to be seen as embarassing and faintly risible – her bitterness and jealousy inappropriate and ridiculous.

Mrs C. was fifty-six when, two days after Christmas, her husband of twenty-five years told her he intended to leave her. She had managed to live with his affairs for several years for the sake of their marriage, the good and happy side of their life together and the esteem in which she held him. 'Why,' she asked when he broke the news, 'do you want to leave me when we are such good friends and have so much in common and when you know I give you freedom to live your own life and don't hassle you about your affairs?' 'Because you shouldn't have to live with me and a whole lot of other women as well; because I want to be surrounded by young and beautiful people and because you are too old to have sex with', came the ugly response from a selfish and irresponsible man unable to find sufficient excuse to break his marriage to an exemplary wife.

Changes

In youth marriage is idealized; if there is a crisis in middle life, it is often about relinquishing hopes and ideals and learning to recognize the reality of the marriage and its quality. In an interview, Evelyn Cleavely, psychotherapist and marriage counsellor at the Tavistock Centre, described middle age as 'a kind of mourning period when we are forced to grieve for the loss of our ideals whether it be the marriage or anything else. It is a time for facing up to the choices we've made and the choices we haven't. At this stage, one either comes to accept the marriage or decides to go different ways. Very often couples who do decide to remain together find that the energy used to encapsulate the new relationship is richly rewarding. Often the greatest changes involve not making the same demands on each other. To recognize that is a shared problem.'

Research has shown that marriages are at their most vulnerable in middle age and a great many couples are divorced in the ten years preceding retirement. Retirement, marriage and the birth of children, the time when the children leave home and divorce itself are periods of transition which require considerable adjustment and adaptation. All transitions are about beginnings and endings, about gains and losses. There is excitement in the knowledge that something is changing, but there is also fear – fear of the unknown in an uncertain future. One of the conditions of a period of transition is that one can be very torn between, on the one hand, having gone so far along the road that it would be satisfying to take it to the end, while, on the other, there is an overwhelming sense of anticlimax: 'Is this all there is?' The pull of continuity is difficult to appreciate until it has been lost. Divorced couples meeting up in later years may be overwhelmed by visions of all that would have been had they kept going and are filled with terrible regrets for the loss of their marriage.

Dr Joyce Brothers's analysis of the five stages in a man's life, *What Every Woman Should Know about Men*,[18] makes it clear that the way in which he emerges from the physically and psychologically stressful period of middle age is crucial in determining the quality of the rest of his life. If he has not solved the problems associated with those years, the resentment, bitterness and fear 'may become somewhat more marked' as he moves through the retirement stage to old age. If he is fundamentally gloomy and pessimistic, Brothers writes,

There is nothing a woman can do . . . except try to make her own life as satisfying as possible. She will not be able to change him. And she has to realize that he needs her more than he ever has. She is wife and mother to him now. He needs her love and her kindness. This may come hard at times, but the fact is, as many widows discover, it is very good to be needed. So do not stint on your affection towards this man you have spent so many years with. You should not underestimate the psychic rewards of knowing that you are the most important person in the world to your spouse.[19]

But is it really too late to change during these years of retirement? Must a man (or woman) be condemned to live what could be a quarter of a lifetime imprisoned by bitterness and fear? Carl Jung, whose thoughts on the psychology of ageing reveal so much wisdom and good sense, felt that as people approach the threshold of old age, they inevitably cast a backward glance at the unlived part of their lives, regretting those things they failed to do or to achieve, and it is at this moment, he insists, that 'a prospect and a goal in the future are absolutely necessary'. Life must have an aim.[20]

Those who follow the psychologist's advice and find 'a prospect and a goal' will also discover they are changed by the experience without having to make any special conscious effort to 'sort themselves out'. They will find that, when they have committed themselves to some absorbing and intellectually satisfying pursuit, the anxiety and fear which so occupied their thoughts has been banished, forced to make way for more important and exciting considerations.

The relative fragility of men – so eloquently and compassionately described by Dr Brothers – is something which women find themselves responding to instinctively, much in the same way as they would respond to the vulnerability of a child. 'A woman should never underestimate the power of the child in the man,' the psychologist warns.[21] One might also add that a woman should never underestimate the fear a man has about losing his sexual potency. Most begin to experience a decline in middle age and if there is an increase in sexual activity outside marriage at this stage, it is more often than not a panic response to the onset of what they feel in themselves to be an intolerable loss.

All this does not make a difficult, tyrannical, demanding, anxious, depressed or faithless man any easier to live with, but it may make him easier to understand, to help and to tolerate, and above all, to love.

Penny Mansfield, assistant director of the Marriage Research Centre at the Central Middlesex Hospital, told me: 'One of the things that emerges very poignantly in our research is that for men and women the meaning of togetherness is so very different. For men, togetherness is a life in common while women see it as a common life. Men talk of marriage as having someone they love to come home to, someone to fall back on, companionship at the end of the day. Women talk about marriage as having someone to love and to share everything with. They use similar words but the emphasis is very different.

'On the whole, it's still women who create the home life, look after the children and care for elderly relatives, so in fact the men's view of marriage is the more realistic. But women adjust to the loss of their ideal of togetherness by getting the additional emotional support they need from their children, from whom they receive a lot of affection, a lot of kissing and cuddling, a lot of reassurance. Therefore, when the children grow up and start leading their own lives, a woman may be drawn outside the home to regain a sense of purpose. The act of going into that new experience, whether it be some kind of training or a return to the workplace, makes her question the quality of her marriage and her family life. It becomes a threat. She may even find that she is drawn to other people who fill the gap in her emotional life. At the same time, her husband, who has been quite happy to have her at home, to be there and to reassure him, now finds she has other interests, other priorities. So – warning bells. Because men are not very good at expressing their emotions, their way of handling a problem is often to take some sort of physical action, and at this point, they may further threaten the marriage by having an affair.'

The Affair

But an affair is not an exclusively male territory. As one man commented: 'If 75 per cent of men are supposed to be unfaithful – and I admit to being one of them – where do they get their partners? Most of mine have been married women.'

Female sexuality is an area which has been greatly under researched, but what literature there is tends to confirm the accepted view that men are naturally unfaithful and women are naturally monogamous – that men's biological sexual urge is greater than women's. While the picture may be broadly true, it by no means tells the whole story. The following experience is not exceptional:

> I love my husband and our marriage has been a long and happy one. I certainly had no intention of leaving him when I met John. Our relationship was based on a mutual sexual attraction the like of which I've never experienced before or since: it was fantastic. I never knew it was possible to have such great sex. The affair lasted about six months but then I made the terrible mistake of telling my husband about it, thinking it was better to be honest about something which in the long run meant very little to me. For a while he went almost mad with grief. He started an affair with his secretary and our marriage very nearly broke up. It

taught me a dreadful lesson but, given the same circumstances, the desire for my lover was so overwhelmingly powerful that I don't think I could have acted any other way. I should have kept it a secret though.

According to Relate, two out of three men and nearly half of all married women are unfaithful to their partners.

Shere Hite, in *The Hite Report on Male Sexuality*,[22] found that the great majority of married men were not monogamous and that 72 per cent of men married for two years or more had had sex outside of marriage. Even if, as marriage guidance counsellors maintain, the vast majority of men involved in extramarital affairs are concerned to protect their marriages, the effect on the wife of her husband's infidelity can be devastating.

Men who have a long history of 'something on the side' have no difficulty in reconciling their dual commitments. One man told me:

I always tell the girl I'm a married man and will never divorce my wife. She usually accepts that and the affair continues until one or other of us has had enough. On the one hand, I have my marriage and the life I have with my wife whom I love, while on the other I have the excitement of being involved with different women. Sometimes the involvement lasts for a month, sometimes six months or a year, sometimes a week or so, or even just a couple of nights. I'm quite certain my wife knows nothing about my other life. I just regard it as something entirely separate.

Maybe his wife knew about his affairs; maybe she did not. Maybe in order to preserve her marriage, she was able to 'turn a blind eye' – many women do just that. But what of the woman who discovers her husband's affair and cannot hide from it. How does she cope with the pain? This is one woman's response:

I suppose I am still very much in love with him or else I would not care so much. We have a very close relationship and spend a great deal of time together and when all is well, it's difficult to see how our marriage could be happier. We normally have a very active sex life; we make love anything from once a day to two or three times a week, depending on the opportunity. But sex is the first thing to go when someone else comes on the scene. I feel at the same time undesirable and miserably rejected. I'm nearly fifty now and I can't help knowing how ugly I must look compared to someone much younger. The first time my husband had an affair during our marriage, I didn't understand what was going on for a month or so. I just knew things weren't right. I thought he might be troubled by a period of impotence and need my help to get things going again, so I went out and bought some new underwear and appeared in it at what seemed like an appropriate moment. It was something which had always pleased him in the past. I don't think I shall ever really recover from the look of absolute disgust and revulsion which crossed over his face. Even after eight years, I am still ashamed of my body. Sex has always been a very important part of our marriage to me. I enjoy it and need it much the same as any man, I suppose, but I never feel free to express myself sexually as I would really like to. Pretty underwear is a prerequisite now. It makes me feel more confident, certainly, and my husband prefers it. But just sometimes, I long to be spontaneous – not to bother about hiding my body, but if I appeared in my husband's presence in the nude, I'm terrified he would find me disgusting again.

Although marriages may heal and relationships often become deeper and more committed following an affair, the scars left by the experience can never be wholly eradicated. If a marriage is strong enough to withstand the battering, it will still require considerable adaptation and change on a wife's part in order to protect her own image and self-esteem, as the following illustrates:

It's difficult not to know when he's having an affair. It's not only the sex that goes; we stop talking to each other. All our conversations, sometimes intimate and important, but usually just comfortable, inconsequential chat and gossip change to a continuation on my part and a lack of response on his. After a while, without the feedback, I find I just lapse into a wretched silence. The nights are bad sometimes too and I get horrible nightmares and wake up crying and shaking.

So far, I don't think my husband has ever wanted to leave me. When life gets back to normal after the affair has finished, he seems for a while not to want me out of his sight. Everything is lovely again. But a few months later, I suppose he just gets bored and along comes someone else. The first time it happened, I couldn't sleep and spent half the days in tears. Sometimes I would leave the house in the night and drive for hours in the car. My husband could see I was in an awful state, but it wasn't about to deter him. Anyway, he always denied the affair until it was all over; then he admitted to it and said he was sorry I had been hurt. I went to my family doctor, who was wonderfully kind and suggested I go and talk to a psychotherapist who specialized in marital problems. I had already spoken to a couple of close women friends who were very supportive, but in this instance, I think one benefits enormously from talking over the problem with an outsider. I have had to come to realize that eventually, there is a chance my husband will leave me and that my age is probably against me. I am gradually learning to think more independently and I have forced myself to take on more interests outside my home. Because your confidence takes such a knock on these occasions, I've found the best way to revive it is to meet more people. I have a part-time job now which fits in with the family life and keeps me much too busy to worry about what my husband may or may not be doing. I love him and I know, despite it all, that he loves me; if I wasn't sure of that, there wouldn't be much point in struggling on. I have made half-hearted attempts to run away, but I really don't want to leave him. I know I should always regret it if I did. Maybe if I can see him through these next few years, he will settle down. Together, I know we have all the ingredients for great happiness in old age.

One woman who lived through the storm and emerged with her marriage and her relationship with her husband intact felt able to offer advice in the light of her own experience:

When it became obvious my husband was having an affair, it was difficult to know what questions to ask and when to ask them. Timing is very important. I told him one evening at supper that I knew what was going on and asked, 'Do you still like spending your time with me or has it all gone; or don't you know?' He was very honest. He said he was sorry; I was right in my assumptions and if I could only hang on, he knew the affair would not last long but he simply had to see it through to the end. In the short term his response was terribly upsetting, but in the long term, when I became adjusted to the idea, I was grateful. I trust my husband; he never lies. It seems rather a contradiction in terms when he is off having an affair, but his honesty helped me to understand his needs. Our relationship was not sterile but it didn't provide him with the sexual excitement he needed. The only thing I would not be able to deal with is the thought that somebody who loves me could lie, deceive and prevaricate, and make me out to be the fool. I was in a position to say at the time, 'Look, if you aren't going to be straight with me, then we have no life together'. People first of all have to be sure they respect and like the person they are married to and whether they want the relationship to continue. If you like someone enough and feel sympathy that they are struggling too, you can distance yourself from what's going on. There has to be a dialogue in which the person having the affair agrees to tell the truth, be considerate and kind and behave well – no phone calls, and no gifts or mementoes to be brought back, which can be identified with the affair and cause pain. One of the first things to go when you are depressed and anxious is the housework, but it's important to keep up a warm and civilized environment where at least friendship can flourish. The home must be welcoming enough to make a man feel pleased to come back to; outside interests have to be developed too – there's nothing more destructive than brooding.

In an interview, Dr Jack Dominian, senior consultant psychiatrist at the Central Middlesex Hospital, and founder of the Marriage Research Centre there, agreed that there is a fragility in men which is both emotional and physical. He told me: 'It really starts when the infant is born. Many more male babies die, for example. Emotionally, I think men are more fragile, in the sense that the affectivity of women is much deeper, much more penetrating, much wider – so for the whole cycle of marriage, it is women's affectivity which supports the restlessness and superficial affectivity of men, especially in the forty-to-sixty period.

'Men have three problems; first, in terms of success – the difficulties of staying at the top. Then you have disappointment – the disappointment of not reaching the top – and finally, you have unemployment. When the children leave home, a man is likely to have less contact with them than their mother. I think therefore, that he finds himself, at this time particularly, not so pertinent to the family structure.

'People talk about a sexual menopause in men. I don't think there is such a thing, but I do think there is considerable anxiety at this time. My experience is that people in their forties and early fifties now want to experiment where they didn't experiment in their adolescence. I think they want to have love affairs, but at the same time, unless they are deeply frustrated and disappointed, they don't want to change their marital status, and I think in that sense, women have to realize that men are looking round without ever ceasing to regard them as their eternal companion.'

Women do not reach a sexual peak until they are in their mid-thirties or early forties. If their marriages are not sexually fulfilling, they too will feel the need to satisfy their sexuality. The problem for them has much to do with society's double standards. Despite the apparently increasing number of married women who have affairs, it is still considered more shameful than it is for married men. The people who are outraged by the illicit sex life of a public figure will wink at each other knowingly over the affair of a friend or acquaintance – provided, of course, that he is male. If a middle-aged woman shows evidence of jealousy on discovering her husband's affair, she is ridiculed and described as 'menopausal'. Part of her jealousy, it is assumed, has to do with her ageing appearance and the youth of her husband's lover, and for this natural reaction she is scorned. Husbands, on the other hand, when their wives turn to another man, are pitied and showered with sympathy, and again the woman is seen as being in the wrong.

These double standards are rooted in the mistaken assumption that biologically men need sex and women do not. Men cannot help themselves; women can, therefore there is no need for them to be tempted into committing adultery. A consultant psychiatrist specializing in psychosexual behaviour expressed the opinion that it was 'a great mistake to think an object of sexual desire is more consciously sought out by men'. He said, 'I think we underestimate badly women's sexuality and sexual needs. It's not fashionable – not part of our culture to say so, but I think in the privacy of the bedroom, many women initiate and desire sex as much as men. The only difference is that for men it is much more a physical and biological urge, while women are generally more emotionally involved. I think women were traditionally far more tolerant of men's affairs than they are today. Now, things are different. Women are becoming much more conscious that they have got to be treated better than they were a generation or two ago. I would say that a great deal of marital breakdown is caused by the increasing non-acceptance by women of treatment in terms of adultery and in terms of cruelty'.

Men and Women – Equal Powers of Communication?

It is often said that women find it easier to communicate their feelings than men and that male reserve forms a barrier against a close marriage relationship. Interviewing the many hundreds of people who contributed to this book, I found men were at least as honest about themselves as women. If anything, women were inclined to be more guarded, especially when describing their sex lives. The fact is that men derive great relief from communicating very closely with members of the opposite sex and are able to talk freely and intimately about their problems and their feelings, provided there is no hint of sexual involvement on either side.

Within marriage, if one or both partners has something to hide, intimate discussion becomes an obstacle course over an eggshell surface. What should you conceal from your spouse in order to protect the marriage and what reveal in order to nurture intimacy? The following extract is taken from an interview with a man close to retirement who found that as age increased so had the joy of his marriage, in which he had discovered unexpected depths of companionship and pleasure, and yet –

> You ask me, if my marriage is as perfect as I describe it what was it that made me so consistently unfaithful over the years? The answer I suppose is that, close as we are, Ann and I, we don't have an exciting physical relationship. The one thing I miss in our lives together is sex, but if I was being strictly honest with myself, I think it is my fault, because there have been quite a number of occasions when Ann has wanted sex and has wanted us to be more intimate when I have shrugged off her advances, or made a joke of it or anyway done something to prevent us making love. That means, for example, I think we have had sex once in the last three months, whereas I know her need is for more than that.
>
> What I can't get now from Ann is an erection. Let's put it this way. Up until the age of about fifty to fifty-five, we were very active as a couple and I was pretty

active elsewhere as well. For the last four years, Ann has had hot flushes and I began to notice a decline in my own potency from about fifty-five. I find I need much more and perhaps more obvious stimulation. I'm not able to do that with Ann. That side of our relationship atrophied.

I am still aroused by particular stimuli – photographs, or being told a story about someone else's experiences, so the urge is still there, but when I've reached a certain stage and want release, I find it much easier and more convenient to do it myself than – I was going to say, 'to bother Ann', but of course, it wouldn't be bothering her, she would be absolutely delighted. But I don't fancy it – it's too much effort. Also I'm afraid it may not work.

Then there was the time when as a symptom of the menopause, penetration was very painful for her and the thought that I might hurt her meant my arousal was soon dissipated. I worked it out that it would be better all round if I didn't expect sex with her and made other arrangements. Now I do find it more convenient the way I've worked it out for myself. I can remember a long time ago a bloke, then in his mid-thirties, who swore by the do-it-yourself method because his wife was always tired or had a headache. Eventually, he gave up trying to have sex with her and decided to do it just for his own satisfaction. That's how it has become with me. Not long ago, I tried to do something different but the experience left me feeling thoroughly ashamed. I responded to some ad in a window – 'Gracie, massage'. I rang up Gracie and went along. I felt really awful. The fact that the person didn't care who I was made the whole thing so degrading.

I argued with myself that I was doing Ann a good turn by not bothering her. I think I've now argued myself into that position even though I know it isn't true. But also she recognized the difficulties there and I think somehow understands why we have very little sex. What she does say, and what she has always said, is that a really close, warm cuddle is quite as good. And we do have lots of kissing, lots of cuddles and lots of hugs, but no sex.

I asked Mr X. whether he had tried to talk to his wife about their sexual differences. He replied:

No, I didn't ever discuss our sex life with her. I knew about the effect of the menopause on women's sexuality and I know about the benefits of HRT, but I was afraid she would wonder where I got that information from. The fact is I got it from someone else with whom I was having an affair at the time. In a strange sort of way – a guilty way – I didn't want to let on that I had this information. Anyway, I was sure she would read about it or go to her doctor. I am certain our problem stems from us both trying to be too considerate of each other's feelings. She perhaps does not discuss sex with me just in case she might reveal that I'm not as potent as I used to be or that sex between us is not as good as it used to be. I also have to face the fact that I kid myself I don't want to trouble her any more when, in reality, I don't want to have sex with her any more.

'Why Can't a Woman be More like a Man?'

The frustrated Professor Higgins who asked this question of his protegée Eliza Doolittle in the musical comedy, *My Fair Lady*, might now be begging her to be more like a woman. The tendency for the gender roles to blur in middle age as men become more caring and thoughtful and women begin to take a little more care of themselves, does not necessarily make the path to adult maturity any less thorny. In fact, it can impose considerable stress upon a marriage. When a woman decides to return to work in the middle years, the differences in her routine are bound to affect her husband, despite the relief of additional money coming into the family: he may welcome the change or – particularly if he is working his way through an emotional crisis – he may react against it. Her job and involvement in a world outside the home may cause him to feel neglected and unloved.

Despite the difficulties inherent in the changing needs of men and women, the passage to middle age is generally marked with equanimity and not a little relief. The following are fairly typical of the responses gained from my own research and would tend to support the feelings of relative comfort and acceptance which characterizes this stage of life:

David, aged fifty-six:

> Ah well, I suppose middle age is progress from sitting on a bench in the park, needing sex every half an hour and not even having the price of a drink in your pocket.

Alexander, aged-fifty-five:

> Six months ago I was very depressed. I felt my life was over. Why? because I discovered that what I wanted was not going to be mine. I wanted the love of more than one woman at once. I was greedy for love and I began to discover the trouble that got me into. I wanted everything and I realized I wasn't going to get it. It was so painful it felt like dying, but now things have changed and I'm happy. I suppose the depression was for the most part due to the consequences of my wife leaving and then getting divorced. A year or so ago she remarried. The whole process took a long time to work through. I thought I couldn't afford to live. I've had to come to terms with loneliness and rejection, and I've had to learn how to be a single parent, to cook for myself and the children.

Mark, aged fifty-nine:

> I was married when I was twenty-one and have a son and daughter born when I was twenty-four and twenty-six. My father died when I was three, and I suppose I married young to escape from my very dominant mother. Pauline and I really had nothing in common and our sex life was a disaster. We separated for many years before we finally divorced when I was

aged forty-four – a year after my mother died. She would have been horrified if we had divorced with her knowledge. Pauline is a tremendously nice person and we are close friends now. My life has been a series of long-term overlapping relationships – from my mother to my wife and to Marion, with whom I was very much in love. Our relationship lasted for about twelve years but broke up a couple of years ago. I still miss her and I miss not having a permanent relationship. It's taken me a long time to adjust to being on my own. I recently had a week's holiday alone and it was a revelation. I suddenly realized how much I had changed. I had spent too many years trying to sort out Marion's various problems without much attention to my own. In a way, you have to find yourself before you have a mature relationship with somebody else. Now I feel I'd like to be with someone else but I've discovered that it's not essential to my well-being. I'd like to have space. I feel lonely some-times but I'd like to form a relationship that is egalitar-ian – not one in which I can see myself as teacher-to-pupil or saviour-of-victim.

Irene, aged sixty:

Although you could say my moment of crisis coin-cided with the onset of my menopause at fifty, I had really very little trouble with the 'change', either psy-chologically or physiologically. But my crisis did have to do with my age. I was out shopping. It was a cold day and I was feeling a bit low. The cold made me hunch up inside my coat and my face felt pinched and icy. Nevertheless, the weather was not responsi-ble for the sight of myself which I caught in the mirror in the shop. I found myself looking at this old lady and it took me several seconds to realize the old lady was me. It was horrible. I was worn, wrinkled and haggard. The reflection I saw was me and yet it wasn't me because it didn't feel like me. It was a terrible experience – such a shock. It was the awful realization that I was an old woman. It is not as though my appearance has ever meant a great deal to me. I have never worn make-up or tinted my hair and I've never had a particular interest in clothes, but from that moment, I decided not to look so sloppy – to look neater. I have reached the point now that I can accept the physical signs of ageing. My husband has helped me over the hump. He is wonderfully reassuring. What made me begin to feel good about myself again was exercise. I swim for half an hour every day and feel very fit and well. Exercise has become very important to both my husband and myself. He prefers to run daily, but together we walk a lot, especially when we are on holiday.

The Second Marriage

Second marriages have a very poor track record. In 1988, according to government statistics,[23] the proportion of partners divorcing for a second or third time rose to nearly a quarter of all the divorces filed. The most vulnerable couples were found to be those in which the man was married in his teens and where the marriage was the man's second.[24]

For the most part, second marriages take place under particularly stressful circumstances. More often than not, they involve a divorce, and children – perhaps from both sides of a relationship – are brought together unwillingly to form a step-family. The process is neither easy nor straightforward and places a great emotional burden on all concerned. It is a far cry from the simple, uncluttered event of the first marriage when a couple could shut the doors on departing wedding guests and concentrate on each other.

Even if a couple manages to overcome all these hurdles and restructure their new family successfully, they may still end up once again in the divorce courts. Why? Well, of course there are never single answers to any of the problems which attach to human relationships, but one possible cause of marital break-up the second time around emerged during an interview I had with a forty-two-year-old divorced father of three. During his first marriage this man had had two very passionate love affairs and rather than deceive his wife, he had decided to confide in her. Some time later, she left him for someone else. He was distraught. He loved her and didn't want her to leave him. 'But why,' I asked, 'did you have the affairs if you loved your wife so much and did not want to lose her?' He replied with great sadness, 'But women have babies, don't they?' At first, I was astonished by this remark. He was a man I knew to be a devoted father, who had always shared the everyday care of his children with his wife and managed to continue to do so even after they were separated. Having his children had been, in his own words 'the greatest experience of my life'. When I had grasped the significance, however, I realized how much his comments underlined the need in many men to be nurtured and loved in a way that is both exclusive and undivided. The demands of motherhood make this impossible. If a man in middle age, full of anxieties and emotionally vulnerable, begins his second marriage with a family of stepchildren and perhaps a new baby, he may feel once again let down, cast aside, neglected and unloved. To boost his crumbling ego at this critical period in his own life cycle, it is quite likely that he will turn to another woman, thus placing his second marriage in jeopardy.

Some time after my talk with the confused and unhappy father, the nature of his predicament was brought to light by an interview with Penny (then aged sixty-six and married to Matthew for forty-five years). Her case demonstrates how a wife's emotional allegiance can be transferred from her husband to her children, and even though this transference may not necessarily be permanent, one can anticipate the consequences. It is not difficult to see how a man might feel abandoned and bewildered by the changes involved in his wife's behaviour towards him and, in the long run, seek an alternative relationship to shore up his damaged ego:

> In mid-life, I was so wound up with my children. Sometimes I would think 'there has to be something more than this', but I was very content. I went back to part-time teaching when I was about thirty-seven and the girls had started school. In my early forties, I went back to college to study for a master's degree in sociology. I then got a job as an academic adviser at

the university where my husband worked. Now that our daughters have left home and have settled down with families of their own, it has meant that Matthew and I can concentrate on each other and upon our own lives. One of the girls asked me recently, 'Whom do you love better, Daddy or us?' I had to think quite a while before answering – 'When you were small, it was the three of you who were most important to me; now it is Daddy.' 'I'm so relieved you said that,' my daughter replied, 'because if you were to ask me that question now, there would be no doubt in my mind that it would be the boys I loved best.' We decided that we both felt that way at the time because young children are so helpless. Now, curiously enough, Matthew seems more vulnerable to me.

If such pressures on a partnership can be brought about by the advent of their own children in a first marriage, how much more complex and heavy will those pressures become on a second marriage, involving stepchildren and a second family. From full-time lover to full-time mother at the stroke of a signature on a marriage licence! If a woman can fill those quite separate roles successfully, she either has an exceptionally unegocentric second husband or she is indeed a wonder. More often than not, her problems begin with the children.

Robert B. is a prison officer. Anna is his second wife and they have two children of eighteen months and three years old. Robert was previously married at nineteen and had five children. His first wife left him. He was unable to care for all the children on his own, so the younger three went to live with an aunt and he had sole care of Simon (sixteen) and Debbie (fourteen). Recently Robert's first wife decided that she wanted to see Simon and Debbie again but soon after renewing her relationship with them, her enthusiasm waned and her contacts are rare. Now Anna and Robert are experiencing serious difficulties with both children. Simon is beginning to steal and Debbie is anxious and acutely depressed. While Anna realizes that her stepchildren need special care and attention, she has her own two toddlers to care for and a demanding part-time job which brings in much-needed income. Now she and Robert have chosen to seek professional help together because they both felt that the stresses involved were beginning to threaten their marriage. They agree that their experience of counselling has drawn them closer together but Anna pointed out, 'It was the joint decision to go for help that was the real turning-point. I felt then that Robert really cared about me and about keeping us all together.'

The Fear of Death

Ask anyone in middle age when they first began to feel 'old' and you will find that the most common response concerns the intimation of their own mortality:

Michael:

> The issue of mortality first really began to occur to me in my forties. The realization that you are going to die just like everyone else really shakes you. My father died when I was forty-two and I was much saddened by his death. I was forty-six when my mother died. Now I look at friends whose parents are still alive and I can see that they are still bracing themselves for the event, while what I now have to face is my own death and the possible deaths of my wife and children.

Robert:

> I have reached middle age without anything to show for my life except my three children. I went to one of the most prestigious universities in the land. It's seen me through but I haven't actually done anything with it. Most of my creative energies in the past have been spent in adulterous relationships. I'm terrified of death and illness, and I suppose I see sex as the only thing which successfully manages to blot out images of the grave.

Patrick:

> Everything went to pieces at forty. Two of my school friends died of cancer that year. It suddenly made me realize how little time I have left.

Anne described her husband's crisis in middle age:

> He wouldn't give in and say what was bothering him, but if I brought it up and started talking, he would let it out. He kept questioning his life's work – 'Looking back over my life, what on earth have I done with it,' he kept saying. He was constantly questioning the value of his scholarship – whether it had been a useful contribution or whether it was really what he had wanted to do. He was also terrified of death. He wanted to live for ever. It was then that he began to swim compulsively. He had to have his exercise or he felt depressed and restless.

Death is a biological inevitability, but it could be argued that the *fear* of death is culturally determined. Death is not universally feared. In some cultures it is welcomed as a move towards a new and happier existence; for the Christian, for example, who believes in life everlasting in the Kingdom of Heaven the fear of death is diminished.

If, then, we begin to regard the fear of death as a cultural phenomenon, theoretically at least it should be within our power to 'deconstruct' that fear. 'Living with the constant fear of death rather than just the awareness of death contaminates life and adversely affects man's capacity to enjoy it,' writes David Cole Gordon in a book entitled *Overcoming the Fear of Death*. 'If we lived with the realization that this very moment might be our last, we would find that many problems and conflicts would evanesce and life would be simplified and become more satisfying,' he suggests.[25]

To strong, healthy, vital youth, death seems too remote to contemplate. For many of us, intimations of our own mortality occur when we experience the ill health or death of our parents, and when we fully come to comprehend that our own death is also inescapable the thought is truly terrifying. Some psychiatrists suggest that the so-called 'mid-life crisis' is not only inevitable but is directly connected to the fear of death, and the way that that fear is resolved is directly related to the development of our personalities in middle and old age.

When both parents die, we suddenly become nobody's child.

To find ourselves without the security of a parental home and the easy familiarity of parental guidance and support is traumatic. Yet, in a sense, it is the loss of our parents, together with the experience of caring for them during periods of illness and debility, which propels us into the final stage of adult development, when we acquire an emotional maturity which, by definition, cannot be established while the bonds of childhood remain. While we are still somebody's child, we cling to the nest in ways that are both conscious and unconscious. However grievous the loss of our parents may seem at the time, standing alone, we have a clear space in which to become our own person.

The human spirit is not something which can be measured empirically, yet whereas it is human nature to fear death, the spirit can overcome that fear. It is the greatest resource we have and the older we become, the more we need to exploit it. The triumph of old age comes when the fear of death is eliminated. A very dear friend told me recently: 'My doctor has just confirmed that I have terminal cancer. Don't worry,' she said, putting her arm around me. 'What do you expect at eighty-four? I'm an old lady. I'm not afraid to die. That doesn't mean I'm giving up. On the contrary, I'm going to make every minute count. I'm off on a trip to the Channel Islands with a couple of friends tomorrow. When I return who knows? I'll just take it from there.' On his eightieth birthday, another friend said: 'You know, it's strange, but I'm not afraid to die. I've had a wonderful life and every day I live now I feel is a bonus.'

Does the fear of death worry women as much as it does men? I can produce no empirical evidence, but my own research based on interviews with people between the ages of fifty and ninety-eight tended to suggest that on the whole women did not fear death in the same way that men appeared to do. If the woman had borne children, the following response was typical, whether they were married or, like the interviewee, bringing up children as a single parent:

> I had just separated from my husband and was living
> the life of a single parent, that is, I was entirely
> responsible for the care and welfare of two very

unhappy teenagers. The responsibility and stress were overwhelming. I used to wake up during the nights covered in sweat, feeling absolute terror. I thought, 'What will happen to the children if I die or suffer from some form of debilitating disease.' Only recently have I been able to look at them – now grown up, settled and happily doing what they want to do – without this fear that I might die before they are ready to take care of themselves. It's such a load off the mind that I almost feel reborn. Of course, I don't welcome the idea of death, especially my own, but I'm no longer so afraid to die.

Implications in research studies would suggest that women generally find the whole process of growing old far less intimidating than men. When the time comes for them to face old age, many of their fears – which concern their children rather than themselves – seem to have already been resolved.

Until Death Us Do Part

Evelyn Cleavely, marital psychotherapist at the Tavistock Clinic, relates the theories concerning the fear of death not only to the so-called 'mid-life crisis' but also to a time of serious crisis within marriage:

'Affairs are probably the most common destroyers of marriage. They happen as often at fifty-five or sixty as they do at forty or forty-five and certainly involve women as well as men. They are very often symptomatic of the fear of death. The anxiety is about losing their partner. One way of dealing with it or denying it is to have an affair. If they're really faced with their husband's affair, women find it very difficult to recover from their sense of failure and humiliation. The biggest problem is really about trust. It is hard not to be always looking over your shoulder.

'It is very rare indeed for couples over sixty-five to come to us – after so many years together, the alternatives are unthinkable – but occasionally we see cases where a man has married a much younger woman. In one instance, a man of seventy came to us quite suicidal because his forty-six year-old wife was having an affair. For her, it was a way of denying his approaching death and a way of coping with her distress in anticipation of it, while at the same time trying to find someone who would care for her after her husband died. His attempted suicide was a way of drawing attention to his own death. In this case, we had to help him over the pain of relinquishing the marriage and tried to make him see that it was his wife's fear of losing him which caused the affair. Understanding this somehow makes the situation more benign.

'For another couple in their early fifties I saw recently, death was involved in a rather different way. The husband had developed a very serious heart condition which required surgery. Instead of acknowledging it and having something done about it, he did everything he was warned against doing by his doctor. He jogged for miles each day and worked out in a gym. His wife was frantic with worry. Her anxiety took the form of hypochondria and she developed a variety of physical symptoms which were stress-related. The marriage was in serious trouble and the family doctor referred the couple to us. We tried to get the husband to accept his heart complaint but two days after coming to us, the wife made a very serious suicide attempt. We insisted she continue seeing us while she was recovering in hospital. We were very tough and she was furious with us. But it was fine. The husband had his surgery and she recovered fully. Their marriage is stable again'.

Coming to Terms with the Physical Signs of Ageing

Physical deterioration is perhaps one of the most difficult aspects of ageing to come to terms with in middle age. The discovery of baldness, greying hair, wrinkles and a spreading waistline provides devastating and inescapable evidence that we are no longer young and therefore no longer seem immune to the inevitable:

Neil, aged fifty-two:

> It's shocking when you look at your own physical degeneration but more shocking to witness the alteration in others.

Mary, aged fifty:

> What makes it so difficult for older people is that one always thinks one is much younger. I still feel I'm twenty-one inside but I look at my contemporaries with horror sometimes when I realize that I must appear to everyone else to be the same age as they are. I am a middle-aged person now and soon I will be an old person. I will have this mask on that says I am old and yet inside I feel I'm young, I want adventure and I haven't yet decided what I want to be when I grow up.

Phillip, aged fifty-eight:

> After my divorce I found making new relationships fraught with difficulties. Mostly, these relationships involved much younger women. They never lasted very long but they weren't really failures. I just discovered that we had nothing in common. You go to a restaurant and at the end of the meal, you find that conversation flags over the coffee.
>
> I want vitality and youthfulness. I like the life in young people. Youth is very attractive. I became very fond of one girl in particular but I found that her being young, as opposed to being youthful, she seemed to me to belong to a different world. There was a terrible barrier of time and of physical deterioration. I remember meeting her with some members of my own generation. 'You've had a haircut,' she exclaimed. Then she whispered: 'You look ever so much younger with your hair cut.' All seemingly affectionate but she could see my bald spot – I couldn't. It isn't so much what time has done to a fifty-year-old, but what time does to twenty-five-year-olds. After a while, you have before you an entirely different person. Now I feel it's spring after winter. I have found someone of my own age whom I find both attractive and youthful.

Wives are well aware of the extent to which husbands cherish the memory of their youthful beauty. 'A husband is someone who has a photo of his wife on his desk in the office showing her as she used to look, not as she looks in middle or old age,' was the wry comment from a company wife trying to come to terms with her ageing face.

I asked a distinguished portrait painter whether any of his sitters had expressed anxiety about the physical signs of ageing. Did they, I wondered, try and persuade him to leave out the lines and wrinkles in their portraits? He replied:

'Women do worry about the way they look when they are older. Not so long ago I painted a lady who was in her late sixties. She was a wonderful woman – the sort of person one hoped to be seated next to at a dinner party. She had irregular features and had never been a great beauty, but there was a vitality and attractiveness in her face which was quite extraordinary. I was very much afraid that I might not have the skill to capture this unique quality, which was after all the result of some invisible power generated from within. However, just before the portrait was finished, friends and family came to see it and were delighted. They said I had captured her exactly. When my sitter came to view the finished work, it was a different story. She was profoundly upset. I asked her, "Don't you think it looks like you?" "Yes", she replied. "It looks exactly like me, but I don't want to look like that. I want my grandchildren to remember me as beautiful. You must straighten my nose and take away some of the lines." I explained to her that I couldn't do that. To do so would have gone against everything I believed in as a portrait painter. So she ordered that the painting be completely destroyed. On the other hand, most of my male sitters don't worry overmuch about their bald heads or their facial lines. Age goes with their success. After all, at thirty, they are still scrambling up their particular working ladder; at sixty or so, they are at the top.'

The stark contrast between images of women as young and beautiful and old, haggard and ugly are deeply engrained in the collective psyche. Beauty in old age is associated with the spirit, not the outward appearance. Our artistic and literary heritage stamps its indelible mark on the female consciousness long before the experience of modern mores have time to undermine the confidence further. Women cannot always avoid the pain and the shock which comes as age transforms them, not perhaps because time marks them so dramatically while they are still feeling vigorous and youthful but because they lose the sexual regard essential to their self-esteem. 'After the age of fifty, or fifty-five if you are lucky, you no longer count as a woman. Men pass you in the street as if you don't exist. They may like you as a person, but they don't think of you as a sexual being', was one woman's reaction to her middle age.

Changes in Sexuality
(See also Chapter 6, Health)

Research has shown that men in their early fifties 'place a higher value on a good sex life than women, as do those in the more affluent socio-economic groups. Some three out of ten men and one in five women were prepared to identify with the statement that a good sex life is important at any age.'[26]

There may not be the physical urgency for either men or women in the second half of life, but sex plays a role no less dominant than in young adulthood, and its importance cannot be overestimated. Apart from physical pleasure, sex fulfils a woman's deeply felt desire for security. Sex in marriage is a sign that her husband loves and needs her and still finds her physically attractive. A sudden change in the rhythm of her sex life may make a wife feel she is no longer wanted and she may become anxious and unhappy – and perhaps not without cause, for sex deprivation may be the first sign she has that her husband is having an affair. Although many women report an increase in affection given to them by their husbands at such times, it does not compensate them for the fact that they are sharing an important aspect of their marriage with someone else.

A psychiatrist explained the changing pattern of sex in the second half of married life: 'In the early years of marriage, sex is much more an expression of immediate physical pleasure. From mid-life on, however, there is a deepening awareness of sex in which the shared life, the shared discovery, the sharing of the increased experience of one another is channelled into sex which may be less frequent but in fact it encapsulates a much deeper representation of what's happening in a couple's non-sexual life. Sex becomes an expression of their fears, their emotions, their social life and their intellectual life. Sex in the second half of married life has more significance and expresses a greater degree of intimacy'.

Women from Forty-five to Fifty-five – a Vulnerable Age

Research is just beginning to show that for many women, the few years prior to the menopause are more likely to cause psychological unhappiness than either the cessation of the menses or the post-menopausal period. Although the subject is dealt with more fully in Chapter 6, I feel it is appropriate to introduce it here because changes now associated with the menopause can occur some years before the onset of any obvious symptoms. Typically, a woman might present herself to the family doctor complaining of irritability, depression, anxiety, insomnia and a feeling of being unable to cope with life, when she was perfectly able to do so before. His inquiries elicit information suggesting she is under considerable psychological stress and under the circumstances her symptoms would seem hardly surprising. All at one time, she is caring for ailing relatives, she is having difficulty with teenage children, she has problems with her marriage and she is trying to keep on top of a demanding job. In response to her concerns, the doctor will probably send her away from the surgery with tranquillizers or antidepressants; but psychotropic drugs will not help her much if her symptoms are due to perimenopausal ('climacteric') hormonal changes which may affect her emotional stability.

In middle age, women's ability to cope is often put to the severest test. That they manage to triumph more often than not is a tribute to their astonishing strengths and adaptability, but in the forty-five to fifty-five age group, particularly if there is a history of premenstrual syndrome or postnatal depression, a normally stable woman may find herself suddenly affected by unfamiliar psychological symptoms which make coping more difficult. If the general practitioner seems unable to help, a visit to a menopausal clinic may relieve much unnecessary suffering (see pp. 288–91, 390–94).

Relationships with the Adult 'Children'

All parents experience changes in their relationship with their children as they move from childhood towards adulthood. Even for the majority of families who do not perceive themselves as having 'problems' with their teenage children, the experience of watching them grow up can still be painful. Nancy P. remembers the sufferings of her husband, William:

> He hated it when the girls brought home their boyfriends. He was miserably jealous. There was a terrible family crisis when one of them, then aged nineteen, went to live with a young man. I have never known him so angry. He refused ever to see the boy and could hardly bring himself to talk to our daughter. In the end, I was so wound up, and the family was so affected, that I had to ask him if he would mind if I discussed the problem with a friend who was a professional counsellor. Since he had no objection, I went and unburdened myself to my friend and felt much better afterwards. Although William could not bring himself to discuss his feelings of jealousy with me, the fact that he knew I was forced to talk to someone else about it made him more conscious of his own behaviour. He never did speak to our daughter's boyfriend and when the relationship broke up he was very relieved. On the other hand, after that particular episode, he seemed to calm down, and I can't remember the girls having any more trouble with their father.

The shared experience of parenthood consists of a common concern for the children. It is a concern which continues to involve us in their lives and remains with us whether the 'children' are aged four or forty-four.

The parallel between the late teenage years and adult middle age is very close. Problems of identity, sexuality and self-confidence are common to both ages and are most likely to exacerbate conflict between the generations at this time. Teenagers are acutely conscious of the behaviour of their parents. The embarrassment caused – from the youngster's point of view –

by an overloud voice or inappropriate laughter can be excruciating. Parents should be seen but not heard and, if seen, should wear garments which blend unobtrusively into the background! While adults should not, obviously, drown their own identity for the sake of their maturing children, the need to be considerate of the feelings of the younger generation also reflects the need to adjust to their own mature status in middle age. No young adult, for example, wants to feel that their mother or father is a sexual rival.

The great majority of young people I interviewed were overwhelmingly positive about their parents' and grandparents' generations. Their positive views placed the process of ageing in its true perspective, namely that it is not just about deterioration but it is also about maturity and development:

Pam, aged nineteen:

> I generally respect older people, not so much for what they are or what they do, but just because they have had so much more experience. If I go to my parents with a problem, or even friends of theirs whom I particularly like, I find that their perspective is so different that very often what I may see as a serious problem becomes to them a minor difficulty which they can show me how to solve in an instant. Older people are a useful source of knowledge.

Negative attitudes were expressed in such complaints as:

Ann, aged twenty:

> The boring thing about older people is that they're always right even when they're wrong!

Bill, aged twenty-one:

> Older people always try to make you think you owe them. You're there to look after them. But they've had their turn. Now it's ours.

Mark, aged twenty-three:

> One often hears older people say: 'We didn't have television in our day yet we always managed to amuse ourselves in other ways'; but so what? We amuse

ourselves in other ways too, but we have television as well. Lucky us! They like to give the impression that young people were nicer and better behaved in their day and that the world was a better place, but that's not how I see it. We have our problems – drugs is certainly one of them – but we have world peace and no Depression. It seems like a pretty good world to me.

These criticisms are well founded and are worth taking to heart when examining our own attitudes and foibles.

The 'Empty-nest' Factor

Couples are most likely to part in the early years of a marriage or at the time when the children grow up and leave home. The so-called 'empty-nest factor' has been commonly applied to women who feel bereaved after their children leave home, but some research tends to deny its existence. The 1989 Mintel report, *The Lifestyle of the Over 50s*, concluded:

The once commonly applied 'empty-nester' label would appear to be very much a misnomer. Relationships with children and grand-children, though valued, would appear to be very much more periph-eral and less central to satisfaction with life than their juniors might suppose. A relatively high proportion of those in this age group actively enjoy freedom from family responsibility and the great major-ity feel that they see as much as they would want to of their families, irrespective of whether they live locally or not.

Not everyone working in the field of marriage research would agree with the Mintel findings that the term 'empty-nester' is a misnomer; although empirically based research studies may prove me wrong, I found in my interviews with men that the loss of children from the parental home, when it was felt, was at least as deeply felt by fathers as by mothers. While many women did indeed rejoice in their freedom to return to work or to pursue their own interests, men tended to mourn their children's independence.

Mr P.E., aged sixty:

My job has become very important to me in recent years since the children have become independent. I loved being a father and when they were young I looked forward to going home to them at the end of the day. It was such a relief to go back to another world. Now all I have is work. I have a grandchild on the way and I'm delighted, but it won't be the same.

Mr A.C., aged fifty-nine:

This is the first year that the children will not be coming on holiday with us – they are all working now and I can't describe to you how awful I feel about it. I can't talk about it to the wife because she'll be hurt thinking I don't want to go on holiday alone with her and she's looking forward to just the two of us spending time together. I just wasn't prepared for missing the children so much. Sometimes I look into their empty bedrooms at night and then lock myself into the bathroom and cry for them.

It is well known that women tend to form closer bonds with their children than do men and, to a large extent, it is the strength of these bonds which can cushion a mother from experiencing the stresses of the empty-nest factor. A mother knows, for example, that she does not 'lose' her children just because they leave home to follow their own lives. She may 'miss' them around the house but she can hardly mourn their loss if she is still expected by them to continue to fulfil her parental role. When children move into the adult world, their need for security does not decrease. Home becomes a safe base – a retreat when things go wrong; the telephone becomes a safety-line. Even after a new family is formed and the first grandchild arrives, an experienced mum is a good deal more comforting than a Dr Spock or a Penelope Leach.

Whatever research may or may not suggest, the 'empty-nest factor' is a very real experience for many people. Consider for example the case of Mrs N.T. The mother of three sons, aged eighteen, twenty-three and twenty-five, she became a grandmother for the first time at the age of forty-seven. Two years after the elder boys had left home and the younger went off to university her marriage was in serious crisis:

My husband has always been an absolute workaholic.

While the children were at home, it didn't matter so much that he would work till three in the morning and that the tables were covered with his papers. It didn't matter that he travelled and that he was away for weeks at a time; it didn't matter that the only time we ever went away together was when I accompanied him on a business trip. But now it does. I'm lonely and I need a companion. I realize I'm the one whose needs have changed and I'm telling him that if he doesn't spend more time with me and if he doesn't relax and begin to take it easy at work so that every moment we do spend together isn't an extension of life in the office, I shall have to leave him. It's terrible, I know, because I love him and don't want to live with anyone else, but equally, I don't want to live alone, which is what I'm doing at the moment. The effect on him of my very serious threat has been devastating. When I try to talk about the problem, he just screams and then sits down and sobs. I understand now that his reaction has much to do with the fact that in the past I have treated him rather as one of the children – just another of my sons if you like. It suited us all as a family then, but it doesn't suit me now.

While the empty-nest factor may not be universally felt, both men and women made more vulnerable by divorce, separation or bereavement can find bringing up children on their own a stressful and isolating experience despite its rewards, and when the children eventually leave home, the loss of their youthful presence can serve only to emphasize the loneliness:

Mrs C.P. was forty-one when her third son, Seth, was born – six years after his elder brother. It was hoped that the joy which his unexpected appearance created would cement his parents' crumbling marriage, but it did not and they separated when Seth was about five. He is now eight years old and at boarding-school.

I've been on my own for about three years now since Seth went away to school. I miss him dreadfully. My eldest son left last year to work in Africa and even though I still have one son at home, I feel more lonely than I would ever have thought possible. Friends have been very kind. In some ways it is easier to be alone than to feel lonely within a bad relationship but it's the discussion over the children's welfare and sharing decisions that I miss. I miss the companionship of marriage much more than the sex. You can't really feel sorry for yourself though. There are plenty of things I could do, especially voluntary work, but sometimes, I'm just so exhausted. Having Seth quite late in life has enabled me to make a number of new friends, several of whom are younger than me, but there are times like weekends when you can't see the friends because they are with their own families. These periods are particularly lonely. I went to a New Year's party and felt dreadful because everyone went home with their husbands looking happy and I had to go back on my own.

I'd like to go back to work but it's difficult to find something that fits in with the long holiday periods. I'd like to move to the country but it could be even more lonely, so I'd only go if I had a job.

Mrs C.P.'s sad experience brings to mind some very sound advice from Gail Sheehy: 'It is imperative that a woman find a sense of importance and a means of independent survival before the empty-nest syndrome leaves her feeling superfluous. She cannot rely on continued health or the constancy of her husband or the largesse of her grown children.'[27]

Concern for the Job

A major part of a man's identity is associated with his work and to say that without it he is lost would be no great exaggeration. That does not necessarily mean he enjoys his work, however – often the contrary is true. Dr Peter O'Connor was astonished to find, while writing his book, *Understanding the Mid-Life Crisis*, that there did not seem to be a single man amongst those he interviewed 'who did not express a feeling of being misplaced in his present occupation. Yet even the word "misplaced" violates the sense of bitterness and anger that many men felt in relation to their work, and the all-encompassing feeling of one's job being one's prison.' The sentiments Dr O'Connor found 'described equally well men who were successful and unsuccessful ... professional or non-professional – work fundamentally was pointless for the majority of men, and one could venture a safe guess that this is valid for the majority of men in general'.[28]

Giving support to Dr O'Connor's 'safe guess' is the fact that 'men in general' seldom choose their occupations. What young lad leaving school at sixteen or eighteen knows what he wants to do for the rest of his life? Even if he does have a burning desire to be a vet or a doctor, his chances of fulfilling those dreams are very small. The jobs or careers most men follow have been essentially chosen for them – by parents, by their education, by their social environment and by the limited choices open to them. The lucky ones kick around the world for a while, broaden their horizons, follow their instincts and wait until they sense their own 'right time' to settle down.

If concern for the job is perceived as part of the mid-life crisis, in middle age the conflict between what a man does and what he might want to do is heightened by the fact that both time and opportunity are fast running out. Should he continue to work his ticket for the next ten years or so until retirement rescues him or should he risk losing a regular pay cheque, take early retirement and look around for another perhaps less well paid but more interesting job? Much will depend on his family and financial circumstances at the time but it will also depend to a very great extent upon the support and encouragement of his wife.

There are few heavier burdens for a wife to bear than her husband's emotional state during a period of redundancy. One counsellor described it as 'a time when good marriages get better and shaky marriages sometimes come apart'. It is very hard for women to accept that no one seems anxious to snap up her talented, hard-working husband immediately he is thrown on to the market. Recruitment is a slow process and if he is lucky he may find another job within three months, but for the most part it takes much longer. Recognizing the strains placed on a marriage by a moody husband pacing the corridors of his home all day, many advisory services offer office space to their clients so that they can concentrate on preparing themselves for a new job and can set out from home each day in their usual way. (See also 'Redundancy', pp. 24–7.)

Concern for Health
(See also Chapter 6, Health)

A Harris Poll for the *Observer* Magazine (18 February 1990) showed that the British were on the whole not very well, but they seldom complained about their health. Researchers found that when they asked the average Briton how he or she felt, the response was likely to be that they were feeling in great shape. They generally did not admit to the fact that, despite 'feeling fine', they were making regular trips to the doctor.

If the famous British 'stiff upper lip' is a genuine character-istic of our island race, then acknowledging our good health is a national social grace: 'How are you?' 'Fine, thank you!' People who moan about their ailments are a bore and even faintly embarrassing – better to be dead than boring. But, if someone is closely and sympathetically questioned about their health, the story is likely to be different. The 'brave face' of a fifty-five-year-old male divorcee crumbled with relief when able to express his anxieties without constraint:

> In my early thirties I had problems with my health. A few months ago complications arose as a result of these problems, and I became ill for about three months. I've completely recovered, but being on my own made me realize how much more concerned about my health I have become. It is frightening to contemplate being ill and alone. I have become more conscious about my diet and I'm aware of eating good healthy food. I eat plenty of fruit and vegetables and almost no junk food. I drink though – a couple of pints of beer at lunchtime and a couple of large whiskies at night. I don't feel I need to drink; I just enjoy that routine. Sometimes I smoke the odd ciga-rette or cigar.

The researchers for the Mintel report *The Over 50s* found

that in middle age 'Concern about health is more a matter of awareness than practical action ... Around half of those in their early fifties and only slightly fewer of those in their sixties identified with the syndrome of being concerned about health but doing less than they should to protect their own health. Some three out of ten of the sample overall claimed to worry about their partner's health.'[29]

The years approaching retirement should be characterized by a growing interest in health and fitness. Where youth immunizes us against the need to trouble ourselves in these matters, age offers no such guarantees.

Concern for Ageing Parents
(See also Chapter 7, Caring for Others)

Mintel's special report, *The Over 50s*, produced in 1989, concluded: 'It is the worry about elderly parents that appears to be one of the principal concerns of this age group. Indeed around a third of those in this age group give regular care to an elderly relative and one in ten have a relative who is totally dependent on them. Among those in their early fifties the proportion looking after relatives rises to nearly half.'[30]

One of the first and most profound experiences with the process of ageing comes in mid-life when we realize that our parents are becoming old and require more and more care and attention. One might think that the first affecting encounter with the ageing process occurs with the experience of witnessing the old age of grandparents, but however beloved a grandparent might be and however severely their loss may be felt, the grandchild in mid-life does not experience the process of ageing in grandparents in the same way as the ageing of his or her parents. Old age in grandparents is expected and, just because they have always appeared old, seems entirely natural. That they will die because they are old is also implicitly accepted by grandchildren, even by those who are very young. The double generation gap which exists between grandchildren and grandparents is insulating in ways which the years separating parents from their children are not. The age gap does not, for example, insulate children from the fear that their parents may die, and it does not insulate them from the psychological and moral bonds which dictate that children should assume responsibility for their parents' welfare if and when they can no longer manage on their own. Even in the closest, most loving adult child–parent relationships the change in roles is bound to be stressful, for when a parent becomes helpless, it is the child who must become parent to the parent; and usually at a time when the demands of a teenage family are at their peak.

The way elderly parents face up to being old is bound to influence the attitude of their adult children towards old age. If their lives are happy and productive, if good health and financial security permit them to remain independent and undemanding, then to their adult children they will seem perennially young. For such a family, old age wears its best and most rewarding face. Essentially, in this case, the parent is still able to function in the accepted role; the adult child has only to make minimal adjustments and the additional burden on family life is light. This positive perception of the ageing process which a happy experience imposes will, however, be very different from that of the adult child who 'loses' an active, intelligent and loving parent to Alzheimer's, or who must take care of a depressed, frightened and angry parent who scourges his child with his own terror.

'For the future I have two fears. The first is if someone I love were to die. This would be quite devastating to me. The second comes from looking at my mother who lived the last twenty-six years of her life on her own. She died at eighty-four, crotchety, difficult and egocentric. I don't want to be like that' (Mr P.W., aged sixty).

Most families manage eventually to find mutually beneficial ways in which to help and care for dependent relatives but the path is not easy and requires a good deal of personal adjustment and give and take on both sides. Chapter 7 looks at the problems in more detail.

On Becoming a Grandparent

In the United Kingdom, the average age at which parents become grandparents for the first time is forty-seven. On the whole, it seems, men and women do not look forward to becoming grandparents. One forty-nine-year-old expectant grandfather expressed his feelings thus: 'The thought of becoming a grandparent is quite horrible to me. It just reminds me of how old I am; and besides, I feel it wasn't that long ago the house was filled with the paraphernalia of our children's lives. It's nice being on our own. I don't particularly relish the thought of nappies and little kids rushing about the place again.'

Yet however daunting the future prospect may seem, when the event occurs, first-time grandparents are generally delighted by their new status: the depth of feeling which they have for their children's children cannot be truly understood by anyone who has not experienced the relationship. Men and women who are deprived of this, their natural family role, often feel a terrible sadness.

At a meeting organized by the Divorce Conciliation Service, a small group of grandparents from various parts of the country and from widely different backgrounds gathered together to express their anguish and frustration. All were fighting for the right to enjoy a relationship with their grandchildren against seemingly impossible odds. Those who had established contact felt they were 'treading on eggshells' and that at any moment, if they put a foot wrong, they would be denied access.

Why are loving grandparents excluded from a joyful and rewarding relationship with their grandchildren? It seems there are three main reasons. In the first instance, divorce is a factor which affects not just the immediate family but the two sets of grandparents as well. Whereas some grandparents may act as mediators between warring couples and be allowed to create a stable background for the children until the families are re-housed or reconstituted, others will be used as scapegoats and become part of the weaponry in the family feud. 'Your parents have something to do with this. I'm never going to allow them into this house again,' an embittered wife might cry in the wake of her husband's departure from the home. Or, a parting shot from an aggrieved husband: 'Your mother is an interfering old cow and I refuse to let her take over the lives of my children. From now on, I want nothing to do with her.'

Divorce also creates a situation where families drift apart; grandparents who lose touch with their children and grandchildren for a period of time do not find it easy to re-establish contact.

The second most common cause of grandparents being denied access to their grandchildren has its roots in their relationship with their adult children. For example, a mother who has had a difficult and antagonistic relationship with her daughter may find that as a grandmother she is not welcomed into her child's family. In fact, she may find that she is cruelly and emphatically excluded. Doors may be barred against her and the grandchildren taught to regard her as an ogre.

Thirdly, no less tragic, is the situation where a grandchild or grandchildren have been taken into care and the Social Services Department for one reason or another refuses to allow the grandparents access to them.

According to a paper produced by Gillian Douglas and Nigel Lowe of the University of Bristol, 'English law accords grandparents no automatic rights in respect of the care or upbringing of their grandchildren. This means that, like any other non-parent, grandparents have to obtain a court order in their favour before they can acquire any formal legal rights over their grandchildren.'[31]

Although, legally, grandparents have no inherent rights over their grandchildren, the law does now give them the right to apply to the courts in certain circumstances. Under the 1991 Children Act, in cases of divorce, adoption and separation, for example, where they wish to be involved in the care of their grandchildren, they now have a universal right to apply to the courts to become parties in the case. Litigation is prohibitively expensive and it is always worth taking advice concerning entitlement to Legal Aid. (See Part III, The Law and Legal Aid.)

No law, however, is going to help grandparents establish a relationship with their grandchildren if the children's parents are hostile. Letters, birthday cards and little gifts may never reach their destination (although this method of contact is perhaps worth pursuing in the hope that one day, a message will be received by a grandchild). Where there is some contact with the parents, it might be possible to persuade them to allow the grandchildren out for a weekly all-expenses-paid trip to the swimming-baths, dancing class or special activity which parents regard as educationally valuable and which they would perceive as involving their children in something else other than their grandparents.

Grandparents who must relate to a step-parent in a reconstituted family sometimes find that keeping in touch with their grandchildren involves eating a great deal of humble pie. A stepmother anxious to stamp her own mark upon her new family might feel that she will be more secure if she can effectively eliminate the relationship between the children and the parents of her husband's previous wife. One grandmother in this position told me that the only way she could continue to see her grandchildren on a regular basis was to swallow much verbal abuse from an aggressive new daughter-in-law. 'I have had a lot to do with my three granddaughters for the last ten years, since they were born in fact. I am used to looking after them for quite long periods, and I've always seen them once a week. It is very hard now to take orders from a woman who tells me what I can and can't do with them, but if it's the only way we can stay in touch, I just have to go along with it.'

The Rewards of Time: Aspects of Love in Middle Age

If women cannot rely upon a loving husband to sustain them as their young beauty fades, then they need look no further than their children for reassurance. Even as adults, children hardly seem to notice the difference time makes to their ageing parents. Until or unless frailty and infirmity take their obvious toll, mother and father look much the same as they have always done.

A friend's memory of her mother illustrates the point:

> Dad always talked about the beauty Mum used to be, not the beauty she was at the time! He talked about her loveliness when they were married and often described the long corn-coloured hair which fell to her waist. A year after they married, when Mum was pregnant with me, he found someone lovelier for a few months. She never really recovered her self-confidence after that and stopped taking any trouble with her appearance when she was about forty I suppose. By the time she was fifty she had lost most of her hair and weighed about thirteen stone, but her

face hardly changed at all throughout her life. She
had a wonderful smile and was beautiful inside and
out. I only really noticed she was old about six months
before she died from cancer at the age of seventy-five
and weighed six stone.

Grandchildren are another great source of reassurance. They
do not seek to compare. Granny's age is what gives her status
in their eyes. Her youth is as remote as history. Even old
photographs fail to describe the person they know and love.

The love of children for their parents and grandchildren for
their grandparents, being non-judgemental, non-sexual and
immutable, is arguably the purest form of love. It is a quality
first recognized perhaps by parents in middle age, being expressed at a time when children – childhood and adolescence
behind them – are able to demonstrate emotions carved out by
their newly acquired adulthood.

Mrs E.B. describes her own experience of a quite dramatic
change in her relationship with her daughter:

She went through a terrible crisis as a teenager. I've
never experienced so much hatred. It seemed to take
years to sort her out – or rather to stick by her until
she sorted herself out. There were times when she
would throw her arms around me and tell me how
much she loved me but they were few and far between. When she finally settled into a job and was
happy, I felt rewarded enough and did not expect
anything more. But to my surprise, even though she
is working and living away from home now, she
comes back regularly, is loving and affectionate and
is interested and concerned about what I'm doing.
Sometimes she telephones just to tell me she loves
me. On her days off, she usually pops over and we go
out together, do some shopping, have lunch – that
sort of thing – and we talk all the time about everything under the sun. I never thought for a moment
she would become a best friend. I haven't quite got
to the stage of telling her my troubles yet; she needs
more time to forget her own and enjoy her happiness,

but in a few years, we'll share our feelings equally, I think.

Another mother described the first time she experienced her adult son's concern and affection:

As a teenager, my son went through a period of being very cross with me and became generally anti-Mum. I rather lost confidence then. I thought perhaps he would not want to have much to do with me as he grew older. He's in his last year at school and I'm pleased to say he has a lot of friends and they are always off together on one kind of adventure or another. He's home but he's not at home if you see what I mean. But I'm beginning to notice little changes which tell me how much he cares. Recently, he was off with friends for the weekend so I didn't expect to see him but suddenly, on Sunday afternoon, the door burst open and there he was – 'Hi, Ma! I just wanted to pop by to see how you are' – and he flung his arms around me and gave me a smacking kiss and a great hug. He spent about twenty minutes checking up on the latest family news and was off again. I was so touched and thrilled. Just for me, he had left his friends and spent an hour travelling to get home to say hello, and he didn't even ask for a loan!

Parents who experience this love from their grown children are surprised by its strength, and overjoyed. Suddenly, after years of giving and loving, of being taken for granted and of generally coming to expect a rather small return for the input of a lifetime, the relationship begins to change and the rewards are without parallel.

Crisis – Looking for Help When Things Go Wrong
(see also Chapter 6, Health, and Part III, Counselling)

For reasons already discussed, middle age is a time of considerable stress for both men and women. For the most part they manage to cope with the various and often simultaneous crises which life heaps upon them at this stage, but quite commonly an individual will be dealt a blow which may lead them to suffer what psychiatrists call an 'abreaction'. In early childhood, for example, they may have experienced an event or feelings which until that moment they had forgotten or repressed. In middle age, a traumatic situation can revive these repressed memories and fears, and the resulting emotional conflict may be accompanied by anxiety, depression and obsessional fears.

The following case history illustrates the experience of abreaction which required and benefited from professional help:

Mrs N.H. was fifty when she remarried. Her new marriage followed a period of three years during which she had been on her own with her two children while a long and bitter divorce struggled to its climax. The happiness and elation which accompanied her second marriage turned to misery and despair when it became evident that her adored new husband had fallen in love with a young woman half his age. Only six months had passed since her wedding day. She had not had time to regain confidence after divorce let alone find the self-possession to 'turn a blind eye' to her husband's affair. For three months, she succeeded in masking her unhappiness in an attempt to help her children and her husband's children over the difficult period of family transition. The affair continued and when it seemed to Mrs N.H. that her husband began in small ways to persecute her, she became afraid that her mind was beginning to show signs of serious paranoia and went to her GP for help. He in turn referred her to a psychiatrist. It was an intense relief to talk about her unhappiness and its cause. She was surprised to learn after about eight visits that she was not quite the person she had imagined herself to be – that was, essentially uncomplicated and easy-going. Although she described her relationship with her parents as ambivalent – dutiful rather than loving – her family background had always seemed to her stable and secure. It had not occurred to Mrs N.H. that the experience of being sent to boarding-school when she was six years old and of having a mother with a serious alcohol problem who found difficulty in showing physical affection had left her extremely vulnerable. Mrs N.H. had learned to accept the fact that her mother never seemed to like her and would often seem angry with her when they were together. She blamed herself for her mother's ambivalent attitude towards her because, despite having wanted to, she had never known quite how to love her mother.

Throughout her life, Mrs N.H. had learned to compensate for two seriously damaging factors – the first, her mother's alcoholism and the second, the apparent lack of her mother's love. When the crisis came, it hit her so hard she began to lose touch with reality. Without professional help, at the very least she might have carried her emotional agony with her into old age, her personality perhaps becoming transformed by bitterness and rage. Her sessions with the psychiatrist ceased when Mrs N.H. felt that she was beginning to know and to understand herself and to value herself. Her husband's affair did not so much diminish her love for him as topple him from his pedestal and place him firmly on the ground along with the rest of the human race.

Many marriage counsellors would like to see the present image of counselling changed. One said: 'It is a mistake to think that counselling is all about people who can't cope. I'm dealing on the whole with people who have not come to me with problems. Everybody goes through changes and for nearly everybody there is strain and a lot of stress. The first thing we do with people is to acknowledge that a change has taken place, and what it really means. Good counselling is actually enabling people to take stock of their lives in the present and to discuss where they might go in the future. Until you actually know where you are, you can't really move forward.'

Professional help does not necessarily make things easier; on the contrary, the process of searching for the self can often be extremely painful, but if, for deep-rooted psychological reasons, we have hidden our true selves in order to escape unpleasant experiences in the past, then self-discovery becomes all the more important. If we first learn to see ourselves as we really are, our response to change becomes more realistic. In this way, too, greater understanding means that we are better equipped to perceive where we stand in relation to those closest to us, and better able to manage the problems involved.

3 The Gains and Losses of Old Age

In the mid 1990s, the United Kingdom will see some 300,000 more people aged over seventy-five, with the numbers of those over eighty projected to rise by more than a fifth.[32] The country now has 800,000 people over eighty-five but within fifty years the figure will probably reach 1·7 million, and could come close to 2 million by the middle of the next century. If the projection is realized, those over pensionable age will, by then, account for one in three of the population.

In our society, the general perception of old age is bleak. We have no particular regard for the wisdom age brings, and our older citizens do not necessarily receive the respect traditionally accorded to those of their years in other societies. Old age threatens – it threatens us with loss, with infirmity, with pain, and ultimately with death. For adult children who assume the responsibility of caring for their elderly parents, it threatens with time-consuming routines and family stress. Fewer people these days are sustained by their religion. Comfort in old age is cold; the young and the middle-aged alike fear growing old. But perhaps the old themselves are partly responsible for perpetuating adverse images of their life stage – having been 'written off' in late middle age, they tend to fulfil the expectations of society by resigning themselves to old age and defending themselves against an uncertain future by living in the past.

In 1986, the American philosopher, psychologist and octogenarian, Erik Erikson, together with his wife Joan and a younger colleague, Helen Kivnick, published *Vital Involvement in Old Age*, in which they describe the effects of our youth-orientated culture on elderly people:

It is not surprising, then, that ageism poses such a problem for all older people. Young is beautiful. Old is ugly. This attitude stems from a stereotyping deeply ingrained in our culture and in our economy. After all, we throw old things away – they are too difficult to mend. New ones are more desirable and up-to-date, incorporating the latest know-how. Old things are obsolete, valueless and disposable. Sometimes they may move into the category of antiques, old ivory or vintage wines, as do the really old elders, those over ninety-five. Preserved like the antique, the ivory and the wine, all old persons might present a braver picture, but that takes affluence, luck and discipline.

The cruellest aspect of this cultural attitude is the elders' vulnerability to the stereotype. Some feel themselves to be unattractive, dull and, quite often, unlovable, and this depressing outlook only aggravates the problem. One response is to avoid looking or acting your own age at all costs. The result is, of course, humiliating failure. Another attitude is to let go, renouncing even rewarding interests and pleasures as unseemly. The acceptance of the stereotype then actualizes the stereotype itself. Perhaps the middle way is the hardest, since it involves accepting who and what you are with active compliance. This process includes a mature appraisal of being just where you are in the life cycle and an appreciation of the great advantages of this position.[33]

I have never met anyone over the age of seventy who actually enjoys being old, but I have met many, many men and women for whom old age has brought great and unexpected pleasures, and some who have admitted to feeling happier and more content in old age than at any other time in their lives. There are the inevitable losses, but there are also gains.

A cardiologist whose patients, in the main, tend to be men and women in the later years of retirement, remarked how much his job had taught him about old age. He said: 'You become acutely aware of the person you don't want to be in old age and just as aware of the dignified, courageous person you would like to be. I can't say what makes the difference, only that it would seem to be related to experience and the spirit; and the only way you can hope to achieve old age in the right spirit is by observing it and becoming aware of the pitfalls – consciously rejecting certain aspects and adopting others.'

Changing the Image – the Association of Retired Persons (ARP)

In May 1988, the *Sunday Times* reporter, Brian Deer, returned to England after visiting a convention held in Detroit by the American Association of Retired Persons (AARP). With twenty-nine million members, the Association is beginning to wield considerable power, both politically (in that year, it had three major bills before Congress) and economically (men and women aged sixty-five and over have more savings and investments per head than any other age group). As an observer, Deer found 'delegates clearly felt that getting older could be fun'. He wrote:

While there were no end of anecdotes about earlier years, at the many entertainment events and private gatherings, you got the sense that this group of Americans, at least, really were glad to be grey . . . For Britain, being older is considered inseparable from being a problem . . . Of course, there are endless exceptions, particularly within families. But, by taking it for granted that older people are a liability rather than an asset, we devise national policies, from television programming to health services, that assume that everyone over sixty is at the last exit from life.[34]

The association's quarterly magazine in Britain, *Retirement, Planning and Living*, gives a good indication of the direction in which men and women over the age of sixty are now travelling, and their present path is decidedly optimistic.

The ARP 'Creed for Successful Ageing' was produced as a result of their research, which showed that people who met its conditions were most likely to experience a fulfilled and healthy older age. It reads as follows:

- People who age successfully . . .
- Accept ageing as a natural process, having no fear of ageing, death or dying. Every age has its own purpose. Don't dwell on ills. Accept and embrace their age and follow the maxim that you're as young as you think you are.
- Are psychologically younger than their chronological age and allow their psychological age to dictate how they look.
- Have a sense of purpose and, through work, family,

volunteer work, project or hobby, feel their role in life is important . . .

- Have nutritious eating habits. They don't combine working and eating. They are lean adults who eat nutritious food which strengthens their immune system and increases vitality. Youthful adults eat just for the needs of their body.
- Exercise regularly. They have a planned programme which includes aerobic exercise to rid the body of toxins and make the bones and body strong.
- Are mentally active throughout their adult years and have a personal achievement programme. They develop their own methods for exercising the brain (crosswords, bridge, learning the piano, for example), as well as physical exercise. They are constantly learning and developing knowledge and interest.
- Understand and practise wise hygiene. Live in the country near water; breathe clean air; enjoy solitude and quiet. Don't smoke or take drugs; drink moderately. Don't drink coffee, which depletes the body of nutrients. Avoid exposure to the sun, which hinders cell renewal.
- Have an ability to manage stress and practise exercises to overcome stress, like yoga and meditation, biofeedback and self-hypnosis; they are calm-centred people.
- Have long, honest and supportive relationships and strong ties; are affectionate, tactile and demonstrative.
- Have a balanced libido, lots of emotional energy, are expressive and sexually active.
- Are optimistic and positive. Difficulties are seen as challenges. They are creative in problem-solving, strong risk-takers, and they laugh at their mistakes.
- Have a sense of humour about life. Have a sense of fun and play, mixing the best of childhood and the best of adulthood.

The only belief one might query in the ARP creed is the need to 'live in the country near water' in order to age successfully. However much they may love and appreciate the countryside, confirmed and enthusiastic city-dwellers, on finding themselves transplanted from familiar concrete environments, could decline very rapidly indeed. A cock's crow at dawn would not do – at least, not for long – for those of us who delight in a day beginning with the comforting roar of town traffic.

How Does It Feel to be Old?

Conversations with some of the residents of a nursing and residential home tended to uphold the notion that people only begin to feel old when they find they can no longer perform essential daily tasks or enjoy those activities which have previously enhanced their lives:

> I've never feared old age but I began to feel old three years ago when I was ninety-five and found I could no longer do the shopping and cooking. That was when I decided it was time to move in here. I don't consider myself old now except that my actions are limited. But my mind's in good shape. If that goes, I want to go. I don't think I've altered much as a person over the years. I'm still very much the same as I was at twenty-five.

Not everyone reaches what they feel to be their old age with such sanguinity, however. For another resident, the age of seventy arrived with all the violent turmoil of a mid-life crisis:

> I remember being forty; there was great excitement and a big party. I was happy to be fifty and sixty, but when I got to seventy I was shocked and frightened. Being seventy meant that I had reached old age – not that anything had happened to me or that I actually felt old, because I was still doing all the things I used to do; but I just couldn't believe that life had run out so fast and that I would have so few more years to live. It was terrifying. I decided immediately that it was time to sell my house and move in here. People said I was too young and active at seventy-one to make such a move but I've been here eight years now and have not regretted the decision for a minute. It was absolutely right for me. I've always known this place; it's local, my sister died here and when I retired, I worked here voluntarily, so you see it's always been

a home from home. Moving was a deliberate preparation for the last stage of life and being here has given
me confidence and security. When I was taken into
hospital suddenly a few months ago for an operation
which I thought would be fairly minor, I came out
with a colostomy and a diagnosis of bowel cancer.
The shock was unbelievable and I'm still suffering
from symptoms of stress. To be looked after during
this time by people who care about you and to be
surrounded by friends has been such a relief. Being
here now is the most wonderful thing that ever happened. I hate to think of what it would have been like
to manage on my own.

What seems to prevent people from feeling old is the continuing sense of well-being which comes from good general health
and an active mind:

At seventy-three, I certainly look old but I'm in good
health. When you've got motivation and when you
keep your mind going in different ways – I mean
exercising it with something as simple as the *Daily
Telegraph* or the *Times* crossword puzzle, and you
read and have an interest that is outgoing, the only
times you are conscious of age is when you look at
your face, and sometimes when you get overtired.

At the age of forty or fifty, we cannot know what it feels like
to be old, neither can we be sure as to the kind of person we
will become in the final stage of life, but if we choose to take
Dr Anthony Clare's advice, quoted at the head of Chapter 1,
and make preparation for old age, our chances of being happy
and at peace with ourselves and the world at large will be
significantly increased.

The two poems set out below were found in the bedside
locker of an elderly patient after her death in hospital. The
nurses there said she had written them herself some time
before she died. I have included them, not just because they
are a very moving account of how it feels to be old, but (and
this has perhaps much to do with the power of poetry to focus
on a subject and distil the essence of its meaning) because

more than anything or anyone else, the writer helps us to understand the importance of communication – not just in family relationships but between the dependent elderly and the independent carer.

Crabbit Old Age

What do you see nurses, what do you see?
What are you thinking when you're looking at me?
A crabbit old woman, not very wise
Uncertain of habit, with far-away eyes,
Who dribbles her food and makes no reply,
When you say in a loud voice, 'I do wish you'd try',
Who seems not to notice the things that you do,
And forever is losing a stocking or shoe.
Who, unresisting or not, lets you do as you will,
With bathing and feeding the long day to fill.
Is that what you're thinking, is that what you see?
Then open your eyes, nurses, you're not looking at me.
I'll tell you who I am as I sit here so still,
As I use at your bidding, as I eat at your will.
I'm a small child of ten, with a mother and father,
Brothers and sisters who love one another,
A young girl of sixteen with wings on her feet
Dreaming that soon now a lover she'd meet.
A bride soon at twenty – my heart gives a leap
Remembering the vows that I promised to keep.
At twenty-five now, I have young of my own
Who need me to build a secure happy home.
A woman of thirty, my young now grow fast,
Bound to each other with ties that should last.
At forty my young ones, now gone, are all grown,
But my man stands beside me and I'm not alone.
At fifty once more babies play round my knee;
Again we know children, my loved one and me.
Dark days are upon me: my husband is dead,
I look to the future, I shudder with dread,
For my young are all busy, rearing young of their own,
And I think of the years and the love that I've known.
I'm an old woman now and nature is cruel;
Tis her jest to make old age look like a fool.
The body it crumbles, grace and vigour depart;
There is now a stone where I once had a heart.
But inside this old carcass, a young girl still lives

And now and again my battered heart gives.
As I remember the joys I remember the pain
And I'm loving and living life all over again.
I think of the years, all too few – gone too fast
And accept the stark fact that nothing can last.
So open your eyes, nurses, open and see
Not a crabbit old woman: look closer –
See me.

Nurses' Reply – The Other Side

What do we see, you ask, what do we see?
Yes, what are we thinking when looking at thee?
We may seem to be hard when we hurry and fuss,
But there's many of you and too few of us.
We would like for more time to sit by you and talk,
As we bath you and feed you and teach you to walk;
To hear of your lives and the things you have done,
Your childhood, your husband, your daughter, your son.
But time is against us. There's so much to do.
Patients are many and nurses are few,
We grieve when we see you so sad and alone
With nobody near you, no friends of your own.
We feel all your pain and know all your fear –
That nobody cares now your end is so near.
But nurses are people with feelings as well,
And when we're together you'll often hear tell
Of the Grandest old Gran in the very end bed,
And the lovely old Dad and the things that he said.
We speak with compassion and love, and feel sad
When we think of your lives and the joys that you've had.
When the time has arrived for you to depart,
You leave us behind with an ache in our heart.
When you sleep the long sleep, not more worry or care,
There are other old people and we must be there,
So please understand if we hurry and fuss.
There are many of you and too few of you.

Talking – a Study in Sociolinguistics

Karen Atkinson, a lecturer at Surrey University's Roehampton
Institute, is currently studying the way in which home helps
talk to their elderly clients in the context of their own homes.
In an interview, she told me: 'The attitude of society towards

elderly people is reflected through the language used in talking to them and about them. Generally speaking, in this country older people are undervalued, underpaid and attributed with low social status. The well-entrenched ageist attitudes mean they are often being expected to fulfil stereotypically negative roles as dependent, helpless, fussy, stubborn, miserly, asexual and communicatively inept. Talked to as though they were small children, they are not treated as autonomous adults and are subsequently marginalized even further.'

By middle age, the chances are that most people have had the experience of taking care of someone older – a parent or relative – who needs their help and consideration. The additional responsibility may impose a severe burden on an already overloaded daily schedule. As the old lady observed in her poem: '. . . time is against us. There's so much to do.' Looking back to the last years in the lives of both my mother and father, I see that I fell into almost every trap. There were just not enough hours in the day to cope with the needs of a large family, teenage crises, the commitments of work and the needs of a sick parent whose vulnerability cried out for attention and companionship. I organized – made numerous telephone calls, spoke to doctors, fetched prescriptions and visited the hospital, but I did not have time to listen; and by not listening, I became patronizing. When my mother complained of pain, it was less time-consuming just to give her an analgaesic, re-arrange her pillow, kiss her and leave her to sleep rather than to sit down by her bedside, take her hand and listen and respond to her memories and fears. When my father became depressed and ill, lonely and frightened, his self-absorption, self-pity and bad temper made me angry and resentful. My language was sometimes brusque and must often have reflected the impatience I felt.

The following extract is a conversation recorded by Ms Atkinson in the home of a seventy-five-year-old woman. Arthritis has rendered her physically dependent, but she is otherwise well and mentally alert. The home help arrives just as her son and daughter-in-law are about to leave. All those involved in the conversation are in the same room throughout:

HOME HELP: How are you today?

MRS J: Oh, I . . . I've got a . . .

DAUGHTER-IN-LAW: She's a bit down because we're leaving.

HOME HELP: I guess that's what it would be today: that's why I came a little bit earlier. I'd finished at Mrs Potts.

DAUGHTER-IN-LAW: Oh.

HOME HELP: So I said I'll go up and see Mrs J., 'cause I thought you would have left, you know.

DAUGHTER-IN-LAW: Now the shopping is done. There's a nice madeira cake in the thing for her and (*turning to Mrs J.*) there's the scones you can have with some jam on like we had last night. You can have that for your tea. (*Turning to the home help*) I bought her a Birds Eye peach melba and a strawberry tri –

HOME HELP: I know what you mean; I know the sort she wants.

DAUGHTER-IN-LAW: They're in the fridge, you see. I'm hoping she will go in there and take them and eat them because she's very fond of them.

HOME HELP: Yes, well, this is it; don't waste them.

DAUGHTER-IN-LAW: They're nice for her tea.

(*There is a knock at the door and a lady from the meals-on-wheels service brings in the lunch.*)

SON: Oh, it smells lovely.

HOME HELP: There you are.

SON: Smells lovely that.

DAUGHTER-IN-LAW: Do you put salt on?

MRS J: No. I put it on later.

DAUGHTER-IN-LAW: You put it on later, do you?

MRS J: Yes.

DAUGHTER-IN-LAW: Yes, it's a bit early, especially for now. Don't open it then.

HOME HELP: Oh, she always opens it to have a look what it's like, then seals the back up.

MRS J: Eh?

DAUGHTER-IN-LAW: Smells nice anyway.

SON: Well, it's a bit late though on a Thursday; you can't do anything about it if she doesn't like it, can you?

MRS J: No.

DAUGHTER-IN-LAW: Well, it all looks good to me.

HOME HELP: Oh, there you are now; that does look nice.

DAUGHTER-IN-LAW: Oh, now, isn't that lovely.

SON: Oh, I think so.

DAUGHTER-IN-LAW: Well, that's really tempting.

SON: Smell it; it's lovely, honestly.

DAUGHTER-IN-LAW: Oh, that's lovely.

MRS J: I've got to find the meat in it.

HOME HELP: She doesn't like the sausage.

While this conversation is filled with kindness and a willingness to help, the woman who is the centre of attention is considered, quite erroneously, to be a person incapable of responding in her own right. Her opinions, feelings and desires are ignored, and she remains as isolated as though she were entirely alone.

Talking is a Lifeline

Sister Frances is responsible for eighty-eight residents over the age of seventy in an Anglican Convent and nursing home in a London suburb. She and her staff are experienced at coping with the needs of people whose powers of communication are severely limited. She spoke of the misery suffered by those who cannot make themselves understood. 'It must be so terrible for them. I can't think of anything more frustrating than not being able to communicate. It's very interesting though – many of our stroke patients who can't talk can manage to sing. When we have groups of entertainers come and sing for us, it's lovely to hear them join in with old favourites like "Daisy, Daisy". Even patients with quite advanced forms of dementia seem to remember the words of old songs and they can often manage the hymns in chapel too.'

When they cannot easily make themselves understood, people become fearful, especially if they are left alone for any length of time. Sister Frances explained: 'If you put yourself in the position of an eighty- or ninety-year-old, and can actually imagine you are helpless in that chair and you want to go to the loo and you see no one around to help and are not sure anyone will come, how would you feel? Very frightened. Therefore, you want to make certain there is somebody near enough if you do want something. Of course, there are bound to be people who are more demanding than others but in our two open wards where so many staff are walking up and down it is really quite easy. We know our residents intimately. One lady, for example, is so polite; she talks a lot of nonsense half the time, but she spent some years of her life in a concentration camp and has some terrible memories which still cause her great unhappiness. She needs a lot of reassurance, but as long as you turn to her and respond with an "I'm coming in a minute", she's happy. She just wants to know you are around and you are there if she needs you.'

Communication is a two-way process and the nuns and nursing staff at the convent sometimes find themselves frustrated by the lack of response from some of their residents. 'When we arrange some special entertainment for them, you wouldn't believe the fuss: "Oh, I don't want to go. It's too late in the evening" or "I don't want to go, it's in the afternoon when I'm resting." Of course, people aren't forced to go if they don't want to, but if the action takes place in the ward, it's difficult for them not to be involved, even if they are in bed. I sometimes wonder why we bother, until a couple of days later, you hear one of them say, "I really liked that concert the other night," or "That was nice, that play." You do get feedback eventually, but you would never know at the time if they enjoyed the occasion, and I'm always apologizing to the artists – "please don't take any notice of the grunts or the groans." I know it's worth it in the long run though. If we didn't have our entertainments and our weekly art classes and music and movement sessions, they'd just sit and look at each other or sit in front of the TV all day. They need the stimulation. When conversation is made difficult by deafness or disease, we can at least try to give them something to think about.'

Friendship in Old Age

There is nothing more precious than friendship in old age and the friendships made in youth are perhaps the most valuable of all. Through them, people remember themselves as they were and value each other as they are. Not long ago, I was having lunch in a restaurant with an old school friend whom I had not seen for twenty years. We had a lot to talk about, but perhaps not as much as the two elderly ladies sitting at a nearby table.

They were reminiscing about their years spent together in the Women's Voluntary Service during the war. 'Do you remember that night we were going to meet the men for dinner all dressed up in our uniform and black-market nylons. We heard the bomb and just before it fell, we threw ourselves at a plate-glass window for protection. Can you imagine! And there were we supposed to be trained!' Between anecdotes, their laughter filled the restaurant. At a table just behind them, Princess Diana entered with a small party of friends but so absorbed were they by each other's company they never noticed her arrival. Not even the presence of Her Royal Highness could interrupt the pleasure of their memories.

Friendship in old age becomes the greatest solace at a time of loss. Mrs T.O. was widowed at the age of sixty-seven. Her husband died suddenly and without warning:

> His death was the most terrible loss I have ever experienced. I did not believe it possible to feel so much grief and sadness. What helped me through those first awful months were my friends and family. Without them, I'd probably have stayed acutely depressed and then goodness knows what would have become of me. One way or another, my friends never left me on my own. There were times when I was especially vulnerable – like birthdays, anniversaries and Christmas. On those occasions, I always had someone to stay, or went away to stay with them. Nearly a year after my husband's death, my son took me on holiday with a couple of old friends of mine, and we went swimming in the sea. It was the first time I found myself saying, 'Gracious, this is fun. I'm actually enjoying life again.'

Again, it is a friend who comes to the rescue of Peggy Wakehurst. She had been married to her husband – Governor of New South Wales and, later, Governor of Northern Ireland – for fifty years. His death 'left a terrible blank'. She writes in her autobiography:

The first years after John died seemed to have passed by in a sort of grey mist. I did not quite know what to be doing and I felt rather desolated. During that time Mrs Haslett, who had been secretary to the governor's office in Northern Ireland when we were there, came over and stayed with me. One day she said, 'Really you must have some young people around you', and she produced two Irish girls who wanted to come over to London for three months to do a Cordon Bleu cookery course. They stayed in the spare room and their enthusiasm and interest in life cheered me up no end. Having young people around me suddenly gave me new heart. I thought, 'I really must get going again.'[35]

The Loss of Old Friends

Although there is always great pleasure in gaining new friends, the loss of old friends is one of the saddest losses encountered in old age.

Mrs A.J.:

> The thought of living to a hundred horrifies me. What on earth is the point? All one's friends would be dead and I couldn't help but be a burden to my family.

Mrs S.T., aged eighty:

> For me, the worst thing about old age has been the death of so many of my friends. In the past, we used to have small dances and parties for about thirty couples. Now there are only six remaining couples. Sixteen are widows and the others are dead. I am very fortunate though. Perhaps because I was an only child and my mother was insistent that unless I made an effort, people wouldn't look out for me, since childhood I have always found it easy to make friends. My husband died fifteen years ago, and I can honestly say that unless I am physically ill and confined to bed, I am never lonely. Many of my friends are younger than I am and without their support and company life would be very dreary. I love travelling but no longer have the confidence to go away on my own, yet I have friends who are widows who also love going abroad, so we team up together.

Mr H.A., aged seventy-one, has never married, but has shared his life with a partner for twenty-three years:

I have always had lots of friends and continually make new friends, but about ten years ago I began losing them, mostly through illness related to their age. At first it caused great sadness – it still does, but I'm more used to it now. The business of going through a friend's illness, then they die, then you go to their memorial service; now it happens so often you get rather used to it.

My father died when I was nine years old, then I went through the Second World War when I lost several friends. My mother died when I was in my twenties. After the war, I went through a long period of being very happy when nobody died, but now it's happening again.

When you're a young man and even in middle age, you don't think much about death, but when older people around you, friends of your own age or a little younger, start dying, you begin to realize that you too are at that age and stage. When I pick up the newspaper in the morning, I glance straight away at the obituary page, and one of the first things I notice is the age at which most people mentioned have died. If everybody on that day is older than you are, then you're sort of happy, but if everybody is younger, you're sort of dismal.

I'm not afraid of loneliness; in fact, I don't think I've ever been lonely. Tom and I share our home in London and being single men of a certain age, we get invited out all the time. Tom loves people and they love him. He is immensely charming and witty and likes lots of company. I'm a little more selective, I suppose. In the old days when we first began to be asked out so much, I thought, 'My God, we're so popular; this is wonderful!' but then I realized that what people really wanted was just another pair of trousers to make up the numbers at some dinner party. Now I refuse as many invitations as I accept, and consequently I'm far less popular!

I do have friends, both men and women, who cannot do anything by themselves. I can. I can happily go to a theatre by myself or dine out in a restaurant, but there are some people who cannot walk down the street by themselves or sit at a counter and have a cup of coffee alone without feeling lonely. Being alone doesn't frighten me at all. Perhaps it's the security of knowing that even if I'm alone for the moment, someone is eventually coming to join me.

I think the easiest way to make friends is by joining different organizations. I know that one of the most charming, most successful organizations I ever joined was one I absolutely never wanted to join in the first place. I had always liked the idea of being a free spirit, of just getting into a car and motoring around, but eventually Tom persuaded me to take part in a summer-school course on all aspects of the decorative arts. I've been back several times now. These courses have opened up a new world to me. Not only have I met a lot of interesting people, but have made some very good friends and all my travels are now undertaken with an entirely different eye.

The Family

Close family ties and grandchildren are potentially a great source of comfort and happiness in old age.

Mr B.P.:

So many of my friends are either dead or live too far away for me to see them regularly, but I've got four children and fourteen grandchildren and I tend to be very involved with the family. When I don't see them, I write to them a lot. They often come and stay — although not all at once, thank goodness — and I spend time with them.

Mrs Z.T.:

I suppose the greatest thing I've gained in old age is the love and affection of my grandchildren. I have four and they are all wonderful to me. They are teenagers now and sometimes it is a relief for them, I think, to come and talk to me when they get a bit fed up at home. They arrive here at times so angry you can almost see the steam coming out of their ears! I have a spare bedroom which I always keep ready for them, and there are occasions when it is occupied for quite long periods.

Establishing New Friendships

Old age in itself does not make it more difficult to establish new friendships; there are plenty of people who continue to make friends throughout their lives because it has always been in their nature to do so. Others who find life in old age increasingly lonely are often those whose natural reticence or way of life has tended to lead them to rely upon a few good companions. One distinguished gerontologist to whom I spoke saw the problem as being especially difficult for men. She explained: 'Women have much richer social networks throughout their lives. Men don't. They have very limited networks once they have left work and so I think they start from a great disadvantage. How they can actually make new friends is more difficult. If people have been loners all their lives they are going to be loners for ever more. It takes a very conscious effort to start being gregarious for the first time, and this does seem to come more naturally to women.'

Readers who decide that they would like to make that 'conscious effort' will find suggestions in Part III, Friendships.

The Need to Feel Needed

People need to feel they are wanted and that, despite growing age and infirmity, life is still worth living:

When I first moved into the nursing home, I felt so lonely. People didn't seem friendly. I had spent my whole life caring for someone and now no one needed me. It's like being made redundant. When I was young, it was my mother who was an invalid for many years, then there were the children and finally I had to look after my husband for a long time before his death. I was used to being needed. When I first arrived here, I felt so useless, although I am always busy. The other day, one of the sisters remarked on how well I seem to be settling down. She couldn't believe it when I told her I was lonely. 'How can you be when you do so much for all those people? Where would they be without you – where would *we* be without you?' she asked. I was really surprised. She made me see that what I expressed was the loneliness in myself and not really the loneliness of this house. I have begun to realize that actually these ladies do need me. There are things I can do for them that they can't do for themselves and I'm beginning to make real friends now.

Low self-esteem and lack of encouragement can lead to what has been described by Dr Seymour Perlin, Professor of Psychiatry at the George Washington University School of Medicine and founder of the American Association of Suicidology, as 'rational suicide'. That is to say, the deliberate decision by an elderly person to take their own life can often be the result of the negative attitude of their family. Someone who no longer feels loved, wanted and needed may decide that there is little point in continuing the struggle against the inevitable losses of old age. Thus, by not protesting strongly enough, children can effectively lead an elderly parent to decide that life is no longer worth living. Dr Perlin was quoted in an article in *The New York Times* as saying: 'Often the neutral stance in favour of rational suicide is actually collusion, because the parent is really reaching out to the child for affirmation of a desire to live. The concept of rational suicide thus creates an expectation of suicide.'[36]

How Changing Attitudes of Adult Children towards Parents in Old Age Can Affect Their Self-image

Not only does the attitude of adult children affect the self-esteem of their parents in old age, but it also has considerable bearing on their struggle to maintain independence. When age turns the table and the older generation begins to need increased amounts of help and attention, the attitudes of their children are almost bound to change. The extent of these changes will partly be dictated by the fundamental relationship between the parents and their older children and partly by the extent and the nature of the caring involved. Yet even if the emotional bond between the generations is characterized by love, friendship and respect, there will still be subtle ways in which adult children become parents to their parents. One lady described the changing roles thus: 'I adore my daughter. We are the very best of friends and consult each other about eveything under the sun but now I'm eighty-one, it amuses me to hear her speak to me sometimes as I used to talk to her when she was a child – "It's very cold outside today, dear. Do make sure to wrap up warmly!"'

Where the relationship has in some way been impaired, the role reversal can be quite dramatic. A friend of mine, nursing her mother, who was ill with severe asthma and angina, had just brought her home from the hospital. When I asked how the patient was, my friend replied, 'Oh, quite impossible. She is querulous and cross most of the time and refuses to leave her bedroom. I know it's sick, but there's an odd way I'm rather enjoying her illness. I've got her under my thumb for the first time in my life.'

It is one thing for adult children to relieve their parents of some of the day-to-day household chores but quite another to deny them responsibility for their own lives. The more an elderly parent allows himself to become a child to his children, the more he may be dominated. Adults tend to treat their ageing parents as they themselves were treated in childhood; patterns of family life are often repeated. In extreme cases, the bullied become the bullies, the abused become the abusers.

Adult children by making decisions for their parents without first consulting them are taking away their independence. 'What mother needs is this', 'What father should do is that' and so on. On the one hand, they feel they know what is best for their parents – and indeed, this might be true in certain circumstances; but on the other, they are wielding power in a way that elderly parents could well find offensive and unacceptable: 'There's no need to discuss the matter with Mum and Dad; they'll just have to go along with it.' But Mum or Dad may strongly disagree with decisions made on their behalf, especially if they have not been consulted, and they may refuse to cooperate, thereby perhaps placing themselves at risk.

While some people are able to come to terms with increasing disability and accept they need help, others fight tooth and nail against it, seeing one more household aid as just another step towards dependence and the nursing home which they dread.

Maintaining Independence

The importance to men and women of being able to maintain their independence in old age cannot be overestimated. But 'independence' is a relative term – it has different meanings for different individuals and can be as much an attitude of mind as simply a self-supporting way of life.

Almost one third of the eight million people over the age of sixty-five in Britain live alone in their own homes. Of these, according to a General Household Survey carried out in 1980, 12 per cent needed help to leave their house, 7 per cent were completely housebound, and 2 per cent were bedridden.

Professor Anthea Tinker, Director of Age Concern, thinks that appropriate housing is the key to independence. 'If somebody has a warm, easy-to-manage home, they can get by with an awful lot,' she says. 'After that, it's the little things that matter most, like taking care of feet, eyes and hearing. It's attention to these details which enables people to remain independent. People say they can't hear, but it may be that they are suffering from a particular condition which is easily rectified. Incontinence is another common deterrent to people's independence. They say they can't leave their homes because of incontinence, but it may be that it has a very simple cause; in most cases, something can be done to help. Modern medical practice is extraordinarily successful in curing or alleviating the health problems which are so common to old age, but if neglected the everyday use of faculties will disintegrate.'

Whether or not they must depend on the help and support of others to sustain their daily needs, independence for some means remaining in the family home in which they have lived for years and they are not afraid to place their physical health and safety at risk in order to pursue these independent ideals. Others, however, see a move into a smaller, more manageable type of accommodation as the best way to guard their independence, and if advanced age produces an increase in problems of health and mobility, many feel comforted living on their own in special accommodation which includes help at the touch of a button. The fact that they decide independently to move house, whether to a residential home or sheltered accommodation, does not mean to them that they have lost their independence; rather, that they have made a particular choice at a particular time.

The art of remaining independent in old age involves never being too proud or too afraid to ask for help, and although the body may fail, nothing can take away the spirit of independence from an active, unaffected mind.

Help around the House

See Part III, Design for Independent Living, and also Chapter 6, Health.

Making a Move
(See also Chapter 7, Caring for Others)

It is hard to admit that the home in which a husband and wife have brought up a family and lived for forty or fifty years is finally just too much for them to manage; sad that roots should have to be pulled up in the last stage of life, at a time when familiar surroundings and years of comfortable habit should be working towards a gentle and peaceful lifestyle. Change is not welcome then. No loving, concerned child dare say to parents or grandparents 'but look on the bright side'. For the older generation, there is little to be seen 'on the bright side' in a move which has been engineered by necessity and physical decline, especially as it has often been prompted by the loss of a spouse. Nevertheless, the relief experienced by those who move from large family homes into a small flat more suited to their needs will probably in the long run outweigh the grief felt by the loss.

Mrs E.M. is seventy-nine and has lived in a retirement home for four years. She told me:

I decided to make the move about three years after my husband died. I lived in a rather large house, full of books and papers and paintings, nothing very important, but I really hated the idea of my son having to cope with all this later on, and perhaps having to cope with me too; so I gave the books to a library and a school and many of the paintings to a college. The boxes and boxes of private papers I have with me in the retirement home, making my flat seem much smaller than it really is. I am determined to sort them out some day.

It took me two years to organize the move into a retirement community which best suited my needs. The flats here vary in size from one large bedsit to three bedroom flats. Mine has two bedrooms and two baths and I have a very adequate kitchen and nice sitting-room with a balcony. There is a health centre and round-the-clock nursing care should the need arise.

When I moved in four years ago, I didn't know whether I'd live another four years, but now I feel I might go on for ever. The change of moving from a home that I'd known for a long time into something new and strange was very frightening. I knew only one person and there are 440 people in this establishment and I said to myself, 'I scarcely need 440 new people in my life at this point.' The change was so great that I thought it would probably be the beginning of the end of my life. I don't know why I thought that really; I was in good health. But the mere fact that there are so many older people here happy and busy makes one see there is much more to life than hanging around waiting to die tomorrow. Lots of people have come from the area and have friends and family outside the retirement community. Others have moved here because they want to be near their families and their children and grandchildren. There is always so much to do here. It's amazing how quickly the day goes and how little one accomplishes. You wouldn't think I have anything to do, but there's so much going on. I've made lots of friends and never feel lonely. Life is much more simple. I'm taken care of in every way; when I had bronchitis, a nurse came to see me every day. I don't have to worry about paying household bills, getting the lawn mowed or the roof mended. I don't even have to cook if I don't want to. Our maintenance covers one meal a day so we eat lunch or dinner together in the main dining-room, although we can actually eat every meal there if we want. Often groups of us get together to make up little parties and meet for a drink beforehand. There have been a lot of deaths of course but you'd expect that with our age group. The average age is about eighty-two, and it's nice to feel I have friends of all ages and I'm actually rather younger than so many people here.

I find that so many of my friends say 'a move to a retirement home is a nice idea, but of course I'm not ready for it'. I feel people should really face up to it a little earlier than they do. I always urge them to look into these retirement communities and get their name on the list because it takes a long time. We have a three- or four-year waiting-list here.

Sheltered Housing

Sheltered housing is accommodation especially designed for the needs of elderly people and can be provided by councils, housing associations and private developers. The great advantage of sheltered housing, whether in the form of self-contained flats or bungalows, is that it allows people to live independently, while a resident warden is available in case of emergency. People can live either alone or as a couple, safe in the knowledge that there is always someone at hand to help, whether they need medical attention or attention to the roof or the plumbing.

Some councils and housing associations and a few private developers extend the services of their sheltered housing schemes to include provision of meals, domestic help and personal care. Local housing associations, council housing departments and Citizens Advice Bureaux are all sources of information in the immediate area. (See also Part III, Housing.) There is a range of options but the choice will ultimately depend on what is available in a particular area and how much money can be spent. An excellent source of information in the first instance is the book published by Age Concern England, *Housing Options for Older People*. This covers all the housing options available to older people, whether they wish to stay at home or move. The sections on moving describe the different types of housing, while the section on staying at home includes advice on home-income plans, getting repair work done, home security, emergency alarm systems and social services.

Supportive Housing

The following account of the Abbeyfield Societies' supportive housing gives the reader an idea of one of the alternative housing schemes currently available. Founded in the late fifties, the Abbeyfield Societies are independent, nationwide organizations with a coordinating group in Hertfordshire. The houses are arranged as far as possible into family units. Depending on the size of the house, there may be six or seven residents, or as many as eleven or twelve. Couples are not usually accommodated because one of the prime reasons for joining the community is loneliness. Twenty-four years ago people arrived in their late sixties or early seventies. Now, according to one Abbeyfield housekeeper, 'hardly anyone comes to us of that age. We are delighted to see them if they do; but they are usually much older. The average age here is eighty-three.'

Funding is generally mixed and derives from a variety of sources. Contributions from residents vary depending on the size of the rooms. If a resident is on income support, they receive all charges plus £12 a week 'pocket money'. People on fixed incomes and those who must rely on state pensions have free milk and help with extra heating such as an electric fire; otherwise there are really no extra expenses. The houses are run by volunteers, and apart from a few exceptions, the only paid staff are the housekeepers.

Application for a place is, according to an Organizing secretary, Mrs Pamela Newton, very simple. She explained:
'Mostly people plan two or three years ahead but sometimes
they want to come in quickly, usually because they find they
can't cope on their own or they have been in hospital and their
health has deteriorated, or their spouse has died and they are
worried about paying bills. We take them to a house to show
them what it is like; then, when a suitable room becomes
available, we invite them to come and have a meal with the
residents and see how they fit in. Occasionally, if there is a
spare room available, we ask them to come and spend a couple
of nights and see if they like staying there. We have a lot of
people from a wide variety of different backgrounds, but they
get along very well by and large. Most come from the local
area so they have a similar experience of the shops and facilities.
They have friends or family living locally. The society was
originally set up to help the elderly and lonely to go on living
where they had always lived. Sadly their families are not
always very involved. The children may find us and help their
parents get into the homes, but after that, they don't see much
of them.'

Each resident has their own room but the society stresses the
importance of communal dining once a day. A spokeswoman
for the society explained: 'In sheltered housing it can be very
lonely. There may be a common room downstairs but often no
one uses it. People just keep themselves to themselves with the
help of meals on wheels. Here we insist that everybody has
their main meal, which the housekeeper cooks, in the dining-
room. They don't have to see each other otherwise if they
don't want to.

'People furnish their own rooms and residents are responsible for keeping their rooms clean. We encourage people to do
their own shopping for breakfasts but if the time comes when
they are unable to go out, someone does their shopping for
them. When someone is unable to care for themselves, they are
moved on to one of our "Extra Care" houses provided there is
a vacancy; if not, we try to make other arrangements.

'People do have to be reasonably fit when they arrive but
there is no age barrier. We can offer good food and good
central heating. We've had people come in with terrible chests,

perhaps a little incontinent, and after a while they get better. People really do get better when they come here. It takes time to get used to the change of life, especially if you've been living on your own for a while, but once you're settled, there really isn't anything to worry about. You know where your next meal is coming from and you know there is someone to care about you.

'We often find in Abbeyfield that people seem to become younger when the stresses of living alone are taken from them. They return to a family situation and it takes years off their lives. They have interests in common and they feel they belong. We try to organize special social things, but not everyone wants to participate. The thing everyone enjoys is the annual garden party. Almost no one likes to go out in the winter. The houses vary enormously. Just like any family situation, it depends on the personalities involved. We have two houses quite close together in one area; in one, all the residents love going out together to plays and concerts, parties and functions, while in the second absolutely no one wants to go out. It is sometimes quite confusing for the staff because if their residents don't want to participate, they feel somehow they have failed them. But it just isn't so; it's simply a reflection of the different ways in which people want to live.

'Abbeyfield isn't for everyone. It's a good solution but if people want to be on their own most of the time, it probably wouldn't work for them.'

Nursing Homes and Residential Care Homes

These are discussed in more detail in Chapter 7. Fees for private homes differ widely and it does not necessarily follow that the highest prices are paid for the best service. The Registered Homes Act (1985) ensures that all homes are registered and inspected at least once a year. The Registered Nursing Homes Association publishes the *Reference Book of Registered Nursing Homes* annually (see Part III, Housing, for details). However, credibility on paper cannot be taken for granted and homes should be chosen only after careful personal inspection.

Last Moves

Preparation for Death
(See also p. 335, Death and Bereavement, and p. 158, Making a Will)

Preparation for death is a uniquely individual affair. Some people find it comforting to prepare for their own death while others cannot bear to contemplate the event, fearing that the very thought could bring it closer. There is no doubt, however, that those who do manage to tidy up the loose ends of their lives before their death leave behind a most grateful family:

> My mother died of cancer. Like most couples, my parents thought that she would outlive my father because he had a heart condition and was diabetic, but she developed cancer and he outlived her by four years. After she died, the big question was whether he should come down to London and be near us. He was interested in the theatre and libraries. He had a huge house, very difficult to maintain, but he decided to stay where he was and I think he had a very pleasant four years before his own death. It was slightly pathetic, I suppose – going through photographs of my mother; doing quite a lot of things like tidying up his financial affairs, giving away a lot of his books to the university, working out the catalogues and so on. But it was useful work tying up his own life, in a way, which of course made things terribly easy for me. I don't think it was a waste of time. There were ways in which these last years were quite appropriate. We tend to think people should ignore death but I think death is something we should prepare for. Acceptance makes things easier. We all die and there comes a time in life when perhaps it's right to get ready for death.

Room to Die
(see also Chapter 7, Caring for Others)

A person's decision to move to more appropriate surroundings
in old age may bring considerable relief to a concerned family,
but to the individual such a move cannot help but be associated
with their death and it is not surprising that delay often means
the final decision has to be taken by someone else.

Mrs P.T. was eighty-three years old. She lived, more or
less bedridden, in a flat on the fifth floor of an old building.
There was no lift and she found it impossible to walk up
and down the flights of stairs. She had no family and had
been helped for some time by neighbours. Twenty-five years
previously, Mrs P.T. had put her name down on the
waiting-list of a nursing home which offers mobile residents
their own bed-sitting-rooms. If they become ill or are unable
to cope for themselves, they are looked after by trained nursing staff in an open ward, but it was her intention to make
the move while she was still able to enjoy the independence
associated with a room of her own. In the event, she could
not bring herself to act upon the decision she had taken so
many years ago, and when her doctor finally managed to
persuade her to move into the nursing home, her infirmity
had become too great to enable her to take up her place in a
bed-sitting-room. She was psychologically unprepared to
spend the remainder of her days in a bed on a ward and
never recovered from the trauma of the move. She died in
the nursing home less than a year after her admission. A
member of staff told me: 'She seemed always so unhappy.
She withdrew into herself and wouldn't respond. From the
moment she came here, it was as though she had decided to
get over the business of living.'

That case history illustrates the often unbridgeable gulf
which exists between having the foresight to make a plan for
the end of life and summoning the enormous courage required
to put it into action. For the physically and mentally active
man or woman, whether their age is forty-five or eighty-five,
the sight of dependent, infirm members of a geriatric ward can
be deeply distressing. Is it possible that we will also become so
helpless? Must we too end our days amidst people we do not

know, totally reliant for every aspect of our daily lives upon the care of others?

The immensely compassionate matron of a Church of England nursing home did not attempt to disguise what are the everyday realities of life before death for many of her residents: 'I think when you get down to ward level, what is there? You get up, you are dressed, you are put in a chair, you watch everybody else getting dressed and got up. You have your coffee and breakfast, go to chapel, you go to the toilet yet again, and have your lunch. You might then go on to do something specially organized in the afternoon, then you are undressed and put back to bed. How can you be enthusiastic about such a life? We all eat together and we all pray together and we have the centrality of our Christian faith. Hopefully, if people can't do anything else, they can still pray, and you can always make them feel useful by telling them that the thing that keeps this house going is prayer. In a sense, we are privileged here to see our residents on to the next life. We have a chapel and can usually have the funeral service here. It's the right way to say goodbye.

'But whatever your religion, however strong your faith, death is frightening for everybody. People come here to die. Whatever people say about death – they don't mind if they die or they don't want to live on without their friends – when the time comes, it isn't so easy. You don't really know what's going to happen and no matter how strong your faith is, I think people do question what it will be like. We may believe what it says in the Bible but it hasn't actually got the answers and in a weakened state, faith cannot always shield you from fear.'

But there is a less bleak side to the final step. The matron continued: 'Although one says, "people come here to die", I think those who choose to come to us have a more positive approach simply because they know they can stay here to die. They won't be moved on. When they arrive here, they are usually able to manage in a room of their own. Then when they get ill or infirm, they move to a ward – so they know we will look after them until they do die. I think there's a kind of security in that. But not everyone gives in to the idea of death. Many of our residents are prepared to live life to the full until they die. We had one lady here of ninety-two who decided to go to Cornwall to help her niece and two children. She came back and died two weeks later – she'd actually exhausted herself to death. But she had lived right to the end. And isn't it lovely? I'm a great believer in letting people do what they want to do. They're much happier. There's another lady who lives upstairs still well able to cope on her own at ninety-seven. She wants to live until she's a hundred – it's her ambition and I'm sure she'll make it.'

Loss of the Car

Readers who have never owned a car and whose life has revolved happily around the public transport system are likely to skim through this section wondering what all the fuss is about. The fact is that one of the hardest losses for older car drivers to endure is having to relinquish their car owing to poor eyesight or lack of mobility.

Mrs M.P., aged seventy-five:

> In recent years, arthritis has meant that I can no longer move around very quickly and easily. I was so accustomed to driving anywhere I wanted to go and now I really can't drive long distances so it has made a great difference to my life. Any travel now has to be in the hands of someone else, whether it be public transport, taxis or friends who take me around. I feel I am no longer entirely independent.

Mrs A.J., aged eighty-eight:

> The worst thing I ever did was to give up driving at the age of eighty-four. I still feel a terrible sense of loss and regret. At the time, it seemed sensible. I had just moved to a retirement home and was about to buy a smaller car but my son who lives with his family a couple of miles down the road, said to me, 'Do you really need one? You live close to the station and there are regular buses from your front door.' I think he was probably worried about me and considered I was a bit too old to continue driving. Anyhow,

at the time, I thought it good advice; but looking back, it seems to me I didn't think about it long enough. I should love just to be able to potter about the area now under my own steam. I see a good deal of my family and I would give anything if I could just drive myself over for my usual Sunday lunch.

Dr P.J., aged ninety-four:

As a doctor with a country practice, I seemed to spend most of my days in my car. Now I live in a retirement home and I'm still driving. In all truth, I don't think I should and the car mostly sits parked outside, but it gives me a feeling of independence just knowing it's still there and I can use it if I want to.

Safe and reliable transport is one of the most important aids to maintaining independence yet car drivers who have experienced dizzy spells or who have poor eyesight should consider whether it is not time to give in to the demands of age and hang up their car keys rather than waiting for some tragic accident to occur before they are forced off the roads by the law. Not only does age force us to slow down, it also tends to blunt reactions and dull awareness.

Not long ago, I was motoring behind a car whose occupants, including the driver, were well past the age of seventy. They drove out of a country village at fifteen or twenty miles an hour, apparently looking for a left-hand turn. There were many choices along the route. Every few minutes, the brake lights went on and the car slowed down to three miles an hour at each turn, before it was rejected. About five miles later – and by this time I had been joined in the queue by four other cars and a farm tractor – the home turn came into view, but not before the driver had passed it by a few feet. There was much gesturing within the car, but not even the vaguest hand signal without as it came to a halt and began backing up towards me at an alarming speed, ready to take aim at the elusive home turning. Panic and self-preservation led me to press the horn. On hearing the noise, the driver visibly jumped in her seat, looked in the rear-view mirror, saw me and gave me a friendly, apologetic wave before she followed the appropriate procedure which propelled them safely across the road. Until that moment, I am quite certain that she had been entirely unaware of being followed out of the village by an increasing line of exasperated drivers hemmed in by continuous white lines and a winding road.

Readers will perhaps think it unfair of me to cite just one incident as an example of the way in which driving habits can change in old age but I would also suggest that sometimes they do not change enough. One dear friend drives as fast at eighty as he did when he was in his twenties and, given the increase in traffic since those early years of the motor car, driving with him is a nightmare from which one can only hope to wake alive.

Any car driver, regardless of age, whose way of life depends on the independence and freedom motoring affords will understand how difficult it is for people to give up driving. In a nutshell, it means dependence – upon an unreliable (and in many country areas non-existent) transport system, upon expensive minicabs and upon friends and family fortunate enough to own cars; but by far the most severe loss is of the wider world of activity and opportunity which the car driver takes for granted over the years. Even diet can be affected when shopping in a supermarket several miles away from home must be confined instead to whatever goods the nearest village store has to offer, usually at higher prices. On cold winter days, visits to friends are reduced and the spontaneous trips encouraged by a morning's sunshine may no longer be possible without the facility of a car parked outside the front door, ready to go adventuring.

When the time comes to examine the pros and cons of moving to a new environment, transport is a vital consideration. Modern, custom-built retirement homes take account of the needs of residents who can no longer drive but not many locations are so convenient.

Driving Test

A licence is issued up to the age of seventy and currently there is no law or test dictating the age at which a driver should relinquish a driving licence. On the eve of the seventieth birthday, application should be made for renewal, after which time, the licence must be renewed every three years. No medical test is required but questions concerning health are asked on the application form. The onus therefore is on the driver to give a truthful account of himself, but even with the best will in the world, he may be quite unaware of a decline in vision or other vital faculties.

Personal Safety
(See also the check-list on p. 125.)

Are elderly people any more vulnerable to attack and harassment than children or young adults? Not according to a Home Office report published in 1988, *Victims of Street Crime in 1987* ('victims' are defined as those people having experience of robbery, theft from the person and/or assault in public places):

Men	Percentage
16–30	8.4
31–60	1.7
over 61	0.7
all men	3.2
Women	
16–30	2.7
31–60	1.2
over 61	0.5
all women	1.4

But the fact is that older people are not impressed by government figures which show them to be statistically safer than young men between sixteen and thirty. Their advanced years makes them feel more vulnerable, and many become increasingly fearful for their personal safety. In March 1989, the government, concerned that older people were shaping their lives around an unreal and unnecessary fear, formed a working party under the direction of Michael Grade, chief executive of

Channel 4 Television, to look into ways of impressing upon the public the true picture behind the statistics. The report, published in December 1989, was critical of the way in which the media represented criminal incidents. The sensational images of what it described as 'crime-scare programmes' tended to fuel the fear of crime, especially in people who were statistically the least likely to be affected. Despite the very low risk of attack, elderly women were imposing an after-dark curfew on themselves, yet they had little to fear but fear itself.

An Emergency Alarm System

Emergency medical alarm companies are often surprised by the hostility which greets them when they call to arrange for the installation of one of their systems. Far from seeing it as a life-saver, allowing help to be summoned at the touch of a button, the prospective client can be outraged and affronted by the very idea that someone thinks they might actually need such an alarm.

Although many inquiries are received directly from clients themselves, the great majority of requests for alarm systems come from families anxious to protect their elderly parents or grandparents. These requests are frequently made without the parents having first been consulted.

The different types of alarm systems available are described in a booklet entitled *Calling for Help: A Guide to Emergency Alarm Systems*, available from Age Concern (see also Part III, Emergency Alarm Systems).

Check-list: Security

- **Crime** – 95 per cent of crimes are crimes against property. Break-ins usually take place in daylight and last about three minutes. Sensible precautions will help to prevent this type of crime. Talk to the Crime Prevention Officer at your nearest police station; he will tell you how best to protect your property.
- **Personal belongings** – valuable items should be marked by engraving or invisible ink using a security marker pen. The postcode followed by the house number is all that is required.
- People should have a **door chain** fitted and never admit

anyone without seeing their credentials. **Large sums of money should never be kept in the house.**

● **Neighbourhood Watch** – there are over 42,000 of these schemes now operating around the country. Retired people are welcome to join. Talk to the local police about joining or starting a scheme in your area.

Check list: Safety

● **Accidents** – most accidents occur at home. They can be avoided by carrying out repairs and alterations to avoid potential hazards. Stairs and landings need to be well lit and worn carpet replaced. Gas and electrical equipment should be regularly serviced. Bathrooms and kitchens should be made accident-proof, with toxic material and medicines clearly labelled.

● **Fire** – death and severe injury resulting from house fires are common. Smoke is usually the actual cause of death. Inflammable plastic materials such as polyurethane, cigarettes, electrical faults and gas leaks are the most frequent cause of fires.

● **Road accidents** – more than half of all pedestrians killed are over sixty. To avoid accidents, use the roads in between the rush hours; cross at safe places and have your eyes and ears tested regularly.

Staying in Touch

The telephone can be the single most important instrument in helping people to continue living independently. Its value is both social and practical – a source of friendship and of food and services.

In 1989, a report was published by Oftel (British Telecom's consumer watchdog) on a special study of the telecommunications needs of disabled and elderly people.

The author of the report, Professor Anthea Tinker, Director of the Age Concern Institute of Gerontology at King's College, London, stressed the importance of being able to keep in touch with friends and family, and the value of the telephone in maintaining human contact, especially for those living on their own. 'You may think this is fairly obvious,' she said, 'but it hasn't really been emphasized enough in the past. The people we interviewed didn't make any phone calls except to friends and relatives and they took the greatest pleasure in receiving calls. For people who are to a great extent housebound, especially during cold winter months, the telephone is the one thing which makes them feel they belong to the world outside their homes. Regular phone calls to elderly parents also proved a great relief to adult children concerned for their safety and welfare especially if they lived too far away to make frequent visits.'

But despite the popularity of the telephone in principle, the Oftel report showed overwhelming evidence to suggest that elderly people feared its costs. It also indicated that a majority of those involved in the study were wary of using anything new, not because they were uninterested in technology, but because, again, they were afraid innovations would be too expensive. This proved to be the case particularly with the mobile telephone, which can be of immense value to people who find standing up and walking across a room to answer the phone an arduous and painful chore.

Fact sheet no. 28, 'Help with Telephones', from Age Concern describes the help available to elderly people for the cost of installing and using a telephone. While there is no national scheme to provide the finance, people may qualify for assistance if they are chronically sick or disabled.

Old Age – the Gains

While no one would deny the losses of old age, there are also gains. One man expressed a common experience of his generation: 'I'm more tolerant now than I used to be and understand people better. I've also got more time for them.'

The ability to enjoy these later years is generated from within but what kind of men and women are they who manage to find excitement and fulfilment in old age?

The following case histories are examples of people who feel themselves to be genuinely happy and fulfilled in their old age. Apart from the fact that they have all been widowed and have managed to adapt to living on their own, their backgrounds, fortunes, styles of living and even their states of health and degree of mobility differ widely; yet what they have in common is the spirit to squeeze every ounce of pleasure from the life that is left to them.

I first met Mrs R.B. when she was ninety-one years old. She looks astonishingly youthful. She has smooth skin and long, thick white hair which flows down her back. When it falls over her face, she flicks it over her shoulder like an impatient schoolgirl. On that day, she wore a dark pink velvet Alice band which matched the frilled collar of her bright coloured blouse. Not that she was in particularly good health. She had just recovered from a bad bout of flu which left her rather weak. She was also having radium treatment for a malignant tumour in her neck. 'I never felt the need for private medicine until I had this bit of cancer trouble. I'm afraid I did pay for the radiotherapy and the private consultation at the hospital. A doctor friend told me that if I delayed going much longer I'd have to have my jaw taken off and stuck back on again and I was alarmed by the three-month wait on the NHS.'

Apart from the cancer, she considers herself to be in a 'fairly rude state of health'. Although she admits to going slightly deaf, she gave no indication to me that this was so. She has no problems with her eyes and only needs glasses for reading. She finds it impossible to get herself in and out of the bath and once a week a friend comes and helps her. For the rest, she manages to take a daily shower. She is troubled by arthritis in both knees but walks easily enough with the help of a stick.

Personally I'm having the time of my life. I enjoy writing. I had an article about my parents published last year, and I'm in the midst of writing two books, one on Newfoundland and another on the two years I spent in Germany after the war. The Fine Arts Society are having an exhibition of my paintings in the spring. In a couple of weeks, I'm off to Labrador to do some painting and sketching. I'm going with a woman companion. She's eighty years old and very sprightly. She's done a lot of travelling and is very experienced. She's organizing the trip – buying the tickets and everything and I'm paying for it. Seems fair. My family have never had much money but the older I get, the better off financially I've become. Relations die and leave me their savings. I'm really very lucky.

I don't worry much when old friends die off. I always make new ones, mostly younger than me. There's an old girl living a few doors away who's my age. She's nice but we don't have much in common and I hardly ever see her. I have a very funny boyfriend who comes to see me once a week and stays for a quarter of an hour. It's the first time in my life I've had a boyfriend. It's a bit tiresome at ninety-one but he's so nice. He knows a lot about women and we have such a jolly time together. He misses me when I'm away and always comes to welcome me home. He's only sixty-seven – a 'toy boy' you'd say nowadays – but I think he's more in love with his dog than he is with me. We argue quite a bit.

I'd like to get married again but you see, I could never leave this house, and it's too small to share with anyone.

Reluctant though she is to leave her house, Mrs R.B. has made preparations for the time when she will no longer be able to cope on her own. 'I've put my name down for the old people's home about a mile away. I've come to know the staff there very well over the years. I don't want to go into the home unless it's absolutely necessary. I've visited friends of mine there and they have all been very well cared for. I think the symptoms of dementia are catching. When I visit my friend there whose mind is beginning to wander, I find myself repeating things and thinking slowly like she does'.

Mrs R.B. and her companion had planned their trip to Labrador during the month of February. I asked her whether she did not think the summer would have been a better time to travel. The winter was exceptionally cold that year. No, she said. She wanted to return to the country just as she thought she remembered it as a girl, under feet of snow. Had she bought special clothing for the occasion? Yes, she said, and thrust out a trousered leg. She had bought the slacks from Marks and Spencer's the previous week and insisted that they were thicker than her usual winter wear. How about footwear? She thought her trainers would do. I reckoned she would have had as much chance of surviving in a bikini at the South Pole. Fortunately we managed to borrow more appropriate clothing from a friend who had just returned from Canada.

The visit to Labrador lasted a month, and while she was there I received a letter. She wrote:

> The clothing, some of it, has been most useful, especially, strangely enough, the boots. I do hope I haven't worn them out. When it was 25 below, I felt the cold a bit but now it's only -8 and a lovely day. The black glasses too I am glad to have. I never used them before when I was here, but now I have to. And it's too cold to sit out and draw. I think when I was here in 1932 it either wasn't quite so cold or I was here before the snow came and after it had gone so there was the autumn and spring to work outdoors. We are a bit late too: March is the worst month.
>
> We had a short ride in a helicopter and the pilot got lost. I addressed the school in Makkovik, have had to do two talks on radio and there is another threatened in St Johns, and we have been invited out to dinner with the Minister for Labrador which means, I suppose, the Newfoundland Hotel and we naturally have no evening dresses. I find it all a bit exhausting so I fear I must be getting as old as I really am. My companion never stops. She's rather outspoken and looks after me like a nanny.

Mrs R.B. lives in fairly ordinary circumstances on a modest income combined with a pension, but she is not an ordinary woman. Her artistic and literary abilities give her the basis for a resourcefulness which most of us do not have; but what makes her a useful example of fulfilment in old age is that she continues to use these resources to the utmost. Neither does she allow illness or infirmity to stand in the way of her natural curiosity and love of adventure. At ninety-one, she has lost nothing of her zest for life and although her horizons may be somewhat wider and more daunting than many people's, her lifestyle shows that old age does not necessarily mean the loss of fun. Her memories are vivid and precious but she is not forced to rely on the past alone for company because in the present she is always busy replenishing the store.

Religious Faith in Old Age

Speaking to members of the generation who are now in their seventies and eighties, one is constantly led to regret the lack of a firm religious belief. People who are committed to their God and have faith in a life after death are comforted and strengthened by a certain knowledge that they have a future and a future that will in some way include being reunited with friends and relatives who have preceded them in death:

> I'm nearly ninety now and I'm the only one left out of a family of fourteen. I've never worried about getting old. Religion means everything to me, so I haven't really regretted the death of my friends and family – I try to think of their gain rather than my loss because I know they are with the Lord and that we will be together again. My faith protects me, I suppose.
>
> My husband and I were out to tea with friends when he suddenly remembered he had left the car lights on. He went out to the car-park and when he didn't return, I went out to find him only to discover him lying on a stretcher about to be carried away by the ambulance. I just knew he was dead without even looking at him. I knew for certain that there was nothing that could be done. The sense of peace which God gave me at that moment was so great it has never gone. When the police offered to take me home, I refused and told them I would prefer to drive myself. You know if you have real faith when it's put to the test in this way. He was fortunate in having such a quick and peaceful death. He was far too active in life to accept being bedridden for any length of time. I miss him terribly but I still talk to him in my

mind and I have absolutely no doubt that we shall be together again one day.

Faith comforts and supports, helps to relieve the pain of bereavement and makes the healing process a little easier, but it does not make us immune to the trauma of death when it occurs. A nursing sister, a member of a Roman Catholic order, told me: 'Death is a stressful event, whether we are the bereaved or, when approaching our own end, we are about to bereave others. I am a nun; I have no doubt about God or my future with him but like everyone else here whom we nurse through their last days till death releases them, when my time comes, I am sure I shall be a little afraid. We are all frightened; we all need help to leave this life and we all need help from family and friends when we are the ones left behind.'

Carl Jung, who recognized man's difficulty in reconciling God and modern science, wrote in 1930:

For the man of today the expansion of life and its culmination are plausible goals, but the idea of life after death seems to him questionable or beyond belief. Life's cessation, that is, death, can only be accepted as a reasonable goal either when existence is so wretched that we are only too glad for it to end, or when we are convinced that the sun strives to its setting 'to illuminate distant races' with the same logical consistency it showed in rising to the zenith. But to believe has become such a difficult art today that it is beyond the capacity of most people, particularly the educated part of humanity. They have become too accustomed to the thought that, with regard to immortality and such questions, there are innumerable contradictory opinions and no convincing proofs.[37]

Yet not everyone who finds happiness in old age is supported by a belief in the certainty of life after death. 'A peaceful, exciting and happy time' was the way one woman – a confirmed atheist – described her life at the age of seventy-six, 'but', she added, 'if somebody had tried to convince me when I was fifty that I would feel so content in old age, I should never have believed them.'

Part II
Choices

4 Finance

This chapter has been written in close collaboration with John Moysey, administrator at the Money Management Council, an impartial and independent charity set up in 1985 to promote education and better general understanding in personal and family finance. Although the Money Management Council cannot give individual personal advice, a series of factsheets is available which will act as signposts, pointing the reader towards a variety of financial services. Details are given in Part III, Finance.

Retirement – the Poverty Trap?

Although it is true that happiness itself cannot be bought, health care, high-quality food and comfortable living conditions can be, and these all take on a greater significance in middle and old age.

The discrepancy between earnings and the state pension – currently (1991) £52 for a single person and £83·25 for a married couple – gives rise to the fear that retirement is inextricably linked to poverty. At the time of writing, there is no research available to enlighten us as to how many of the nation's ten million pensioners depend solely on their state pension but, in 1990, figures produced by Age Concern show that 60 per cent rely on the state for 80 per cent of their income. It is unlikely that life in old age will be accompanied by many luxuries for those who must depend on the state for such a small weekly allowance. The table overleaf gives some indication of the financial gulf which exists between the employed man and woman and the pensioner:

Average weekly pay

	Men	Women
Manual workers	£217.80	£134.90
Non-manual workers	£323.60	£195.00

(Government statistics: *New Earnings Survey, April 1989*, Part A, HMSO, 1989. National average wage at this time, £239·70 per week. Figures include overtime pay at £57·90 for male manual workers; £22·20 for female manual workers; £26·20 for male non-manual workers and £9·50 for female non-manual workers. It is noted that women on average worked 4·7 hours less than men.)

Financial Planning for Retirement – the Need for an Early Start

To ensure that the quality of life does not suffer in retirement, early preparation is essential. Income may be reduced, but it can to an extent be offset by a reduction in travelling expenses and clothing costs. In the years before retirement, houseowners are usually beginning to feel the freedom of life without burdensome mortgage repayments and enjoying the financial relief of adult children earning their own money. A retired office manager described it this way:

> I found with three children at home we were very strapped for cash for quite a long time while I was working, really right up to the time they started leaving school. Even so, I used to try to put a little bit away each month, even if it was only ten or fifteen pounds. I invested it in one of the National Savings schemes which allows the money to build up into a capital sum. It's surprising how quickly it mounts up and even more surprising – you find you don't miss it and can actually do without it.
>
> Eventually, when the children were off our hands and I was pretty much near the peak of my employ-

ment, we suddenly found we had more money than
ever before. We actually had some spare cash! We
decided, my wife and I, to spend most of the money
on more luxuries and less worry but we also managed
to put a little aside each month towards a world
cruise to celebrate my retirement.

Where to Go for Help and Advice?

The range of financial advisers offering advice as to how, on
your behalf, they can best spend your money is bewilderingly
wide. It should be borne in mind that some professional
advisers have a vested interest in promoting their own schemes,
which may not necessarily be suited to a particular client's
needs. To protect consumers against this built-in bias, the
1986 Financial Services Act asserts that under the law people
must be offered 'best advice' to satisfy their own individual
requirements and should not be persuaded to put their money
into a scheme simply because it benefits the adviser.

But even the 'best advice' is not enough to prevent the
customer from losing their savings if the company in which
they have placed their trust defaults. There are rogues in every
industry who will cover their tracks so cleverly that it takes a
long time before their dealings are discovered.

However, provided a client has sought advice from a firm
authorized under the Financial Services Act, if he then loses
money through negligent advice or fraud, or business failure
on the part of the financial adviser, under the Act he is entitled
to compensation up to a maximum, at present, for any one
investor, of £48,000.

Another area of concern centres on the 'roll-up' schemes
mostly provided by building societies, in which a person can
be provided with an income without paying interest on the
loan – at least, not immediately. The unpaid interest is 'rolled
up' and added to the loan until perhaps ten years later, a
demand is made for a substantial repayment. In February
1990, the Labour MP for Grimsby, Austin Mitchell, raised
questions in the House of Commons about the lack of control
over unscrupulous advisers who persuade pensioners to boost

their meagre incomes in this way by using their valuable homes as security. It is one thing to buy an annuity or an income for life in which repayment of the interest on the loan is taken into account, but quite another to use the money for everyday purposes. When interest is not paid, the amount added to the loan can quickly reach the total value of the property. Without means to repay the debt, the lender forecloses and the property owner is made homeless.

(For problems involving debt, see pp. 160–61.)

Taking Stock – Questions to Ask

In the financial world, there is only one certainty and that is inflation. Unless money is invested in a way which allows it to keep pace with rising prices, its real value will be diminished. So how can you obtain the best financial advice in the light of your own individual requirements?

In the first instance, there are certain fundamental questions to consider: is money required immediately or can it be set aside for a period of time? Is your financial future to be planned taking a spouse and family into account or are you single and likely to remain so? Do you pay tax and if so, at what level? What sums of money are you likely to have from pension schemes on retirement? What are your current expenses; what are they likely to be in the future? Are you prepared to oversee a portfolio of stocks and shares or would you prefer to hand the responsibility of investing your savings to others? Are you prepared to risk the consequences of a stock-market crash?

The Need to Budget

Before making any decisions it is essential to sit down and work out the annual budget. List *income* (pension, earnings, investment income, etc.) and *anticipated expenditure* (house, car, travel, housekeeping, personal expenditure, leisure and holidays). Sort out the latter into 'Priority' (e.g. mortgage/ rent) and 'Non-priority' expenses (e.g. eating out). It is important to overestimate expenses in order to allow for inflation. Include also savings and an amount to be set aside for emergencies and unforeseen bills.

The figures should be prepared on an annual as well as on a monthly basis. They will immediately highlight tight spots in your cash flow. At a glance, you will see whether you can manage comfortably, or with care, or not at all. If it appears that you are unable to manage, what do you plan to do about it? Every detail should be included. What is a luxury to one person will be a necessity to another and without a close examination of the ways in which money flows into and out of the household it will not be possible to find ways of financing the necessities if cutbacks are needed.

Budgeting will also be a useful exercise in assessing investment needs because it will indicate whether extra income is needed, or capital growth, or a mixture of both.

Shopping Around

With a fairly modest amount to invest, where the investor cannot afford to take risks, banks, building societies and National Savings schemes offer maximum security and reasonable – albeit fluctuating – rates of interest. Most of the banks have teams offering all-round financial advice to their customers. In a simple, straightforward situation, where the money to be invested is around £15,000–£20,000 or less, it may not be necessary to go to a financial adviser. With a relatively small sum, self-help can save money. By sifting through the literature (see Part III, Finance) and targeting the investment area which seems to offer the best deal, and then going along to the bank or building society concerned, or picking up the relevant information and forms from the Post Office, the fee charged by a financial adviser can be avoided.

Some of these schemes require notice before money can be withdrawn. This is an important factor to be taken into consideration, as some money should be kept available for dealing with emergencies, but obviously the longer you are able to tie your money up, the higher will be the rate of interest.

Finding the Best Professional Advice

The situation becomes much more complicated when a larger sum of money is involved or where someone with only a modest amount to invest is prepared to take some risk. At a time when so many agencies offer the same service – banks like building societies now operate mortgage schemes; building societies have entered the banking world and now run cheque accounts – some kind of professional advice is necessary. But how can the best advice be obtained?

In the first instance, the financial adviser must be an authorized member of one of the organizations set up under the Financial Services Act, (see p. 142), which gives the consumer protection under the law and means that the adviser has the necessary status and credibility, and also that he or she has met the conditions imposed by the Financial Services Act, has a certain financial status and has achieved the necessary high standards of expertise. Letters after an adviser's name will indicate the professional examinations passed.

Provided this basic rule is adhered to, personal recommendation by a friend or family member who has been satisfied with the work of a particular financial adviser and trusts his judgement is one of the best sources of guidance. Failing that, there are really only three options open to customers:

1. They can write to one of the umbrella organizations set up under the Financial Services Act covering the particular business in which they are interested in investing their money, and asking for a list of member firms in their area. They will be supplied with the names of perhaps ten or a dozen firms which they can then investigate personally.
2. The Yellow Pages telephone directory is a useful source of information.
3. Thirdly, a customer can tramp the High Street looking for people who advertise themselves as insurance brokers or independent financial advisers or financial consultants, and who have displayed in their premises and on their headed notepaper a badge of one of the organizations set up under the Financial Services Act. They can go in and see how they get on; if they feel comfortable with the adviser concerned and confident that he or she can do a good job and that the level of charges estimated for the work is acceptable, then let business commence; but if they do not feel happy, it would be better to try elsewhere. In any

event, comparisons are useful. It is worth bearing in mind that a local broker or adviser relies very much on word-of-mouth recommendations in order to build up his business, so it is in his interest to give you 'best advice'.

Even personal recommendation from friends or family cannot guarantee success. Where one customer might feel satisfied, another could feel let down. Shopping around for a financial adviser is much the same as employing a builder to do some work on the home. Two or three might be invited to give an estimate; one will eventually be chosen, probably for a combination of reasons – because his price was right, he was a pleasant man to deal with and because he seemed to know what he was talking about.

The single person, whether widowed or unmarried, may find the fact of being alone makes them a little more vulnerable to the charm of a financial adviser. Does his kindness and willingness to listen also mean that he will invest your money in a way that is most suited to your needs? In an interview, two heads are often better than one – one will pick up nuances which escape the other; where one may be less willing to ask questions, but another will demand to know the adviser's performance record – what he has done with people's money in the past. There is an advantage too in being able to go away and think about the advice given, talking over the plans together. With this in mind, a single person, who perhaps does not feel very confident about approaching an adviser for the first time, might consider taking along a friend or a member of the family to the interview.

If you are beginning investigations into your financial future without any prior knowledge or guidance, free and impartial advice is always available from the local Citizens Advice Bureau. (The telephone number will be in the local directory.) Their leaflet Finding Your Way Through the Financial Minefield offers a menu of services involving help and advice on mortgages, banking loans and credit, investment protection, finding the best financial advice, taxation and pensions.

Questions Asked – What the Financial Adviser will need to Know

The Independent Financial Advice Promotion booklet, *A Guide to Independent Financial Advice* (see Part III, Finance, for further details), lists the information an adviser needs to know (and, under the Financial Services Act, is entitled to know) before 'best advice' can be given. The list is as follows:

> your income
> mortgage repayments
> details of any other investment, unit trust, etc.
> what pension arrangements you have
> family commitments
> personal investment philosophy – do you like taking risks or
>   do you prefer cast-iron-solid investments
> expectations
> lifestyle
> tax bracket

Charges

The client will be charged by the adviser, either by a fee or by commission from the companies in which you have invested, or a combination of both. If commission is involved, it should be made clear what percentage is taken and whether or not it affects the investments. The client should insist upon a written account of all charges.

Financial Organizations

Devised with the help of the factsheet 'Who Will Give Me "Best Advice"?', available from the Money Management Council (see Part III, Finance), the following section gives descriptions of the organizations from which, under the Financial Services Act, all advisers must have authorization in order to operate. They must be authorized either through one of the Self-Regulatory Organizations (SROs) or through a Recognized Professional Body (RPB).

From the outset, advisers have to decide whether to be *independent*, whereby they are entitled to offer the whole range of financial services, or *tied*, in which case, they may offer only the products of a single company or group. Their individual position must be clearly acknowledged.

There are firms of financial advisers who specialize in advising retired and elderly people. Information will be available from one of the umbrella organizations listed below.

Securities and Investments Board (SIB) and Self-Regulatory Organizations (SROs)

Securities and Investments Board (SIB)
Gavrelle House, 2–14 Bunhill Row, London EC1Y 8RA
  Tel. 071–638 1240
This is the supervisory organization which controls the Self-Regulatory Organizations set up under the Financial Services Act. It has available a comprehensive list of all authorized firms and individual advisers and produces a free booklet, 'Self-defence for Investors'.

The SROs will supply lists of their member firms in your area. A firm's letterhead should indicate their membership.

Financial Intermediaries, Managers and Brokers Regulatory Association (FIMBRA)
Hertsmere House, Hertsmere Road, London E14 9AB
  Tel. 071–538 8860
FIMBRA regulates the *independent* financial intermediaries who offer advice and arrange deals in life assurance, pensions, unit trusts, stocks and shares and provide management services.

The Life Assurance and Unit Trust Regulatory Organization (LAUTRO)
Centre Point, 103 New Oxford Street, London WC1A 1QH
  Tel. 071–379 0444
Regulates the marketing activities of companies providing life assurance, pensions and unit trusts.

The Securities and Futures Authority
The Stock Exchange Building, Old Broad Street, London EC2N 1EQ
  Tel. 071–256 9000

Formed in April 1991 by the merger of The Securities Association (TSA) and the Association of Futures Brokers and Dealers (AFBD). The authority mainly covers those who advise and deal in stocks and shares, government securities (gilts), and 'futures' and 'options'. It also covers advisers whose secondary activities involve unit trusts, life assurance, 'futures', 'options' and investment management.

The Investment Management Regulatory Organization (IMRO)
Broadwalk House, Appold Street, London EC4A 2LL.
Tel. 071-628 6022
Regulates investment managers, including unit-trust managers and trustees and those providing a discretionary management service for their clients.

Recognized Professional Bodies (RPBs)

Insurance Brokers Registration Council
15 St Helen's Place, London EC3A 6DS
A statutory body set up under earlier legislation to register insurance brokers. It does not provide brokers' names and addresses to the public.

The Law Society of England and Wales
113 Chancery Lane, London WC2A 1PL

The Law Society of Scotland
26 Drumsheugh Gardens, Edinburgh EH3 7YR

The Law Society of Northern Ireland
90–106 Victoria Street, Belfast BT1 3JZ
Sometimes solicitors' work involves them in areas which require registration under the Act, but this is covered by membership of the Law Society, which can provide names and addresses of solicitors in your area. Similarly, chartered accountants must register with the Institute of Chartered Accountants.

Institute of Chartered Accountants
England and Wales: PO Box 433, Chartered Accountants
Hall, Moorgate Place, London EC2P 2BJ

Scotland: 27 Queen Street, Edinburgh EH2 ILA

Ireland: Chartered Accountants House, 87/89 Pembroke
Road, Dublin 4

The Chartered Association of Certified Accountants
29 Lincoln's Inn Fields, London WC2A 3EE
Will provide a list of certified accountants.

The Institute of Actuaries
Staples Inn Hall, High Holborn, London WCIV 7QJ
Can provide a list of practising actuaries.

Other Organizations Providing Information on Where to Go
for 'Best Advice'

IFA Promotion Ltd (IFAP)
4th Floor, 28 Greville Street, London ECIN 8SU
  Tel. 071–831 4027
IFAP offers a service by which the consumer can telephone
081–200 3000 to obtain a list of independent financial advisers
in their home or work area according to postcode. The organization also produces a free booklet called 'A Guide to Independent Financial Advice' designed to help choose an adviser and
pinpoint the relevant questions a client is likely to be asked in
order that 'best advice' can be given.

Association of British Insurers
Aldermary House, Queen Street, London EC4N ITT
  Tel. 071–248 4477
The trade association for insurance companies, which, although
it cannot recommend particular companies, provides a list of
companies and produces general literature on pensions and life
assurance.

British Insurance and Investment Brokers Association
BIIBA House, 14 Bevis Marks, London EC3A 7NT
  Tel. 071–623 9043

Society of Pension Consultants
Ludgate House, Ludgate Circus, London EC4A 2AB
  Tel. 071–353 1688
The last two both provide lists of individual brokers and
consultants, all of whom should be authorized through
FIMBRA or LAUTRO.

Investing a Lump Sum

National Savings Schemes

Some National Savings schemes offer guaranteed tax-free returns, for example:

National Savings Fixed-interest Certificates which provide
safety and a tax-free capital gain over five years; if they are
kept for longer than that period, the investor will only be
entitled to the *general extension rate* of interest – a variable rate
set well below other current interest rates.

The current *Index-Linked Issue of National Savings Certificates* has the advantage of guaranteeing a return above the rate
of inflation but because of this it is not possible to assess
exactly what they will be worth at the expiry time.

Yearly Plan, which is a regular monthly savings scheme
offering a tax-free return guaranteed over a full five years.

National Savings Schemes for Non-taxpayers

Other National Savings Schemes are ideal for non-taxpayers
because, although the interest is taxable, tax is not deducted at
source from the interest paid to the saver. These include:
Capital Bonds which offer a way of investing a lump sum with
a guaranteed growth over a full five years with absolute safety,
the interest rate rising each year; *Income Bonds*, which are also
suitable for lump-sum savings, have the added advantage of
giving the investor a regular monthly income; and the *Investment Account*, which operates like a bank account except that
one month's notice is required for withdrawals. There are no
withdrawal penalties.

Before investing in these schemes, your income-tax position
should be checked, since non-taxpayers could become taxpay-
ers with the additional National Savings interest.

(The latest leaflets describing all the current National Savings are available from most Post Offices or from the Department for National Savings, Marketing and Sales Information Dept, Charles House, 375 Kensington High Street, London W14 8SD.)

Banks and Building Societies

These have a variety of savings schemes and most of them compete with National Savings. Although income tax is normally deducted by banks and building societies before the money is paid to the customer, since April 1991 it has been possible for a non-taxpayer to complete a form (R58) which enables the bank or building society to pay the interest 'gross', i.e. without prior deduction of tax. It pays to compare schemes and watch the advertisements when interest rates climb. Sometimes offers emerge which beat the money market.

Free publications available from
Banking Information Service, 10 Lombard Street, London
EC3V 9AT
Building Societies Association, 3 Savile Row, London W1X
1AF

Insurance Investments

Insurance investments are numerous and varied. Purely as an investment they tend to be cautious, but they also provide life-assurance cover. Since most schemes tend to tie up money for longer periods, they are not suited to investors who may want easy access to their funds. Help from a first-class broker or adviser is essential: then go for big-name companies with high reputations to protect.

Free publications available from
Association of British Insurers, 51 Gresham Street, London
EC2V 7HQ.
Tel. 071–600 3333

The Stock Market

Gilt-edged Stocks ('Gilts')

The term is used to describe shares in the government or its enterprises, and was coined at a time when the certificates were edged with gold. A stock bears a redemption date on which the holder will be repaid the full face value. So, for example, the investor may buy a gilt now for £90, knowing that he will receive £100 in five years' time. Depending on the redemption date and type of gilt, the different categories are called 'shorts', 'mediums', 'longs', 'undated' or 'index-linked'. Holders usually receive interest twice a year and any capital gain on gilts is free of tax. Experienced advice is needed for this type of investment.

Stocks and Shares

These are for the punter. Prices fluctuate daily, sometimes violently, and while the gains are there, so are the losses – which could have serious consequences for the lifestyle of the investor, especially in retirement, when the ability to recuperate from loss is less robust.

Futures and Options

This is a specialist market in which the investor speculates on the future price of the stock he wants to buy or sell.

For all dealings in the stock market, professional advice is essential.

Free publications available from:
The London Stock Exchange, Publications Department, Old Broad Street, London EC2N 1HP

Unit Trusts

Unit Trusts are collective investments in which small or large sums of money from investors are pooled and invested by experienced professionals into a wide spread of stocks and shares. This wide spread cushions any losses while regulations set out by the Department of Trade and Industry ensure that unit trusts take few risks with your money. In consequence, units are less likely to soar but also less likely than stocks and shares to tumble dramatically.

Free publications available from:
Unit Trust Association Information Unit, 65 Kingsway,
London WC2D 6TD

Investment Trusts

These are companies whose shares are quoted on the Stock Exchange. They themselves deal in and hold the shares of other companies so, like unit trusts, they are collective investments. Their funds are managed by experts who have a close ear to the money market and can take advantage of situations by being on the spot. Not being subject to the same intense government regulations, they have more flexibility than unit trusts.

Free publications available from:
Association of Investment Trust Companies, 6th Floor, Park House, 16 Finsbury Circus, London EC2M 7JJ

Management Fees

For collective investments like unit trusts and investment trusts, the management fees will be reflected in the buying and selling prices and in the 'distributions' (dividends) the investor receives, usually twice a year.

If you arrange for a financial organization such as a bank to manage your investments for you, there will normally be an annual management charge and sometimes a dealing charge after buying and selling transactions.

Capital Gains Tax
(See also Taxation, below)

For investments which are not in gilts or National Savings, the investor's profits will be liable to capital gains tax – but only when these exceed a fairly generous tax-free annual allowance, which rises in line with inflation.

An investment adviser's service must cover the tax implications of the options open to you.

Investing in Local Companies

Good local companies, often not quoted in the press but handled by stockbrokers and stock exchanges in the regions are worth bearing in mind. The large London stockbroking firms generally prefer to handle substantial investments. Although theoretically it is possible to invest £500 in stocks and shares, it is difficult to find a dealer willing to invest a sum which is considered small by market standards.

Pensions

There are still choices to be made by men and women coming up to retirement. Most of the larger companies make fifty years old the cut-off point for embarking on a pension scheme. On the other hand, if the employee is made redundant or given early retirement at that age, it is not unlikely he or she will be offered a full pension provided the company's own length-of-service regulations have been fulfilled. Women are no longer forced to retire at sixty but if they decide to continue until the age of sixty-five, the extra years are not as yet counted as pensionable service. On the other hand, if they do not claim their pension at sixty, they will still receive an annual increment until they retire at sixty-five.

Between October 1987 and July 1988 new laws were passed which brought radical changes to the rules governing pension schemes. The following are the rules as they now stand.

Personal Pensions

The scheme was introduced in July 1988 to replace the old Section 226 policies which related to employees of firms which had no occupational scheme. Currently, however, it is also possible to opt out of an employer's pension scheme and replace it with a personal pension.

Three types of personal pension scheme exist, one which is linked to a unit-trust investment, the second to an insurance

Age	Percentage of earnings
35 or less	17.5
36–45	20
46–50	25
51–55	30
56–60	35
61–75	40

policy, and the third to a bank or building-society account. On retirement, up to 25 per cent of the fund built up in a personal pension plan can be paid as a tax-free lump sum. The remainder must be used to set up a regular pension income (called an annuity) from an approved insurance company.

The limit on tax-free contributions to an occupational pension scheme is 15 per cent of your earnings. Tax-free contributions to a personal pension scheme may not exceed the following proportions of your earnings:

Only contributions from earnings up to £71,400 (1991) per annum qualify for tax relief, a ceiling which is raised annually in line with inflation. Provided total contributions remain within these limits, it is possible to have more than one personal pension. Although there are no limits to the final pension received, the amount will depend on the success of the investment and the type of scheme involved. If you want to retain your occupational scheme, you may also have a personal pension but it can only be used to contract out of SERPS (see below) and your own contributions may not be added.

State Earnings Related Pension Scheme (SERPS)

At the moment, all employed people paying National Insurance contributions are in one of two possible categories:

Either their employer has adopted the SERPS scheme, in which case the employee pays a higher National Insurance contribution and in return, on retirement, receives a state flat-rate pension *plus* a top-up, called SERPS;

Or their employer has contracted out of the SERPS scheme,

in which case the employee pays a lower National Insurance contribution and on retirement receives only the basic flat-rate state pension. However, the loss of SERPS should be compensated by additional benefits under the employers' occupational pension scheme.

This all sounds simple enough, but because of the enormous increase in the number of people living well beyond the age of retirement, the government has become concerned that there may not be enough money in the SERPS scheme to pay everyone due to retire from the year 2000 onwards. They have therefore decided to encourage people to opt out. This is being done in two ways:

1. by making it known that after the year 2000, benefits under SERPS will be reduced;
2. by offering a cash incentive to leave SERPS and instead pay money into a new personal pension scheme. This means that you continue to pay the higher National Insurance contributions, but the amount previously set aside for SERPS is instead placed in the personal pension scheme. In addition to this, *until 5 April 1993*, you receive a cash incentive from the government to add to your personal pension contributions.

Although it depends on individual circumstances, as a general rule it will be advantageous for younger people to opt out of SERPS because their benefits under it have not had time to reach full value.

Occupational Pension Schemes

If you leave your employment or opt out of the pension scheme, no benefits are lost provided you have been employed with the firm for at least two years. If you are involved in one of the occupational pension schemes but decide to opt for early retirement or are forced to retire early, the 1985 Social Security Act secures additional protection against inflation. Since the employer is meeting a considerable part of the cost of the benefits provided, it is important to ascertain just how much of an advantage it will be to you to leave the scheme. (The value of remaining in SERPS, for example, is that it increases with age.) Employers are not required to contribute to personal pension arrangements.

Additional Voluntary Contributions (AVCs)

The extra contributions paid to boost occupational pensions are known as Additional Voluntary Contributions. All occupational pension schemes must now offer AVC facilities. It is also possible to make 'free-standing' AVCs to a pension plan outside the company scheme. However, since 7 April 1987, those paying AVCs are only allowed to increase their pensions or death benefits; they are not permitted to increase any lump sum available to them on retirement.

Advice and Information on Pensions

Advice and information may be obtained by contacting one of the Self-Regulatory Organizations provided under the Financial Services Act (see p. 137), or any of the following:

Occupational Pensions Advisory Service
8a Bloomsbury Square, London WC1A 2UA
   Tel. 071–831 5511
Those who feel they have not received adequate information from their scheme's managers can contact this organization, which offers advice and guidance to anyone who may have rights under an occupational pension scheme.

Department of Social Security
Freefone 0800 400 472 for a free information pack.

Society of Pension Consultants
Ludgate House, Ludgate Circus, London EC4A 2AB
Will provide lists of independent brokers.

The Association of British Insurers
Aldermary House, Queen Street, London EC4N 1TT

BIIBA
BIIBA House, 14 Bevis Marks, London EC3A 7NT
   Tel. 071–623 9043

Pensions and Long-term Hospital Care

Pensions and any social-security benefits are affected by a hospitalization which lasts longer than a few weeks. After a period of six weeks, a retirement pension is considerably reduced and there are further reductions after one year. Housing benefit remains unchanged up to one year but widow's benefit, invalidity benefit and severe disablement benefit, income support, attendance allowance and invalid care allowance are all affected. It is important to inform the Social Security office before admission to hospital. NHS leaflet N19, 'Going into Hospital', is a useful source of further information. For further details about benefits, see Part III, Benefits and Rights.

Pensions and National Insurance

It is possible to defer a pension for up to five years after retirement age. 'Your State Pension and Carrying on Working', Age Concern's Factsheet No. 19, describes the current situation for people who wish to carry on working after sixty or sixty-five.

Taxation

It is essential for people coming up to retirement to ensure they claim all the tax allowances to which they are entitled. The reason that your date of birth is requested on tax returns is to enable the Inland Revenue to transfer the information on to their computer, which should then indicate the time when a particular age allowance becomes due. Unfortunately, the results are not always very reliable and sometimes people do not automatically receive the age allowances. To make absolutely certain, the allowance should be claimed at the age of sixty-five. Married couples are entitled to the age allowance as soon as either of them reaches the age of sixty-five. Additional allowances can be claimed at age seventy-five. Helpful leaflets, produced by the Inland Revenue, are available free from any tax office.

Independent Taxation and the 1990 Changes Affecting Husbands and Wives

Until April 1990, a wife's income was usually combined with that of her husband for tax purposes. He was normally responsible for completing a joint tax return and for paying the income tax on their combined incomes. The married couple's allowance covered them both. The only allowance a wife received was the £2,785 wife's earned income allowance, which was offset against her earnings before tax was assessed. This allowance could not be used for any other purpose so, if she had no earnings, or if they were less than £2,785 per year, all or part of the allowance was lost.

From 6 April 1990 there were four main changes:

1. Husbands and wives each have their own separate personal allowances, which can be offset against their income from whatever source. To ensure confidentiality, each will be responsible for completing their own tax return and for paying their own tax.
2. In addition, husbands will receive a further allowance called a married couple's allowance.

    If a wife does not use up all of her personal allowance, because her income is too small, she will lose it – it cannot be transferred to her husband. Thus it behoves married couples to arrange for the wife to receive earnings or other income, preferably not already taxed, in order to take advantage of her allowance.
3. There are now special rules for husbands on low incomes. If a husband is unable to use all his married couple's allowance, he is entitled to apply to his (or his wife's) local tax office to transfer the unused part to his wife. Once the allowances have been transferred to his wife, her husband cannot demand them back.
4. Income from assets held jointly: unless a couple elect otherwise, each will be taxed on half the annual income received from joint assets – e.g. interest on savings.

Also, unless the couple elect otherwise, tax relief on mortgage interest will be given to the partner who actually pays the interest.

All these rules apply only to married couples and do not include couples living together or to long-term homosexual relationships.

Useful Publications

Information concerning independent taxation for married couples and personal taxation is available from a number of sources, including:
Inland Revenue booklets:

IR80, 'A Guide for Married Couples'

IR81, 'A Guide for Pensioners'

IR82, 'A Guide for Husbands on a Low Income'

IR86, 'A Guide to Mortgage Interest Relief for Married Couples'

IR90, 'A Guide to Tax Allowances and Reliefs'

IR91, 'A Guide for Widows and Widowers'

IR92, 'A Guide for One-parent Families'

IR93, 'Income Tax – Separation, Divorce and Maintenance Payments'

Allied Dunbar Tax Guide, ed. W. I. Sinclair, Longman Law, Tax and Finance

Daily Mail Income Tax Guide, ed. K. R. Tingley, Chapmans Publishers.

Booklets and leaflets are available from the Institute of Chartered Accountants, PO Box 433, Chartered Accountants Hall, Moorgate Place, London EC2P 2BJ.

Capital Gains Tax

If your savings are not in gilts or National Savings, you will be liable to capital gains tax on your profits when you sell. However, before the tax is assessed, there is an annual exemption which usually rises in line with inflation. An allowance is also given, based on the Retail Price Index, for any rise in value due to inflation.

Your home is normally exempt from capital gains tax, although this will be affected if you rent out part of it to a lodger or use part of it for business purposes. Also, you will be liable for capital gains tax on any profit you make over your CGT exemption when you sell a second home or holiday cottage.

From 6 April 1990, independent taxation rules (see p. 155) give husbands and wives separate capital gains tax allowances, instead of only one, as was previously the case.

Inheritance Tax

This affects the estates of people who own (6 April 1991) £140,000 or more, including their home, at the time of their death. It is also payable on gifts over that amount made within seven years prior to the death of the donor. The rules are complicated, but there are a number of important exemptions, particularly gifts between spouses (either during lifetime or on death), to UK charities and to major political parties.

If your estate is substantial, you should seek professional advice if you want to try to reduce the amount of inheritance tax your family will pay.

The Inland Revenue produce helpful booklets on both capital gains tax and inheritance tax (obtainable free from their offices), and many of the larger firms of chartered accountants also produce free guides.

Widows' Benefits and Tax

The amount of money a widow receives depends on her age when her husband dies, whether she remarries or cohabits, and whether she has dependent children. The following organizations offer the relevant advice and information:

Cruse, 126 Sheen Road, Richmond, Surrey TW9 1UR
   Tel. 081–940 4818
National Association of Widows, 54–7 Allison Street,
Digbeth, Birmingham B5 5TH
   Tel. 021–643 8348
National Council for One Parent Families, 255 Kentish Town
Road, London NW5 2LX
   Tel. 071–267 1361.
See Part III, Bereavement and Death, for information on these organizations.

Making a Will

An astonishing two out of three people in this country do not make a will. By dying intestate, they allow the law to 'interpret' their wishes and the laws governing estates in cases of intestacy are rigid. The order of relatives entitled to benefit is set out. If there are children, the surviving spouse will receive the personal belongings, a lump sum (at present £75,000) and the income for life from half the remaining estate. The other half will be divided equally between the children. If any are under eighteen, their share has to be held in trust until they reach that age.

The house, if it is jointly owned, usually passes automatically to the surviving partner, but if it is in the sole name of the spouse who has died and it is worth more than £75,000, as the law stands at the moment, it might have to be sold. Without the authority of a will, unmarried couples living together have no legal rights of inheritance; neither do stepchildren.

There are three ways in which a will can be made: it may be done through a solicitor or by going to a bank or an insurance company, or it can be drawn up personally on a form bought from a stationer's shop. Although this latter method has the virtue of being almost cost free, there are also drawbacks. Certain words have different meanings in law and may lead to misinterpretation after your death. If the DIY method is adopted it would be wise to have the wording checked by the Citizens Advice Bureau. All wills must be signed by two witnesses, but these may not be a beneficiary of the will or the spouse of a beneficiary.

A will drawn up by a solicitor usually costs between £35 and £60, but for a more complex document the cost can run into hundreds of pounds. Banks also charge varying rates for their service, so it is essential to ask for an estimate.

Once drawn up, a will must never be altered except by means of a codicil, which involves much the same procedure as making the will, but the two witnesses do not have to be the same people as those who initially witnessed the will.

The will must be available after your death so it should be kept in a safe place and its whereabouts made known to a trusted friend or relative. It can be kept at home or with the solicitor or bank, or, for a nominal fee, it can be lodged with the Principal Registry (Family Division), South Wing, Somerset House, Strand, London wc2. (Note: The laws of succession are different in Scotland. The address of the Law Society of Scotland is given on p. 144.)

Financing a Funeral
(Again, some of the procedures are different in Scotland.)

Usually, a death should be registered within five days of the event. The registrar will require the 'cause of death' certificate issued by the doctor, hospital or coroner, and the deceased person's medical card. A *white* certificate of death will be produced for DSS purposes together with a *green* disposal certificate for burial or cremation, which will be required by the undertaker.

Funeral costs will vary according to individual needs but the undertaker will often be prepared to provide an estimate which includes payment for minister's and organist's fees, doctor's charges for certificates, cemetery charges, newspaper announcements, etc. The convenience of this arrangement is that all fees may be paid with a single cheque. If there is no family grave, a plot of ground in a local cemetery will have to be purchased for a burial.

Financial Help

A visit to the DSS office will ascertain what money you are entitled to. If a low income means you will find it difficult to pay for the funeral, the Social Fund may provide temporary relief. It is important to take the *white* form with you to the DSS.

If the deceased was employed at the time of death, it is possible that certain funds are available through the employers. It is worth contacting them. Another immediate source of money would be an insurance policy or a joint bank or building society account. Failing these, a family member may be persuaded to give temporary financial help, or a bank might help with an overdraft (although the interest involved makes this an expensive option).

Funeral expenses are normally payable out of the money

which comes into the estate but if the outstanding bills exceed the amount of money available to meet them, help should be sought from a financial adviser. Another source of help and advice is the local Citizens Advice Bureau.

Debt

The 1980s saw an enormous increase in the number of people running into debt. Citizens Advice Bureaux are now finding that debt and consumer inquiries form the second largest category of advice given. In five years the inquiry figure, now standing at 1·4 million, has almost doubled. The easy availability of credit, higher mortgage interest rates and cuts in social-security benefits in real terms are just a few of the factors leading to financial hardship and debt.

The experience of being in serious debt is psychologically traumatic. The leaflets available offering advice in this situation – for example 'Debt – a Survival Guide' free from the Office of Fair Trading (see Part III, Advice, for details) – may not go far enough in relieving the anxiety and stress involved in individual cases. According to the Consumer Use of Credit Survey, commissioned and published by the Office of Fair Trading in 1988, the Citizens Advice Bureau is seen as by far the most obvious place to turn to for advice on credit payment difficulties. They have the huge advantage of being free of charge and have responded to the increase in debt inquiries by providing specialist Money Advice Support Units (MASUs), debt counselling and in-depth training on how to deal with problems of debt.

Debtline

National Debtline is a telephone advice service available to anyone in England and Wales who is worried about money. The telephone lines are staffed by debt experts who can give immediate advice to callers. Callers also receive a comprehensive information package which includes:

● working out a personal budget
● dealing with priority debts

- working out offers of payment to creditors
- dealing with court papers and procedures.

The information package may also be obtained by leaving your name and address on the twenty-four-hour answering-machine service.

To contact National Debtline, telephone 021–359 8501. The lines are open on Mondays and Thursdays, 10 a.m. to 4 p.m., and Tuesdays and Wednesdays, 2 to 7 p.m.

Insurance

'Insurance is not a luxury, it is a necessity and should not be allowed to lapse on retirement,' is the advice given by the Association of British Insurers. Most people approaching retirement will already be covered by some form of insurance – motor, life, house, etc. – and will not be contemplating changes to their policies. But security of property, personal safety and health are all aspects of life about which older people tend to feel increasingly vulnerable.

In retirement, where there is likely to be a drop in the annual income, the need to make absolutely certain that house and contents insurance is adequate to cover the costs of a major loss is crucial.

A holiday insurance policy covers most of the risks which can arise on holiday – personal accident, personal liability, medical expenses, cancellation, delay, etc.

The following advice leaflets are available free from The Association of British Insurers, Dept T, Aldermary House, Queen Street, London EC4N 1TU (tel. 071–248 4477): 'Home Contents Insurance', 'Home Safety', 'Watch Out for Winter!', 'Domestic Frost Precautions', 'Claiming on Your Home Insurance Policy', 'Beat the Burglar', 'Holiday Insurance', 'Buildings Insurance for Homeowners 1990', 'Bogus Callers: The Knock Code', 'Motor Insurance', 'Holiday Insurance' and 'Intruder Alarms'.

Health Insurance.

Only 10 per cent of retired people have health insurance even though they may have belonged to a group scheme provided by their employers.[38] Private health insurance, it seems, is one of the first 'luxuries' to be dropped on a retirement income. Despite the fact that tax relief is now allowed on *some* premiums paid for private medical insurance, many people find the cover too difficult to maintain as individuals. Once they leave the firm's group scheme, premiums become much higher and increase sharply with age. At the time of writing, only one health care group, Private Patients Plan, offers a special 'Retirement Health Plan'. Under this scheme, anyone over the age of sixty-five and under seventy-five can enrol. In the London area, for example, the monthly payment for a person aged between sixty-five and sixty-nine is £16·25.

If you do decide to take private medical cover in later life, personal contact with the insurance company involved is probably the best way to make certain you know exactly what your premium covers and to eliminate the possibility of missing vital information in the small print. Premiums and benefits should be linked to inflation, and it is as well to remember also that at the present time, there are no options which offer financial support for long-term chronic illnesses and geriatric care. Private health care may seem a less attractive investment if it fails to cover possible needs in the future.

For further information, see Chapter 6, Health, and Part III, Benefits and Rights.

Money Goes Further in Retirement

To end the chapter on an optimistic note, it would seem that money really can go further in retirement – a *Sunday Correspondent* financial research team published the following on 22 April 1990, under the heading 'How the Grey Pound can Buy Twice as Much':

We compared the costs of Mr and Mrs Retiree using existing perks during a typical stay of a few days in London with the costs for other adults. Starting with a train from, say, Moreton-in-Marsh, in Oxfordshire, to London at £14·50 each (standard return £28) and using cut-price London fares, we estimate Mr and Mrs Retiree could save £61·60 on the normal cost of £121·80. Mrs Retiree had her hair done (half price at £2·50) before their trip; in London they visited the Cabinet War Rooms (£1·50 instead of £3) and took in HMS Belfast at £1·75 (half price). They spent the next day at the Planetarium and Madame Tussaud's on a special retiree ticket of £4·60, and the next afternoon went to a matinee performance at a London theatre under the Senior Citizens' scheme, which gives them concessionary seats (saving £14). The following morning they popped into the Globe Museum for 50p and took in the view from Tower Bridge for £1 instead of £2·50. They finished off their week in London with a half-price visit to the Hayward Gallery.

Including train fares, Mr and Mrs Retiree spent £60·20 on their week. Mr and Mrs Worker would have spent £121·80 – they would also have averaged £1 each on London fares each way, each trip. Mr and Mrs Retiree get concessionary fares.

5 Leisure and Working for Pleasure

This chapter has been compiled with the help of Rosemary Brown's *Good Retirement Guide 1990*, the Greater London Association for Pre-Retirement and Age Concern.

The years of retirement bring with them the chance to achieve all those things one has always wanted to do but never quite had the time for. The choice of adventure is so varied now that just delving through the literature will provide a fund of stimulating ideas.

Leisure should surely be one of the greatest, most joyful words in the English language. *Chambers 20th Century Dictionary* defines it as 'time free from employment; freedom from occupation ... free from necessary business'. But wonderful though this may sound to the commuter waiting on a platform in the freezing cold for a train which never arrives, or to the secretary who has been asked to take an urgent letter just as the clock strikes 5·30, when the time comes to leave the confines of the regulated working day breaking down those years of habit is not always easy. Unhurried hours spent gardening, playing bridge, bounding about a tennis court, learning new skills or listening to music is many people's idea of pleasure – but not everyone's. Some people even find going on holiday a trial.

Taken in its wider context, however, 'leisure' can also mean simply a 'convenient opportunity' (ibid.) and it is in this positive sense of the word that we shall explore those options which become available in the second half of life. 'Convenient opportunities' exist not only for play but increasingly for a return to paid employment.

The information which follows is arranged under these headings:

SPECIAL INTERESTS

Adult education	Jigsaw puzzles
Animals	Keep fit
Archaeology	Languages
Architecture	Models and miniatures
Arts and crafts	Music
Astronomy	Pen-friends
Books for people with	Photography
special needs	Politics
Coins	Radio
Collecting	Railways
Conservation	Retreats
Dance	Silver
Dolls	Social
Film	Sports
Food	Stamp collecting
'Friends'	Theatre
Games	Weather
Gardening	Wildlife
Geography	Wine
Geology	Writing
History	
Holidays	

THE VOLUNTARY SECTOR
Voluntary organizations

BACK TO BUSINESS
Starting your own business
A new career?

The voluntary sector has always been a rich source of varied and rewarding work, but in the present economic climate, not only are more people looking for pay to supplement their retirement income, but there is a growing band of enterprising individuals whose idea of leisure in the retirement years is to start up their own businesses.

SPECIAL INTERESTS

This section describes a wide range of activities and interests and some of the related holidays, tours and courses currently available. Those who are already committed will know that this part of the chapter only scratches the surface. It is impossible in such a small space to present a comprehensive list of all the groups and associations involved in the world of leisure, but I hope the information provided will at least indicate the enormous range of options.

Adult Education

Depending on the ambitions and aspirations of the potential student, there are many different ways of obtaining a formal education as an adult, ranging from full-time degrees at colleges of higher education or universities or polytechnics, to studying for a degree at home with the Open University, or to taking correspondence courses and courses at an adult education institute.

At first sight the choice of subjects to study seems almost limitless, but it is ultimately dependent on the topics offered by the educational facilities in a particular locality, which in turn can be determined by the individual skills of teachers and lecturers living within range of the college.

Adult education courses usually begin in September and follow through the academic year, but there are also short courses in some subjects which may only last one term and others which are flexible and allow a student to join the group at any time.

The public library will have details of all educational opportunities available locally. The reference section will contain copies of publications which list full-time university, college and polytechnic courses and degrees.

The Open University
Central Inquiry Service, PO Box 71, Walton Hall, Milton
Keynes MK7 6AG.
 Tel. 0908 653231
Provides educational opportunities for all adults, regardless of
educational qualifications, who wish to study in their own homes
and in their own time. As with all universities, it can grant
degrees and other qualifications. Degree-level and short courses
are supervised and a tutor helps with course material, marking
and commenting on assignments. Correspondence with a tutor
is the university's main form of teaching although most courses
have occasional group tutorials in large urban centres.

The University of the Third Age (U3A)
U3A National Office, c/o BASSAC, 13 Stockwell Road,
London
 Tel. 071–737 2541
U3A is a self-help organization which offers a variety of educational, creative and leisure activities. The courses and social
programmes are determined by the interests of members of the
local branches through which it operates. The Third Age
Trust is the governing body of U3A nationwide. The National
Office liaises between local U3As and provides a range of
goods, services, travel opportunities and support for the establishment of new groups. It also has available lists of names and
addresses of local organizations. Local U3As decide their own
programmes and raise whatever funds are needed by subscription or donation. The periodical, *The Third Age*, gives details
of conferences and events.

Council for the Accreditation of Correspondence Colleges
27 Marylebone Road, London NW1 5JS
 Tel. 071–935 5391
The council was established to raise and maintain the standards
and effectiveness of postal tuition and to safeguard the interests
and progress of students. They will supply a list of correspondence colleges currently accredited.

National Extension College
18 Brooklands Avenue, Cambridge CB2 2HN
 Tel. 0223 316644

Courses, which can lead to a wide range of qualifications, are specially prepared to meet the needs of adult students who would prefer to study at home. NEC also specializes in training teachers and other trainers in most of the main aspects of open learning.

National Adult School Organization (NASO)
MASU Centre, Gaywood Croft, Cregoe Street, Birmingham
BI5 2ED
   Tel. 021–622 3400
NASO is a voluntary organization promoting 'Friendship through Discussion' groups throughout the country. Groups meet weekly or fortnightly in a variety of settings and are linked through local area organizations or directly to the national organization. A study handbook is published each year containing a variety of topics which form the basis for discussion. Groups also arrange social activities; one-day, weekend or week-long courses are arranged locally and nationally. International visits are also arranged.

Workers' Educational Association
Temple House, 9 Upper Berkeley Street, London WIH 8BY
   Tel. 071–402 5608
The WEA is an independent, voluntary and national movement which aims to interest people in their own continued education. Their evening or day-time courses are on a part-time basis and are open to all beyond school-leaving age who wish to continue or resume their studies. There are no entry requirements, examinations or tests. Teaching includes discussion with like-minded people and a skilled tutor, with the aim of improving, understanding and enriching the quality of life.

University extramural departments
Many universities have a department of extramural studies which arranges courses for adults. These generally take place either in the evenings or during the holiday periods.

Age Concern England
Education and Leisure Officer, Astral House, 1268 London Road, London SWI6 4EJ
   Tel. 081–679 8000

Factsheet No. 30, 'Leisure Education', gives a list of useful contacts; there is an information network for anyone interested in education and older people.

Short Residential Courses and Study Holidays

The National Institute of Adult and Continuing Education
19b De Montfort Street, Leicester LEI 7GE
Twice a year publishes *Time to Learn, a Guide to Residential Study Breaks,* giving details of weekend or week-long residential courses. Accommodation is usually in study bedrooms, which are well suited to the needs of a single person.

British University Accommodation Consortium (BUAC)
Box 609E, University Park, Nottingham NG7 2RD
  Tel. 0602 504571
BUAC publishes a brochure with activity and study holidays at universities throughout the UK.

Many of the old public schools are historic buildings situated in some of the most beautiful countryside. Their facilities – swimming-pools, tennis and squash courts, libraries, etc. – offer ideal surroundings in which to combine a holiday with leisure. Millfield and Marlborough are just two of the many schools which have summer-holiday programmes.

Marlborough College
The Secretary of the Summer School, Marlborough College,
Marlborough, Wiltshire SN8 IPA
  Tel. 0672 513888
Summer courses cover a wide range of special interests in the arts, history, music, language, finance, wine appreciation, gardening and sporting activities.

Millfield Village of Education
Millfield School, Street, Somerset BA16 OYD
  Tel. 0458 42291
The summer programme offers a choice of 370 different courses. The value of these short courses is that they provide a starting-point for people who think they might be interested in

a particular activity but who feel they need to test the water before committing themselves further, whether it be a new sport or the first step towards a new career.

Scotland

For details of adult educational possibilities in Scotland, *The Scottish Handbook of Adult and Continuing Education* can be obtained either from the local library or from the Scottish Institute of Adult and Continuing Education, 30 Rutland Square, Edinburgh EHI 2BW (tel. 031–229 0331).

Continuing Education Gateway
199 Nithsdale Road, Glasgow G41 5EX
   Tel. 041–422 1070
An adult information and advice service, set up by Strathclyde Regional Council, which exists to help anyone who wishes to further their education in college, school or community education centre. They have information on sources of financial help and on every type of course available, and can also advise on open learning centres and centres able to provide for adults with disabilities.

Continuing Education, Lothian Region
Community Education Section: Hilary Kirkland
   Tel. 031–229 9166

Animals
(See also Wildlife)

Home and Pet Care
PO Box 19, Penrith, Cumbria CA11 7AA
   Tel. 06998 515 (24 hours)
A nationwide service which involves looking after a home and pets while the owners are away. (See also Holidays – Home-sitting.) Carers are between the ages of forty and seventy and should be fit enough to walk a dog or dogs for half an hour twice daily. Payment is approximately £40 a week plus food and travel expenses. (Note: the service has recently been extended to include the care of an elderly or infirm relative.)

Cinnamon Trust
Poldarves Farm, Trescowe Common, Germoe, Penzance,
Cornwall TR20 9RX
  Tel. 0736 850 291
The trust seeks to relieve the problems faced by elderly pet
owners and the terminally ill who are concerned for the future
of their animals. A network of volunteers has been established
to provide help at home – for example, walking the dog and
fostering pets when owners are temporarily hospitalized, and
there is a sanctuary for pets whose owners have died or have
been admitted into residential care. The services of the trust
are free of charge but it is hoped that, where possible, owners
will contribute towards the costs.

Pet Fostering Service Scotland
  Tel. 041–332 7910
Dial this number for a list of local pet fostering services
throughout Scotland.

British Beekeepers' Association
National Agricultural Centre, Stoneleigh, Kenilworth,
Warwickshire CV8 2LZ
  Tel. 0203 696 679
Membership of a county association or one of its branches
offers affiliate membership of the BBKA, an introduction to
bees and beekeeping and advice on how to set up a colony and
market the honey. There are summer field meetings, winter
programmes and social events, evening classes, weekend conferences and educational and special-interest tours.

Pro-Dogs
Rocky Bank, 4 New Road, Ditton, Aylesford, Kent
ME20 6AD
  Tel. 0732 848 499
A national charity which aims to stop cruelty to dogs by
educating both their owners and the public. In the pro-Dogs
Active Therapy (PAT) visiting scheme, members take suitable
friendly dogs on regular visits to people in hospitals and homes
for children and the elderly. Older people often deny them-
selves the pleasure of owning a dog because they worry about

the animal's future in the event of their death. In recognition of this problem, Pro-Dogs has recently initiated a nationwide 're-homing' scheme which helps to find temporary or permanent homes in an emergency. The founder of Pro-Dogs, Leslie Scott-Ordish writes in the booklet 'Your Dog Without You' (available from the address above): 'By availing yourself of our emergency procedure, you will be able to keep a pet right up to the end, secure in the knowledge that Pro-Dogs will take over caring when you are no longer able to do so yourself. This should give you peace of mind concerning your animals. This is particularly important to people living alone, who value the love, affection and companionship that a dog can give.'

The Kennel Club
1 Clarges Street, Piccadilly, London W1Y 8AB
   Tel. 071–629 5828
Exhibiting at dog shows can become an absorbing hobby. The Kennel Club will provide details on how to transform a pet into a potential champion.

National Canine Defence League (NCDL)
1 Pratt Mews, London NW1 0AD
   Tel. 071–388 0137
The policy of this charitable organization is to ensure that no healthy dog in its care is ever destroyed. Its aim is to find new owners, but those dogs who are not re-homed become permanent residents at one of the thirteen rescue centres. Rescue and rehabilitation are the main concerns, but staff are always available to offer advice and assistance to people who need help with their dogs.

Membership of the NCDL costs £7·50 per year or £3·50 for senior citizens. Copies of the League's newsletter and annual report keep members informed as to events and benefits.

Our Dogs
5 Oxford Road Station Approach, Manchester M60 1SX
   Tel. 061–236 2660
Publishes *Our Dogs*, the specialist newspaper for dog lovers; also *Cats* and *Obedience Competitor Magazine*.

The Monkey Sanctuary
Looe, Cornwall
  Tel. 05036 2532
Home of a natural colony of woolly monkeys, the sanctuary
needs volunteers to help all the year round. Board and lodging
are provided.

Chickens' Lib
PO Box 2, Holmfirth, Huddersfield HD7 1QT
A non-violent pressure group dedicated to the total abolition
of battery cages and any other systems for poultry keeping
which impose severe restrictions on the birds, depriving them
of a reasonably natural lifestyle.

Lynx
PO Box 509, Dunmow, Essex CM6 1UH
A group campaigning against the fur trade.

Whale and Dolphin Conservation Society
220 West Lea Road, Bath BA1 3RL
Campaigns to prevent the slaughter of whales and dolphins.

Redwings Horse Sanctuary
Hill Top Farm, Hall Lane, Frettenham, nr Norwich, Norfolk
NR12 7LT
  Tel. 0603 737432
The society's aim is to rescue horses, ponies and donkeys from
neglect and slaughter, and provide them with a home for life.
Membership allows you to 'adopt' an animal and visitors to the
sanctuary are welcomed.

Royal Society for the Prevention of Cruelty to Animals
(RSPCA)
Causeway, Horsham, W Sussex RH12 1HG
  Tel. 0403 64181
There are 209 RSPCA branches throughout England and
Wales, each registered as a separate charity. The branches and
the voluntary workers who make up their membership form
the backbone of the society. By way of fund-raising, they
contribute towards the cost of the inspectorate and undertake

their own animal-welfare activities. For many, this involves running an animal home, clinic, welfare or advice centre, finding new homes for unwanted or abandoned animals and monitoring the welfare of those they re-home. Others help raise funds to pay veterinary bills in cases of financial hardship and board unwanted or stray animals until they are found suitable homes. Details of membership may be obtained from the Membership Department at the above address. Their journal is *RSPCA Today*.

Wood Green Animal Shelters & National Pet Register
Head Office: Highway Cottage, Chishill Road, Heydon, Royston, Herts SG8 8PN
  Tel. 0763 838329
The charity operates from three centres: in Wood Green, London; Heydon, Hertfordshire; and Godmanchester, Cambridgeshire. These shelters take in, care for and find homes for abandoned and abused animals. Since they are entirely dependent on contributions, there are many ways in which to become involved in fund-raising events. There is also an adoption scheme for people who are unable to keep a pet at home. Pets can be chosen from any one of the three sanctuaries and for a sum of £5 a month, will be fed and looked after and may be visited at any time. For a lifetime registration fee of £5, the National Pet Register offers a twenty-four-hour service which aims to rescue and reunite lost and stray animals with their owners.

Cat Protection League
Head Office: 17 Kings Road, Horsham, W Sussex RH13 5PP
  Tel. 0403 65566
The objects of the league are to rescue stray, unwanted and injured cats, rehabilitate them and rehome them where possible. There are eleven CPL shelters and two hundred branches and groups operating throughout the country. Encouragement is given for 'active cat work' to be done by local people raising money in their own town and village and spending it in the area.

Governing Council of the Cat Fancy (GCCF)
5 Penel Orlieu, Bridgwater, Somerset
  Tel. 0278 427 575

Many cat shows are held each year at various venues all over the country. The GCCF has details of cat shows and will advise on how to become an exhibitor. The Cat Fancy does not allow the showing of half-pedigree or part-pedigree pet cats, and hybrid or variant cross-breeds are allowed only in special assessment classes. *Cats*, the official journal of the GCCF, is published by *Our Dogs* Publishing Co., see above.

The Cat Association
CA Central Office, Hunting Grove, Lowfield Heath,
Crawley, W Sussex RHI IOPY
An alternative registering and showing body, the CA has a register for non-pedigree and part-pedigree pet cats, and those officially registered with the association may compete for such titles as Junior Pet Champion, Champion Pet, Grand Pet and Supreme Pet.

Feline Advisory Bureau (FAB)
350 Upper Richmond Road, Putney, London SW15 6TL
  Tel. 081–789 9553

The Conchological Society of Great Britain and Ireland
The Hon. Sec., School of Geography and Geology, College
of St Paul and St Mary, The Park, Cheltenham, Glos
GL50 2RH
Collecting shells is one of the great pleasures of visiting beaches in exotic parts of the world. The Conchological Society promotes the international study of all kinds of molluscs including fossils. Members receive a newsletter and journal and are invited to attend lectures and field meetings.

Lifewatch (Friends of the London Zoo and Whipsnade Park)
Zoological Gardens, Regents Park, London NWI 4RY
  Tel. 071–722 3333
There are five categories of membership to Lifewatch, all of which offer wide-ranging privileges. Exclusive events and activities, publicized in the regular members' magazine, allow a special insight into the life, aims and aspirations of London Zoo and Whipsnade Wild Animal Park.

Archaeology

Council for British Archaeology
112 Kennington Road, London SE11 6RE
   Tel. 071–582 0494
An annual subscription of £9 to *British Archaeological News* will give professionals and amateurs details of excavations where help is needed, courses, day schools and tours of interest. The CBA series, 'Practical Handbooks in Archaeology', is designed to meet the needs of amateurs and extramural students.

Archaeology Unit
Milton Keynes Development Corporation, Bradwell Abbey Field Centre, Bradwell, Milton Keynes MK13 9AP
   Tel. 0908 312475
Every year the unit organizes archaeological excavations between Easter and late autumn. The sites change from year to year, requiring short-term and long-term volunteers. The work is often physically hard and applicants need to be fit and well. An accommodation and subsistence allowance is paid.

Architecture

Architectural Heritage Society of Scotland
43b Manor Place, Edinburgh EH3 7EB
   Tel. 031–225 9724
The society has a network of regional groups throughout Scotland. Activities are organized for members to help them to become better acquainted with their architectural heritage. These activities may include day-trips, walks or weekend excursions, lectures, conferences and social events. In addition, the society publishes a regular newsletter and an annual journal, both of which are distributed free to members.

The Society for the Protection of Ancient Buildings (SPAB)
37 Spital Square, London E1 6DY
   Tel. 071–377 1644
The SPAB has prime responsibility for safeguarding the country's pre-Georgian heritage. It is a leading authority on the ways of repairing and maintaining old buildings and per-

forms a vital advisory, campaigning and educational role. The society also organizes courses on the treatment and repair of old buildings, produces a range of publications on their care and arranges lectures and visits. Membership includes architects, surveyors and specialist builders as well as those who are simply drawn to the society by their concern for the protection of the nation's heritage.

Historic Houses Association (HHA)
38 Ebury Street, London SW1W 0IU
   Tel. 071–730 9419
Over a thousand stately-home owners responsible for maintaining and financing their own properties belong to the HHA. Becoming a Friend of the association entitles you to visit 270 properties free of charge and to become involved in the HHA's work at a regional level. Each region is headed by a house-owning member of the HHA as a voluntary chairman. Most regions organize at least one meeting each year to which Friends are usually invited, and many organize social events as well, giving house-owners and Friends the opportunity to meet. *The Historic House*, the HHA's quarterly magazine, publicizes tours and events.

Arts and Crafts

Arts Council of Great Britain
Information Unit, 105 Piccadilly, London W1V 0AU
   Tel. 071–629 9495
The Arts Council acts as the major channel for public funding of the arts. For the individual who is interested in becoming involved but is uncertain about the possibilities, the council's Careers Pack is very helpful. It gives information about careers in arts administration, in museums and galleries, music, and the music business, in the theatre, films and in dance administration. The pack also contains information on courses and voluntary work and for people interested in working for Regional Arts Associations, there is a list of useful contacts.

Artsline Telephone Advice Service
5 Crowndale Road, London NW1 1TU
   Tel. 071–388 2227

London's information and advice service on arts and entertainments for disabled people. As well as giving news of events and entertainment, they will also advise on courses and classes, transport, booking arrangements and catering.

Arts Development Association
Room 110, The Arts Centre, Vane Terrace, Darlington, County Durham DL3 7AX
Keeps information on local arts councils.

National Association of Decorative and Fine Arts Societies
8a Lower Grosvenor Place, London SW1W 0EN
  Tel. 071-233 5433
There are over 240 member societies of the NADFAS in the UK. Specialized lectures, study courses, visits and overseas tours are organized at local and national levels. Membership is through individual societies, details of which may be obtained from the above address.

Friends of the Royal Academy of Arts
Burlington House, Piccadilly, London W1V 0DS
  Tel. 071-439 7438
Membership allows Friends and one guest to attend exhibitions free of charge. A regular magazine keeps members informed of the very wide range of events and benefits. They also have the advantage of having their own comfortable sitting-room.

Contemporary Art Society
20 John Islip Street, London SW1P 4LT
  Tel. 071-821 5323
The CAS is a registered charity which exists to promote the understanding, appreciation and collecting of contemporary art in Britain. One of its principal aims is to acquire works by living artists for gift or loan to public collections. Members are encouraged to participate in the activities of the CAS. There is a full annual programme of events, including lectures, courses on collecting and visits to exhibitions, studios and private collections. Members are invited to a private view of the annual market/exhibition and trips are arranged in Britain and

abroad to see major exhibitions and to visit leading art centres. Regular newsletters keep them informed of news and events.

Friends of the Tate Gallery
Millbank, London SW1P 4RG
  Tel. 071–821 1313
Benefits include special events, lectures, invitations to private previews and subsequent free entry to all the gallery's exhibitions. Selected sections of the collection are open every Sunday morning exclusively for members, who may bring two additional guests.

Crafts Council
12 Waterloo Place, London SW1Y 4AE
  Tel. 071–930 4811
The council was set up to promote fine craftsmanship in the decorative and applied arts throughout England and Wales. *Crafts* magazine is published six times a year and has a comprehensive calendar of craft events. The inquiry service has information on full-time and short courses.

The Basketmakers' Association
The Hon. Secretary, Threadgolds Farm, Great Braxsted, Witham, Essex CM8 3ER
  Tel. 0621 891 340
The association gives information on teachers, speakers, demonstrators, courses and training, and holds a national index of makers working in cane, rush, straw and willow. They can also recommend sources for materials. Members receive a quarterly newsletter.

Brass Rubbing
Monumental Brass Society, c/o Society of Antiquaries of London, Burlington House, Piccadilly, London W1V 0HS
Members attend four meetings a year and are invited to an annual excursion and conference. The society's magazine, *Transactions*, is published once a year.

Weaving, Spinning and Dyeing
Martin and Nina Weatherhead, Snail Trail Handweavers,
Penwenallt Farm, Cilgerran, Cardigan, Dyfed
    Tel. 0239 841 228
Courses, which run from Saturday to Saturday, are suitable
for the absolute beginner or the experienced weaver. Subjects
covered include natural and chemical dyeing, rug weaving,
weaving for wall-hangings, off-loom weaving, basic spinning
and making simple weaving equipment.

The Royal School of Needlework
Apartment 12a, Hampton Court Palace, East Molesey, Surrey
KT8 9AU
    Tel. 081–943 1432
Summer-school classes are held in the Georgian wing of Hampton
Court Palace. The art studio creates designs to order and provides
all the materials necessary to complete the project. The Friends of
the Royal School of Needlework can be contacted at London
House C3, 26–40 Kensington High Street, London W8 4PF.

The Embroiderers' Guild
Apartment 41, Hampton Court Palace, East Molesey, Surrey
KT8 9AU
    Tel. 081–943 1229
Offers a quarterly magazine for the enthusiast. Workshops and
lectures are held during the academic term and the programme
caters for embroiderers of all levels from beginners to professionals.

Reading

Hobbies Handbook (annual), Hobbies (Dereham) Ltd, Dereham, Norfolk NR19 2AZ

Courses

West Dean College
West Dean, Chichester, W Sussex PO18 0QZ
    Tel. 0243 63 301
The summer school combines art and craft courses with a
programme of social, theatrical and musical events.

Open College of the Arts (OCA)
Houndhill, Worsbrough, Barnsley, S Yorks s70 6tu
  Tel. 0226 730 495
The OCA uses methods broadly similar to those of the Open
University: specially written course manuals guide students
through a programme of activities lasting up to nine months.
These are backed up by regular help from tutors who are
practising artists, writers or teachers in universities, polytechnics and colleges. Courses include art and design, painting,
textiles, sculpture, garden design, photography, starting to
write, history of art, and music.

Studio 1D (China Restorers)
Kensington Church Walk, London w8
  Tel. 071–937 7583
The studio restores ceramics for private customers, the Victoria
and Albert Museum and antique dealers; they also offer a two-
week course in ceramic restoration for beginners which is
especially popular with people who have built up a collection
over the years and find in retirement that they have the time to
patch up the cracks and identify the pieces in question. Once
the skills have been learned, it is then easy and relatively
inexpensive to work from home, and, according to a spokesman
from the studio, it is possible to earn an amount somewhere
between 'pin money and a moderate income'.

Christie's
63 Old Brompton Road, London sw7 3js
  Tel. 071–581 3993/071–589 0383
Christie's run evening courses on furniture, ceramics, English
silver, music and painting. They also offer one-year diploma
courses and a selection of short daytime courses covering the
history of modern art from 1848 to the present day.

Arts and Other Cultural Holidays and Guided Tours

Artscape Painting Holidays
Units 40–41, The Vintners, Temple Farm Industrial Estate,
Southend-on-Sea, Essex ss2 5rz
  Tel. 0702 617 900

A company which combines painting holidays in the UK and Europe with at least thirty-five hours of art tuition a week. Courses are tailored to suit the needs of both beginners and professionals.

Alderney Craft Holidays
The Alderney Pottery, Alderney, Channel Islands
   Tel. 0481 822246
The pottery operates as a cooperative, the four partners living and working together to produce hand-crafted items and teach some of their skills. Their 'Dabblers' craft holidays offer an opportunity for people who would like to try their hand at pottery, hand-spinning, landscape watercolour painting and calligraphy. Holiday prices include tuition and craft materials.

Specialtours
81a Elizabeth Street, London SW1W 9PG
   Tel. 071–730 2297
Tours are sponsored mainly by the National Art Collections Fund, but sponsors also include the British Museum Society, the Folio Society, the Friends of the Royal Academy, of the Royal Scottish Academy and of the Courtauld Institute, the Royal Geographical Society and the Sunday Times Wine Club. Membership of the organization sponsoring the tour must be taken out in advance and donations are included in the cost.

Ace Study Tours
Babraham, Cambridge CB2 4AP
   Tel. 0223 835055
Tours and courses with a cultural theme – architecture, art history, archaeology, music, drama, ecology or wildlife. There are a number of joint ventures with the University of Cambridge Board of Extra-Mural Studies and Temple World Tours.

Swan Hellenic Cruises
77 New Oxford Street, London WC1A 1PP
   Tel. 071–831 1515
Specializes in professionally guided tours around the Mediterranean, the Aegean and the Black Sea.

Serenissima
21 Dorset Square, London NW1
   Tel. 071–730 9841
The company specializes in art, history, music and painting tours in locations around the world. All are accompanied by a lecturer and a tour manager, and employ the services of local guides when necessary.

Jules Verne
10 Glentworth Street, London NW1 5PG
   Tel. 071–486 8080
Specializes in tours which concentrate on botany, natural history, birds and painting.

British Museum Classics Tours
Kent House, Regent Street, London W1R 8LS
   Tel. 071–734 7971/2
Itineraries are planned to coincide with archaeological work or ethnographical research involving the musum.

Page & Moy Ltd
136–140 London Road, Leicester LE2 1EN
   Tel. 0533 552 521
The company offer arts and music holidays, tours of castles, country houses and stately homes, and journeys to ancient historical sites.

Prospect Music and Art Ltd
454–8 Chiswick High Road, London W4 5TT
   Tel. 081–995 2163
A company which organizes holidays in music, opera, art, history and archaeology in Europe and the Middle East. Tours are accompanied by art historians, archaeologists or musicians who act as lecturers and guides.

G.W. Henebery Ltd
Kareol, Islip, Oxford OX5 2SU
   Tel. 08675 6341
Specializes in opera and music festival holidays. Prague, Vienna, Florence, Verona, Salzburg and Bratislava are just some of the tours available.

Martin Randall Travel
10 Barley Mow Passage, London W4 4PH
   Tel. 081–994 6477
Brochures detail lecturer-accompanied tours centred on archaeology, history, art, music and architecture.

Past Times
Wootton Business Park, Abingdon, Oxon OX13 6LG
   Tel. 0865 326111
Offers special-interest weekends in conjunction with a hotel chain. Each event includes accommodation and all meals, admissions, guided tours and travel. Tours change annually but popular examples have included 'A Victorian Christmas' and 'Buying Antiques'.

Astronomy

British Astronomical Association
Burlington House, Piccadilly, London W1V 9AG
   Tel. 071–734 4145
Membership is open to everyone interested in astronomy. The association holds regular meetings inside and outside London and organizes or supports a number of residential weekend courses. Dates, venues and topics are published in the newsletter which is distributed with the *Journal*. There is an annual *Handbook* – an almanac which gives all data necessary for observational work – and there are over three hundred instruments available for loan to members.

Books for people with special needs

RNIB Talking Book Service
Mount Pleasant, Wembley, Middlesex HAO 1RR
   Tel. 081–903 6666

National Library for the Blind
Cromwell Road, Bredbury, Stockport, Cheshire SK6 2SG
   Tel. 061–494 0217

Calibre
Aylesbury, Buckinghamshire HP22 5XQ
   Tel. 0296 432339/0296 81211
This lending library has three thousand recorded books on standard cassette tapes for anyone who is unable to read printed books due to disability.

Talking Books for the Handicapped (National Listening Library)
12 Lant Street, London SE1 1QH
   Tel. 071–407 9417
A special tape player and a wide range of titles are provided on loan to the disabled.

British Wireless for the Blind
34 New Road, Chatham, Kent ME4 4QR
   Tel. 0634 832501
Radios or radio-cassette recorders on free permanent loan are offered to any registered blind person who is a resident of the UK and over the age of eight.

Cassette Library for Blind Gardeners
48 Tolcarne Drive, Pinner, Middlesex HA5 2DQ
   Tel. 081–868 4026

Coins

The British Association of Numismatic Societies (BANS)
Dept of Numismatics, Manchester Museum, The University, Oxford Road, Manchester
An umbrella organization which aims to coordinate the activities of local societies throughout the country. Two conferences are arranged each year.

Collecting

The 1980s saw the enormous rise in popularity of the car-boot sale, which goes to show how much everyone loves a bargain and that one man's junk is another man's treasure. Almost any article one can think of is collectible. Although the rewards might not necessarily be lucrative, the most unlikely objects can have their price and to the enthusiast there is nothing more thrilling than to take off across the country in pursuit of an addition to his collection.

Conservation

National Trust
36 Queen Anne's Gate, London SW1H 9AS
   Tel. 071–222 9251
Individual membership of the National Trust costs £19, a sum which includes free admission to properties, a comprehensive annual guide and three issues of the *National Trust Magazine*. National Trust associations or centres and supporters' clubs are run exclusively for members. They organize a wide range of activities including lectures, coach outings, rambles, films, social events and holidays.

National Trust for Scotland
5 Charlotte Square, Edinburgh EH2 4DU
   Tel. 031–226 5922

The London Ecology Centre
45 Shelton Street, Covent Garden, London WC2H 9HJ
   Tel. 071–379 4324
Acts as a focal point for education and awareness of ecological issues and activities, both locally and globally. An information service is provided on all subjects related to ecology and the environment. There are opportunities to become involved in practical conservation projects and Friends are welcomed.

The British Trust for Conservation Volunteers
36 St Mary's Street, Wallingford, Oxfordshire OX10 0EU
   Tel. 0491 39766
BTCV is a national charity which aims to protect the environment. There is a diverse programme for volunteers and staff which ranges from learning about practical conservation techniques to publicity and understanding environmental politics. You can join a local group, take a conservation working holiday or become part of a midweek group – the opportunities are many and varied.

Council for National Parks (CNP)
45 Shelton Street, London WC2H 9HJ
  Tel. 071–240 3603
The CNP is a small administrative charity with scope for
volunteers who wish to be involved on a regional basis. One
example of this would be to become part of their network of
speakers, who give illustrated talks to a wide variety of groups
on the National Parks and the role of the council. Friends of
National Parks are kept in touch with the issues and events
through their own magazine.

The Council for the Protection of Rural England
4 Hobart Place, London SW1Y 0HY
  Tel. 071–235 9481
Campaigns to protect and preserve the countryside. There are
forty-three county branches and associations. The skills of
individual members can be used in a number of ways whether
they be organizational, business or artistic (paintings or
sketches of landscapes and photographs are published in the
CPRE books and leaflets).

Friends of the Earth
26–8 Underwood Street, London N1 7JQ
  Tel. 071–490 1555
A politically impartial national and international environmental
pressure group whose campaigns have focused public attention
on, for example, the ozone layer, tropical rainforests, acid rain,
water pollution, toxic wastes and global warming. Almost all of
their income derives from supporters.

Inland Waterways Association
114 Regent's Park Road, London NW1 8UQ
  Tel. 071–586 2510/2556
Campaigns to restore, retain and improve our two-hundred-
year-old network of inland waterways. The national quarterly
magazine has news of events and contacts, and members are
brought together through meetings, rallies, trips, film shows
and festivals. There is work for volunteers on restoration
projects, and discounts are offered on boating holidays and insurance.

Scottish Inland Waterways Association
139 Old Dalkeith Road, Edinburgh EH16 4SZ
  Tel. 031–664 1070

The National Council for the Conservation of Plants and Gardens
c/o RHS, Wisley Garden, Woking, Surrey GU23 6QB
  Tel. 0483 224234
See also Gardening, below.

The Open Spaces Society
25a Bell Street, Henley-on-Thames, Oxon RG9 2BA
  Tel. 0491 573 535
The recognized authority on common land and public footpaths; members benefit from free advice and receive the magazine *Open Space* three times a year.

The Royal Society for Nature Conservation
The Green, Nettleham, Lincoln LN2 2NR
  Tel. 0522 752326
Membership can involve helping in the wardening and management of one of the society's 1,800 nature reserves. A wide variety of activities are organized by local trusts.

The Woodland Trust
Autumn Park, Dysart Road, Grantham, Lincs NG31 6LL
  Tel. 0476 74297
A national charity whose job is to safeguard trees, in small areas as well as large, by raising money to buy and look after woods that might otherwise be destroyed. Members receive a woodland directory and are kept in touch by regular newsletters.

Greenpeace
30–31 Islington Green, London N1 8XE
  Tel. 071–354 5100/359 7396
An environmental pressure group independent of all political parties. Campaigns and takes non-violent direct action to protect the natural world.

Farming Information Centre
Agriculture House, Knightsbridge, London SW1X 7NJ
   Tel. 071–235 5077
Details of 'pick-your-own' centres.

Dance

London City Ballet
38 Ebury Street, London SW1W 0LU
   Tel. 071–730 9419
Membership of the Friends of the London City Ballet provides
an opportunity to attend rehearsals and meet the dancers.
There is a quarterly newsletter with advance information on
performances.

Association of Retired Persons' Grey Panther Dance Clubs
There is dancing for all ARP members at local Grey Panther
dance studios. For further details, see Part III, Retirement.

National Resource Centre for Dance
University of Surrey, Guildford, Surrey GU2 5XH
   Tel. 0483 571281
A computerized data base and dance archive provides a wide
range of information. Inquiries which can be dealt with quickly
are answered free of charge, but for more detailed information
there is a fee for the research work undertaken.

English Folk Dance and Song Society
Cecil Sharp House, 2 Regent's Park Road, London NW1 7AY
   Tel. 071–485 2206
The society has details of the local clubs nationwide which
organize regular and special events.

Royal Scottish Country Dance Society
12 Coates Crescent, Edinburgh EH3 7AF
   Tel. 031–225 3854
The society has a worldwide membership of all ages. A summer
school is held annually at St Andrew's University in Aberdeen
and local branches offer instruction to members at all levels.

Imperial Society of Teachers of Dancing
Euston Hall, Birkenhead Street, London WC1H 8BE
    Tel. 071–837 9967
The society lists dance teachers throughout the country, many
of whom organize classes for older people.

Voluntary Work in Dance

Voluntary assistance is usually welcomed by companies,
venues, dance centres and festivals. See also Extend, p. 209.

Dance Administration

There are employment opportunities within the specialist departments of major dance companies or in the administration
of smaller groups, many of which can afford only part-time
administration by one person. There are also careers in theatre
administration, front-of-house and box-office management and
publicity. (Contact the Arts Council, see p. 177)

Dolls

Making dolls – and collecting them – is a thriving industry.
The UK Doll Directory and *The UK Teddy Bear Guide* are
available by post direct from Hugglets, PO Box 290, Brighton
BN2 1DR

Film

British Film Institute
21 Stephen Street, London W1P 1PL
    Tel. 071–255 1444
Membership privileges include priority bookings, access to the
BFI library reading-room, an illustrated monthly programme
booklet and a copy of their annual publication, *The British
Film Institute Film and Television Yearbook*. There are special
concessions – tickets at half price, for example – for senior citizens.

British Federation of Film Societies
21 Stephen Street, London WIP IPL
  Tel. 071–255 1444, ext. 343 or 344

Institute of Amateur Cinematographers
63 Woodfield Lane, Ashstead, Surrey KT21 2BP
  Tel. 03722 76358
Members receive the bimonthly magazine *Amateur Film Maker*, and may seek advice on all related topics, from scripting to animation. The institute also runs an amateur film festival.

National Film Theatre
South Bank, London SEI 8XT
  Tel. 071–928 3232

Food

The Royal Society of Health
RSH House, 38a St George's Drive, London SWIV 4BH
  Tel. 071–630 0121
The society offers a course on the basic principles of food and health, suitable for those interested in becoming involved in the catering trade or for those wanting to learn more about the properties of food and how to balance the family menus. The course involves twenty hours of lectures, discussions and practical work, and can be taken at local colleges around the country or studied at home.

Food from Britain
301–44 Market Towers, New Covent Garden Market,
London SW8 5NQ
  Tel. 071–720 2144
Offers help and advice on marketing agricultural produce and food.

Organic Meat and Poultry

Factory farming methods are abominably cruel. Meat produced by more humane methods is healthier and is becoming more widely available. The giant supermarket chains – Marks and

Spencer, Safeway, Tesco and Sainsbury – now offer a variety of free-range or organic meat, and the more we buy, the more they will have for sale.

The following welfare-minded suppliers will deliver food to your door. Orders are taken over the telephone and payment can be made by credit card.

Ian Miller's Organic Meat
Jamesfield Farm, Newburgh, Fife
  Tel. 0738 85498
Offers a nationwide twenty-four-hour delivery service of fresh vacuum-packed organic beef and lamb, free-range pork, bacon, chicken and game-shot venison.

The Pure Meat Company Ltd
Coombe Court Farm, Moretonhampstead, Devon
  Tel. 0647 40321
The company supplies beef, veal, pork, lamb, sausages, bacon, ham, Christmas turkeys, poultry and game, and delivers anywhere in Britain.

Greenway Organic Farms
Freepost, Edinburgh, Lothian EH1 0AQ
  Tel. 031–557 8111
The company also supplies organic beef and lamb, and also a range of French organic poultry – chicken, duck and guinea-fowl.

The Real Meat Company Ltd
East Hill Farm, Heytesbury, Warminster, Wiltshire
BA12 0HR
  Tel. 0985 40501
Home deliveries of additive-free meat from traditionally reared livestock provided the order is at least 12 lb.

Reading

Audrey Eyton, *The Kind Food Guide*, Penguin Books, 1991

'Friends'

Museums, art galleries, orchestras and dance groups have followed in the tradition of hospitals in creating organizations of Friends. In return for an annual subscription, the Friend is entitled to certain privileges which can in some cases mean very considerable discounts. Being a Friend enables an enthusiast to become closely involved in their hobby at relatively little cost. It is also an excellent way of meeting people who share the same interests.

Games
(See also Sports)

British Chess Federation
9a Grand Parade, St Leonards on Sea, E Sussex TN38 0DD
    Tel. 0424 442500

English Bridge Union
Broadfields, Bicester Road, Aylesbury, Bucks HP19 3BQ
    Tel. 0296 394414

Scrabble Club
The Coordinator, 42 Elthiron Road, London W6 4BW
    Tel. 071–731 2633

Gardening

National Centre for Organic Gardening
Henry Doubleday Research Association (HDRA)
Ryton-on-Dunsmore, Coventry CV8 3LG
    Tel. 0203 303517
Ryton Gardens is the home of the HDRA, which publicizes methods of gardening which do not involve the use of harmful chemicals. Membership includes free admission, regular magazines, use of the reference library, access to outlawed vegetable varieties and the chance to take part in experiments in your own garden.

The Herb Society
PO Box 415, London SWIP 2HE
  Tel. 0803 867 823
Open to anyone interested in herbs. Members receive the
quarterly magazine, *Herbal Review*. Regular lectures and open
days are arranged to enable members to meet informally.
Additional benefits include discounts on plants and herbal
products and information on local herb groups, courses,
sources and literature. There is a small specialist library open
to members, and the society will also provide specialist information in answer to queries.

The English Gardening School at the Chelsea Physic Garden
66 Royal Hospital Road, London SW3 4HS
  Tel. 071–352 5646

Gardens for the Disabled Trust and Garden Club
Hayes Farmhouse, Hayes Lane, Peasmarsh, nr Rye, E Sussex
TN31 6XR
  Tel. 0424 882345
The trust exists to provide practical and financial help, and offer
advice to disabled gardeners. There is a quarterly newsletter and
members are encouraged to meet or be in touch with each other.

Horticultural Therapy
Goulds Ground, Vallis Way, Frome, Somerset BA11 3DW
Gives advice, information and training for those working with
people with disabilities.

*National Association of Flower Arrangement Societies of Great
Britain*
21 Denbigh Street, London SWIV 2HF
  Tel. 071–828 5145; 047 483 2380 (publicity)

The Royal Horticultural Society
Vincent Square, London SWIP 2PE
  Tel. 071–834 4333

For an annual subscription of £18 a year, members of the RHS receive a monthly copy of the society's colour journal, *The Garden* and, at no extra charge, individual advice on gardening questions and problems is provided. Free to members are visits to many gardens throughout Britain including (with a guest) Wisley and Rosemoor, and to all twelve RHS flower shows in Westminster. There is also an opportunity to receive surplus seeds from Wisley.

National Gardens Scheme
Hatchlands Park, East Clandon, Guildford, Surrey GU4 7RT
  Tel. 04873 211535

Scotland's Garden Scheme
31 Castle Terrace, Edinburgh EH1 2EL
  Tel. 031–229 1870

National Society of Allotment and Leisure Gardeners Ltd
Hunters Road, Corby, Northants NN17 1JE
  Tel. 0536 66576
Financially supported by its members only, the society encourages the formation of gardening associations, seeks to safeguard their interests through improved legislation and advises and assists generally on all the problems encountered by the amateur gardener.

Garden Tours
Premier Suite, Central Business Exchange, Milton Keynes
MK9 2EA
  Tel. 0908 609551
The tours cover some of the world's most beautiful gardens but the terrain is often rocky and precipitous and means that the traveller must be of a reasonable standard of mobility and fitness.

Land Use Volunteers
Goulds Ground, Vallis Way, Frome, Somerset BA11 3DW
Projects are run in horticulture, farming and gardening for handicapped, disabled and disadvantaged people.

Friends of the Tradescant Trust
The Chairman, 74 Coleherne Court, Old Brompton Road,
London SW5 OEF
    Tel. 071–373 4030
St Mary-at-Lambeth is the home of the Museum of Garden
History. The museum was founded by the Tradescant Trust
and has links with societies in America and Australia.

Garden History Society
5 The Knoll, Hereford HR1 1RU
    Tel. 0432 354470
Three newsletters a year and a journal, *Garden History*. Organizes visits and lectures, a summer conference and foreign tours.

Reading

Isobel Pays, *Gardening in Retirement*, Age Concern England,
    1985
*Directory of Scented Gardens and Gardens for the Blind/Dis-
abled; Directory of Nature Trails for Blind People*; and Kathleen
Fleet's *Gardening Without Sight* (Royal National Institute for
the Blind, 1989) are all available from the RNIB.

Genealogy
See under History.

Geography

Royal Geographical Society
1 Kensington Gore, London SW7 2AR
    Tel. 071–589 5466
A national source of geographical information and a focal point
for British geographical and exploration activity.

Geology

The Geologists' Association
Burlington House, London W1V 9AG
    Tel. 071–434 9298

History

British Association for Local History
Shopwyke Hall, Chichester, W Sussex PO20 6BQ
   Tel. 0243 787639
Membership is open to anyone interested in local history.
Courses are offered on topics of special interest to the local
historian, such as the use of computers, writing local history
and the development of market towns. Visits are arranged to
places not normally open to the general public, for example,
the Public Record Office, the College of Arms, the Borthwick
Institute and the Bodleian Library. The official journal of the
association is *The Local Historian*, and there is a twice-yearly
newsletter of national and local events.

CADW Welsh Historic Monuments
Brunel House, 2 Fitzalan Road, Cardiff CF2 1UY
   Tel. 0222 465 511

National Museum of Wales
Cathays Park, Cardiff CF1 3NP
   Tel. 0222 397 951
A main starting-point for anyone interested in Welsh tradition
and culture. Free leaflets and a calendar of events are available.

English Heritage
Historic Buildings and Monuments Commission for England,
Fortress House, 23 Savile Row, London W1X 2HE
   Tel. 071–973 3250
Members of English Heritage contribute to the preservation of
England's past for the benefit of future generations. In return,
they receive the quarterly magazine, an illustrated guidebook,
a map showing the location of all sites and a diary of special
events and concerts.

Friends of the Scottish Monuments
Historic Buildings and Monuments, Scottish Development
Department, 20 Brandon Street, Edinburgh EH3 5RA
   Tel. 031–244 3144; 031–244 3099 (membership inquiries)
For £10 a year (£5 for senior citizens) members are entitled to

free entry to sites and half-price entry to English Heritage and Welsh CADW sites. There is a free directory with maps, and special site visits for Friends are guided by professional staff. A regular newsletter announces activities.

The Saltire Society
13 Athol Crescent, Edinburgh
   Tel. 031–228 6621
Scottish culture and traditions are enjoyed by members of the society. Local branches organize musical evenings, dancing, dinners, tours and lectures.

Garden History Society
See under Gardening.

Historical Association
59a Kennington Park Road, London SE11 4JH
   Tel. 071–735 3901
The association aims to develop public interest in history in all periods at all levels, and caters for beginners, amateurs and experts. Membership includes a free quarterly magazine, *The Historian*, and gives access to specially organized tours, an annual conference, the vacation school – a short intensive summer course in a university environment – and activities and lectures all over the country. There are over eighty branches offering local lectures and social events. Membership of a local branch is included in the basic subscription.

Age Exchange Reminiscence Centre
11 Blackheath Village, Blackheath, London SE3 9LA
   Tel. 081–318 9105
The Reminiscence Centre recognizes the precious value of memory and produces plays, books and exhibitions based on the memories of old people. More recently Age Exchange has been working in old people's homes, hospitals and nursing homes, running reminiscence sessions and developing ideas and methods with residential and nursing staff. Training sessions are also held at the centre throughout the year.

Oral History Society
Department of Sociology, University of Essex, Wivenhoe Park,
Colchester CO4 3SQ

City of London Information Centre
St Paul's Churchyard (Southside), London EC4
   Tel. 071–606 3030 (ext. 1456)

Streets of London
32 Grovelands Road, London N13 4RH
   Tel. 081–882 3414

The Georgian Group
37 Spital Square, London E1 6DY
   Tel. 071–377 1722
Besides its role as an architectural watchdog, the group runs an
imaginative and lively programme of activities for its members, including visits to buildings not normally open to the
public and to buildings under threat; lectures on subjects as
varied as cooking and cabinet-making, as well as an academi-
cally oriented annual symposium; conversation weekends and
country-house weekends, town walks and foreign study tours;
some grand and costumed, others more intimate and informal. Membership entitles you to take part in the activities
and to receive free copies of the newsletter and illustrated
annual report.

Victorian Society
1 Priory Gardens, Bedford Park, London W4 1TT
   Tel. 081–994 1019
The society is first and foremost a pressure group which exists
in order to save the best examples of Victorian architecture.
The headquarters are in London but there are thirteen regional
groups. Membership involves learning about Victorian and
Edwardian history and culture, with special reference to architecture and the decorative arts. Lectures, conferences, walks
and tours are held throughout the year. The society also runs
an intensive three-week summer school in collaboration with
the Victorian Society in America.

Genealogy

Society of Genealogists
14 Charterhouse Buildings, Goswell Rd, London ECIM 7BA
 Tel. 071–251 8799
Tracing ancestors is a time-consuming but fascinating study
and seems especially appealing in retirement for the opportunities it offers to discover hitherto unknown family members.
Members of the society and non-members have access to a
unique library of parish registers and family histories. There
are open lectures in the winter and courses for beginners are
run twice a year in the spring and autumn.

Historic Battlefields and War Graves

Commonwealth War Graves Commission
2 Marlow Road, Maidenhead, Berkshire SL6 7DX
The commission will give information on the location of particular graves.

The Royal British Legion
The Pilgrimage Department, The Royal British Legion
Village, Aylesford, Maidstone, Kent ME20 7NX
 Tel. 0622 716182

Major and Mrs Holt's Battlefield Tours
Golden Key Building, 15 Market Street, Sandwich, Kent
CT13 9DA
 Tel. 0304 612248
There is a choice of over forty battleground tours in all parts
of the world in all periods of history. 'Feats of the Longbow-
men at Crécy and Agincourt', 'The Alamo', 'The Zulu and
Boer Wars', 'The Battle of Britain', 'Vietnam' and the most
recent option, 'Both Sides of the Berlin Wall', are among the
battle zones covered.

Martin Middlebrook's Battlefield Tours
Battlefield Tours, 48 Linden Way, Boston, Lincs PE21 9DS
 Tel. 0205 64555
Mr Middlebrook, a well-known military historian, writes books

in the winter and, in the summer, guides parties of not more than twenty people around First World War battlegrounds – the Somme, the Ypres Salient and Verdun. His book *The First Day on the Somme – 1 July 1916* is published by Penguin.

Period Costume – Dressing Up and Acting the Part

Kentwell Hall
Long Melford, Suffolk, CO10 9BA
 Tel. 0787 310 207
The owner of this sixteenth-century manor-house, Patrick Phillips, offers enthusiasts a chance to re-create history by living the everyday life of the period. Each summer, in an event lasting three weeks, participants of all ages dress, behave and talk as Tudors. Everyone makes their own clothes and shoes.

Holidays

To visit a travel agent's and return with brochures promising adventure and enchantment is one of life's great pleasures. At no expense and from the depths of an armchair on a cold winter's evening, the homebound voyager can roam the world in imagined sunshine, dressed for the tropics or a mountain walk, eating lobster or yak steak, living in lofty tower or leaky tent.

 While special-interest holidays can be found in this chapter under the heading of the interest or activity concerned, this section, for the most part, looks at holidays for older people and people with special needs.

Holidays in the British Isles

The British Tourist Authority (BTA)
Central Information Services, Thames Tower, Black's Road, London W6 9EL
 Tel. 081–846 9000

Scottish Tourist Board
23 Ravelston Terrace, Edinburgh EH4 3EU
 Tel. 031–332 2433

Wales Tourist Board
Brunel House, 2 Fitzalan Road, Cardiff CF2 1UY
   Tel. 0222 499909

Northern Ireland Tourist Board
48 High Street, Belfast BT1 2DS
   Tel. 0232 246609

Irish Tourist Board (Bord Failte)
Ireland House, 150 New Bond Street, London W1Y 0AQ
   Tel. 071–493 3201

Holidays for the Older Traveller

Age Concern Factsheet No. 4, 'Holidays for Older People', is an excellent source of basic up-to-date information, ideas and advice; No. 26, 'Travel Information for Older People', includes information on financial assistance and travel for those with mobility problems.

Below is a guide to just a few of the many commercial organizations which arrange holidays especially for the older traveller. Further information can be obtained from travel agents and the tourist boards mentioned above.

Saga Senior Citizens Holidays Ltd
The Saga Building, Middleburg Square, Folkestone, Kent
CT20 1AZ

All telephone calls to Saga are free: 0800 300 500 (reservations); 0800 300 600 (inquiries); 0303 85 75 22 (public relations).

SAGA is often described as being 'in a class of its own'. The company was originally created exclusively for holiday-makers over the age of sixty but has now extended its boundaries, moving into the retirement-housing market and offering advice on health and finance. (See also Part III, Friendships.) Saga holidays are all 'off-peak', so travellers are spared the crowds. Long winter holidays of up to five months, which some people say are almost as cheap as staying at home, are offered.

Saga's special-interest holidays include bowls, walking, archaeology, painting, golf and bird-watching.

Saga publishes Paul Lewis's *Saving and Spending on Longer Holidays Abroad* and *Leisure* (a Saga Retirement Guide).

Co-op Holiday Care
PO Box 53, Corporation Street, Manchester M60 4ES
   Tel. 061–832 8248
   Specializes in group holidays.

Cosmos
Cosmos South, Tourama House, 17 Homesdale Road,
Bromley, Kent BR2 9LX
   Tel. 081–464 3400

Golden Rail Holidays
PO Box 12, York, YO1 1YX
   Tel. 0904 628992

National Holidays
George House, George Street, Wakefield, W Yorkshire
WF12 6AG
   Tel. 0924 387387 (reservations); 0924 383838
      (administration)

Portland Travel Trust
218 Great Portland Street, London W1 5HG
   Tel. 071–388 5111

Wallace Arnold Tours
8 Park Lane, Croydon, Surrey CR9 1DN
   Tel. 081–688 7255 or 686 2378
Coach holidays.

Young at Heart
Thomson Holidays, Greater London House, Hampstead
Road, London NW1 7SD
   Tel. 071–387 8484 or 387 9321

Butlins Ltd
Senior Citizens' Office, Bognor Regis, W Sussex PO21 1JJ
   Tel. 0243 820202

The Independent Traveller

Saga
(See also above and Part III, Friendships.) Arranges 'Specially for Singles' holidays which Saga says are 'the ideal way to meet new friends and enjoy their companionship'. An experienced 'host' arranges excursions, entertainment and a series of activities and works hard to ensure that no one feels left out.

Chips (Cultural Holidays for Independent People – Single)
c/o Pamela Pile, Hillside, Mitford, Surrey GU8 5JJ
Organizes specially arranged breaks for single people over forty who are interested in the theatre, historic houses and gardens.

Travel Companions
89 Hillfield Court, Belsize Avenue, London NW3 4BE
  Tel. 071–431 1984 or 071–202 8478
Provides a nationwide service for people aged between thirty and seventy-five who like to share their holidays. Arrangements are made to enable you to meet your travel companion before you decide to holiday together.

Travelling Partners
20 Mount Pleasant, Norwich, Norfolk NR2 2DG
  Tel. 0603 53446
This is an introduction service for those who want to team up with a travelling companion. Their monthly magazine, *Contact*, lists current members and gives brief details of each person's interests, holiday plans or ideas but, with the single traveller in mind, the firm also publishes a selective guide to some tours, educational, small group and individual holidays in which people travelling on their own can comfortably participate.

Travelmate
6 Hayes Avenue, Bournemouth BH7 7AD
  Tel. 0202 393398
Travellers not wishing to travel alone may find this a useful service. The company acts as an introduction service and, for

an annual fee of £25, guarantees a minimum of six introductions, taking into account, age, sex and planned destination.

Solo's Holidays Ltd
41 Watford Way, Hendon, London NW4 3JH
   Tel. 081–202 0855 (reservations, 24-hour); 081–202 1922
   (administration)
The company organizes overseas and UK holidays and weekend breaks for single men and women over thirty years old. They are anxious to welcome women, although not on every occasion as the following extract from their brochure makes clear:

Although we make a considerable effort to achieve a reasonable balance between the sexes and also age groups, a recent analysis of our holidays has shown that the average age of our lady clients is between five and ten years older than that of the men, and as you will appreciate this somewhat distorts the social balance. For the time being therefore we are not accepting bookings from new clients over fifty-five years of age, and we are restricting numbers in the fifty-to-fifty-five age group. If however, your age is between fifty-five and seventy, welcome to Senior Solo's. As it will not be possible to balance numbers between the sexes for Senior Solos, we anticipate the groups being mainly female, but hope the programme of sightseeing, theatre visits, quizzes, general conviviality and companionship will hold wide appeal.

Longstaff Leisure
Hartrigg Country House, Buckden Skipton, N Yorkshire
BD23 5HA
   Tel. 0756 76246
   The company specializes in country-house holidays in the Yorkshire dales for single people in the thirties-to-fifties age group. Although they try to maintain a reasonable social balance between the sexes, the organizers are anxious to dispel the notion that 'singles holidays' are 'only about sex and booze'.

Solitaire Holidays Ltd
118 London Road, Sevenoaks, Kent TN13 1BA
   Tel. 0732 464777

Offers holidays and short breaks for single, divorced and widowed people of all ages.

Odyssey International
21 Cambridge Road, Waterbeach, Cambridge CB5 9NJ
　Tel. 0223 861 079
For a yearly membership fee of £20 this nationwide club with members between the ages of seventeen and seventy arranges introductions and organizes holidays and weekend breaks abroad and in the UK.

Reunion Holidays

For people wishing to visit relatives who live abroad and for organizers of reunions, the following agencies may be helpful:

Canuspa (Canada, Australia, New Zealand, United States Parents and Associates)
Secretary: Mr T. Serwood, 24 Florida Court, Reading RG1 6NX
　Tel. 0734 574757
Postal secretary: Mrs J. White, 6 Sheepcote Road, Windsor, Berks SL4 4JQ
　Tel. 07535 60137

Lion World Travel 'Friendship' Foundation, Worldwide Reunion Travel
53 Gresham Road, Staines, Middlesex TW18 2BD
　Tel. 0784 64261
　Membership of these organizations includes newsletters and discount flights.

Homesitting

Taking care of someone else's home while they are away can be a real bargain, especially if you believe that 'a change is as good as a rest'. Homesitters receive travel expenses and food and a fee if pets are to be looked after. The organization to contact is:

Homesitters
The Old Bakery, Western Road, Tring, Herts HP23 4BB
  Tel. 0442 891188

Holidays With Care for Special Needs

Holiday Care Service
2 Old Bank Chambers, Station Road, Horley, Surrey
RH6 9HW
  Tel. 0293 774535
This is the United Kingdom's central source of holiday information for people with special needs. Through the Holiday Helpers scheme, volunteers are introduced to elderly and disabled
people as carers or companions to enable them to take independent holidays. The service aims to help anyone who is elderly
and frail or in poor physical or mental health. It also offers help
to others who may be experiencing difficulties – single parents
and their children, widows and families affected by long-term
unemployment – anyone, in fact, whose personal or family
circumstances mean that a break is especially important.

ATS Travel
9 River View Terrace, Purfleet, Essex RM16 1QT
  Tel. 0708 863198
The company organizes special holidays which are carefully
arranged to suit the needs of the individual traveller.

Camping for the Disabled
20 Burton Close, Dawley, Telford, Shropshire
  Tel. 0743 77489 (day); 0952 507653 (evening)

Disabled Drivers' Association Holiday Hotel for Disabled People
Ashwellthorpe Hall Hotel, Ashwellthorpe, Norwich, Norfolk
NR16 1EX
  Tel. 050 841 324

Leisure Link
48 Chiltern Avenue, Bushey, Herts WD2 3QB
  Tel. 081–950 2976

Holidays are especially designed for the elderly and disabled elderly.

Reading

Guides to holidays in the UK and abroad, covering hotels, holiday centres, transport arrangements, self-catering and special-interest holidays are available from the Royal Association for Disability and Rehabilitation (RADAR), Publications Dept, 25 Mortimer Street, WIN 8AB (tel. 071-637 5400).

'Care in the Air – Advice for Handicapped Airline Passengers' (from Air Transport Users Committee, 2nd Floor, Kingsway House, 103 Kingsway, London WC2B 6QX; tel. 071-242 3882)

'British Rail and Disabled Travellers' (available from mainline stations)

AA Travellers' Guide for the Disabled and *The World Wheelchair Traveller*, Automobile Association, 1990

'Holidays for Older People' (from Age Concern England)

Jigsaw Puzzles

British Jigsaw Puzzle Library
8 Heath Terrace, Leamington Spa, Warwickshire CV32 5LY
· Tel. 0926 311874
This is a lending library and puzzles are exchanged mainly by post. Subscription rates vary according to the period of time involved. All the puzzles are wooden, without guide pictures, and a team of cutters ensure the selection is constantly being extended. The wide variety of styles and degrees of difficulty enable the librarians to select puzzles to suit the needs and interests of individual members. Unless requested, the same puzzle is never supplied twice!

Mandolin Puzzles
9 Elia Street, London NI 8DE
   Tel. 071-278 2756
The brochure contains some unusual and challenging puzzles, all available by post.

Keep Fit

The Central Council of Physical Recreation
Francis House, Francis Street, London SWIP IDE
  Tel. 071–828 3163/4

Keep Fit Association
16 Upper Woburn Place, London WCIH OQG
  Tel. 071–387 4349

Look After Yourself Project Centre
Christ Church College, Canterbury, Kent CTI IQU
  Tel. 0227 455564

Extend
la North Street, Sheringham, Norfolk NR26 8LJ
  Tel. 0263 822479
Extend is a registered charity which aims to enhance the
quality of life for senior citizens and the mentally and physically
disabled of all ages by providing recreational movement sessions to music. The organization offers a basic training to
people allied to the medical profession or to those with an
appropriate knowledge of anatomy and physiology. After continuous assessments, students who reach the required standard
are awarded a certificate of qualification and are invited to
affiliate to Extend. Teachers then work in a variety of ways
with elderly and disabled people, either from independent
classes or under the adult education authority and in hospitals,
day centres and residential homes.

Languages

Courses in foreign languages are offered by all adult institutes
of education, but for opportunities to test and improve language skills further, there is nothing quite like putting them
into practice in the countries concerned.

General

The Central Bureau for Educational Visits and Exchanges
Seymour Mews House, Seymour Mews, London WIH 9PE
  Tel. 071–486 5101
The national office for information and advice on all forms of
educational visits and exchanges. Publishes *Study Holidays*
(£5·50 plus 70p. p&p)

En Famille Agency (Overseas)
The Old Stables, 60b Maltravers Street, Arundel, W Sussex
BNI8 9BG
  Tel. 0903 883266
Concentrates on France, but also deals with other European
countries.

French

French Institute, 15 Queensberry Place, London SW7
  Tel. 071–589 6211

German

Goethe Institute
50 Princes Gate, Exhibition Road, London SW7 2PH
  Tel. 071–581 3344
PO Box 20 10 09, D-8000 München 2, Germany

Italian

Italian Institute
39 Belgrave Square, London SWIX 8NX
  Tel. 071–235 1461

The British–Italian Society
172 Regent Street, London WIR 5DF
  Tel. 071–437 9479

The British Institute, Florence
Palazzo Lanfredini, Lungarno Guicciardini 9, Firenze 50125,
Italy
   Tel. (from the UK) 010–39 55 284031

Spanish

Spanish Institute
102 Eaton Square, London SW1
   Tel. 071–235 1484

Estudio General Luliano
c/o John Galleymore, 25 High Street, Portsmouth PO1 2LZ
   Tel. 0705 824095

Others

Scots Language Society
60 Victoria Road, Falkirk FK2 7AX
   Tel. 0324 21567

Universal Languages
45 High Street, Kensington, London W8 5EB
   Tel. 071–938 1225
Offers courses at all levels of ability, either in small groups or
individually, six days a week at various times during the day
and evening.

Models and Miniatures

British Model Flying Association
Chacksfield House, 31 St Andrews Road, Leicester LE2 8RE
   Tel. 0533 440028
With responsibility for all branches of the nation's model
flying activities, the BMFA organizes competitions and special
events and offers practical guidelines for flying and third-party
insurance. Indoor free-flight or radio-controlled flying particularly appeals to older members.

Miniature Armoured Fighting Vehicle Association (MAFVA)
15 Berwick Avenue, Heaton Mersey, Stockport, Cheshire
SK4 3AA
   Tel. 061–432 7574
This international society gives advice and information on tanks and other military vehicles and equipment, and also provides links with local branches and overseas members with similar interests. The society publishes a bimonthly magazine and organizes meetings, displays and competitions.

Music

National Federation of Music Societies
Francis House, Francis Street, London SWIP IDE
   Tel. 071–828 7320
For professionals or amateurs, the association has the addresses of around 1,300 affiliated choral societies and orchestras nation-wide. Most of these charge a small membership fee.

Benslow Music Trust
Little Benslow Hills, Ibberson Way, Hitchin, Herts SG4 9RB
   Tel. 0462 459446/455175
A registered charity pioneering work in music education and the development of amateur music. Adult courses for both professionals and amateurs at all levels of accomplishment are run throughout the year, including most weekend and holiday periods. Programmes which include chamber music, choral and orchestral work, solo instruments, early music and jazz, and recording techniques, are supported by theory, apprecia-tion and lecture courses.

Summer Music
22 Gresley Road, London N19 3JZ
   Tel. 071–272 5664
Organizes a variety of music courses, workshops and events throughout the year. The Summer Music Summer School is held during July at Wellington College in Berkshire and the year ends with a Christmas Music House Party for string players and choral singers. Other events include weekly musical evenings in which participants bring and sing their own songs, and choral weekends.

Extend
A national network of teachers providing scientifically structured music and movement sessions; see above, under Keep Fit.

Aldeburgh Foundation
High Street, Aldeburgh, Suffolk IP15 5AX
Tel. 0728 452 935
The Aldeburgh Festival of Music and the Arts is held in June and presented by the foundation as part of a year-round programme of concerts and recitals and master classes in the Britten–Pears School for Advanced Musical Studies.

Edinburgh International Festival Office
21 Market Street, Edinburgh EH1 1BW
Tel. 031–226 4001

The Friends of Covent Garden
Royal Opera House, Covent Garden, London WC2E 7QA
Tel. 071–240 1066

The Friends of the English National Opera
The London Coliseum, St Martin's Lane, London WC2N 4ES
Tel. 071–836 0111

Handbell Ringers of Great Britain
2 Holt Park Approach, Holt Park, Leeds LS16 7PW
Tel. 0532 677711

National Association of Choirs
21 Charmouth Road, Lower Weston, Bath BA1 3LJ

Society of Recorder Players
469 Merton Road, London SW18 5LD
Tel. 081–874 2237

Reading

The British Federation of Music Festivals publishes a *Year Book* listing festivals throughout the country.

Arts Festivals in Britain and Ireland (price £7·95, available from bookshops or through Rhinegold Publishing Ltd, 241 Shaftesbury Avenue, London WC2H 8EH). This is the most comprehensive list of festivals in the United Kingdom and the Republic of Ireland.

Pen-Friends

Friends by Post
6 Bollin Court, Macclesfield Road, Wilmslow, Cheshire
SK9 2AP
   Tel. 0625 527044
This is a free service (enclose s.a.e. however) which aims to bring together pen-friends with interests in common.

Saga Magazine Club (Pen-friends)
The Saga Building, Middelburg Square, Freepost, Folkestone
CT20 1AZ
Annual membership of the club includes ten issues of the magazine, which gives information on pen-friends.

Photography

Royal Photographic Society of Great Britain
The Octagon, Milsom Street, Bath BA1 1DN
   Tel. 0225 62841
Membership includes access to workshops, field days and social events, meetings, lectures, conferences and exhibitions.

Politics

Conservative Party Central Office
32 Smith Square, Westminster, London SW1P 3HH
   Tel. 071–222 9000

Labour Party Headquarters
150 Walworth Road, London SE17 1JT
   Tel. 071–703 0833

Social and Liberal Democratic Party
4 Cowley Street, London SW1P 3NB
   Tel. 071–222 7999

Green Party
Station Parade, Balham High Road, London SW12 9A2
   Tel. 071–673 0045

Plaid Cymru
51 Cathedral Road, Cardiff CF1 9HD
   Tel. 0222 231944

Scottish National Party
6 North Charlotte Street, Edinburgh EH2 4JH
   Tel. 031–266 3661

Social Democratic and Labour Party (SDLP)
38 University Street, Belfast BT7 1FZ
   Tel. 0232 323428

Ulster Unionist Party
3 Glengall Street, Belfast BT12 5AE
   Tel. 0232 324601

Radio

Radio Society of Great Britain
Lambda House, Cranbourne Road, Potters Bar, Herts EN6 3JE
   Tel. 0707 59015 (between 10 a.m. and 4 p.m.)
Help and advice for amateur radio operaters.

Railways

Railway Correspondence and Travel Society
97 Greenhill Road, Kettering, Northants NN15 7LN
   Tel. 0536 85575
Members receive the monthly magazine *The Railway Observer*, which keeps them in touch with events and with fellow enthusiasts. There are regular meetings, visits and rail trips at home and overseas.

Retreats

The National Retreat Centre
Liddon House, 24 South Audley Street, London WIY 5DL
    Tel. 071–493 3534
The centre publishes a journal, *Vision*, which gives details of
retreat houses in the United Kingdom.

Some examples

Allington Castle
Maidstone, Kent ME16 0NB
    Tel. 0622 54080
Carmelite.

Parcevall Hall
Skyreholme, Skipton, N Yorkshire BX23 6DG
    Tel. 0675 672 213/283
Anglican.

Pluscarden Abbey
Elgin, Grampian IV30 3UA
    Tel. 034 387 257
Benedictine, RC. In winter, men only.

The Iona Community
Iona, Argyll, PA76 6SN
    Tel. 06817 404
Ecumenical. Pilgrimage each Wednesday around the island.

Caldey Abbey
Isle of Caldey, Tenby, Dyfed SA70 7UH
Cistercian, RC. Open Easter to 1 November. The monks own
the small rocky island and make their own scent. Apply by
letter.

The Hen House Club
Hawerby Hall, North Thoresby, Lincolnshire DN36 5QL
    Tel. 0472 840278
A women's holiday and retreat centre, the Hen House Club is
also a venue for meetings, special events and courses.

Reading

Away From It All: A Guide to Retreat Houses and Centres by Geoffrey Gerard lists over a hundred retreat centres in Britain. (Available from the National Retreat Centre – see above.)

The Good Retreat Guide by Stafford Whiteaker, Century, 1991.

Silver

Wolds Silver Courses
   Tel. 065385 485
Offers tuition and accommodation at Rothay Cottage, Leppington, Malton, N Yorkshire YO17 9SL.

Social

ARP/050 Companions Programme
ARP Companions, Borough Woods House, Shillingford, nr Bampton, Devon EX16 9BL
Companions is a club founded by the Association of Retired Persons in response to requests from single members who felt that the retirement scene is geared to couples. The club welcomes ARP members on their own who like to travel, make new friends, share new experiences.

Sports

The Sports Council
161 Upper Woburn Place, London WC1H 0QP
   Tel. 071–388 1277
The Sports Council is the country's main central source of information and data about sport. The headquarters is based in London, but there are nine regional offices, details of which can be obtained from the above address. Sports Council publications include advice on health and fitness and leisure provision. Their booklet, *50+ All to Play For* is a useful starting-point for people contemplating sport in middle age.

Central Council of Physical Recreation
Francis House, Francis Street, London
Offers advice, support and training for providers of recreational activities.

Angling

National Anglers Council
11 Cowgate, Peterborough, Cambridgeshire PE1 1LZ
    Tel. 0733 54084

The Angling Foundation
23 Brighton Road, South Croydon, Surrey CR2 6EA
    Tel. 081–681 1242

Archery

Grand National Archery Society
7th Street, The National Agricultural Centre, Stoneleigh,
Kenilworth, Warwickshire CV8 2LG
    Tel. 0203 696631

Badminton

Badminton Association of England Ltd
National Badminton Centre, Bradwell Road, Loughton
Lodge, Milton Keynes, Bucks MK8 9OA
    Tel. 0908 658822

Bicycling

Just Pedalling
9 Church Street, Coltishall, Norfolk NR12 7DW
    Tel. 0603 737201

Cyclists' Touring Club
Cotterell House, 69 Meadrow, Godalming, Surrey GU7 3HS
    Tel. 04868 7217

Cycling for Softies
Roy and Susan Madron, 11 Norman Rd, Manchester
    Tel. 061–834 6800
The company organizes bicycle tours in France. Although the
basic formula for every holiday is always the same, a range of
tours is offered to suit the abilities and needs of the cyclist.

The first two nights and the last night are spent at the home-base hotel, where the tourist is given the choice of bike and equipped for the holiday.

Billiards and Snooker

The Billiards and Snooker Control Council
Coronet House, Queen Street, Leeds LS1 2TN
 Tel. 0532 440586

Boating – Canals

The Association of Pleasure Craft Operators
35a High Street, Newport, Shropshire TF10 8JW
 Tel. 0952 813572
Covers all areas of canals.

Inland Waterways Association
See under Conservation.

UK Waterways Holidays Ltd
1 Port Hill, Hertford SG14 1PJ
 Tel. 0992 550616

Boating – Passenger-carrying Cargo Boats

Gray Dawes Travel
Chatsworth House, 76 St Mary Axe, London EC3
 Tel. 071–623 2450
or 3 Cathedral Place, London EC4M 7DT
 Tel. 071–248 6474

The Strand Cruise Centre
Weider Travel, Charing Cross Shopping Concourse, Adelaide Street, London WC2N 4HZ
 Tel. 071–836 6363

Bowling

English Bowling Association
Lyndhurst Road, Worthing, W Sussex BN11 2AZ
 Tel. 0903 820222

English Women's Indoor Bowling Association
8 Oakfield Road, Carterton, Oxon OX8 3RB
   Tel. 0993 841344

Women's Bowling Association
Darracombe, The Clays, Market Lavington, Wilts FN10 4AY
   Tel. 0380 813 774

English Indoor Bowling Association
290a Barking Road, London E6 3BA
   Tel. 081–470 1237

Clay Pigeon Shooting

Clay Pigeon Shooting Association
107 Epping New Road, Buckhurst Hill, Essex LG9 5TQ
   Tel. 081–505 6221

Cricket

National Cricket Association
Lord's Cricket Ground, St John's Wood Road, London
NW8 8QN
   Tel. 071–289 1611

Women's Cricket Association
16 Upper Woburn Place, London WC1H 0QP
   Tel. 071–387 3423

Croquet

Croquet Association
c/o The Secretary, Hurlingham Club, Ranelagh Gardens,
London SW6 3PR
   Tel. 071–736 3148

Darts

British Darts Organization Ltd
2 Pages Lane, Muswell Hill, London N10 1PS
  Tel. 081–883 554

Falconry

Falconry Jollys
  Tel. 071–607 7577
Will arrange a two-day break including a half-day falconry course and b.&b. in a small farmhouse hotel.

Golf

English Golf Union
1–3 Upper King Street, Leicester LE1 6XF
  Tel. 0533 553042

Golfing Union of Ireland
Glencar House, 81 Eglinton Road, Donnybrook, Dublin 4
  Tel. 010–3531 269 4111

Scottish Golf Union
The Cottage, 181a White House Road, Barnton, Edinburgh
EH4 6BY
  Tel. 031–339 7546

Welsh Golfing Union
5 Park Place, Cardiff
  Tel. 0222 238467

Land Yachting

British Federation of Sand and Land Yacht Clubs
23 Piper Drive, Long Whatton, Loughborough, Leicester
LE12 5DJ
  Tel. 0509 842292

Riding

Riding for the Disabled Association
Avenue R, National Agricultural Centre, Kenilworth,
Warwickshire CV8 2LY
   Tel. 0203 696510

Rifle Shooting

National Small Bore Rifle Association
Lord Roberts House, Bisley Camp, Brookwood, Woking,
Surrey GU24 0NY
   Tel. 048 676969

Rowing

Amateur Rowing Association (ARA)
6 Lower Mall, London W6 9DJ
   Tel. 081–748 3632
Neither age, sex, physical disability nor lack of experience
should prevent an enthusiastic would-be oarsman from applying to join a local rowing club. Most welcome beginners and
the necessary degree of fitness will be achieved with growing
proficiency. Novices are expected to train once or twice a week
and this may gradually increase to four times a week. Information and addresses of local clubs may be obtained from the
ARA.

Running

The Running Sixties
120 Norfolk Avenue, Sanderstead, Surrey CR2 8BS
   Tel. 081–657 7660
Membership is open to all men and women over the age of
sixty.

Sailing

Royal Yaching Association
RYA House, Romsey Road, Eastleigh, Hants SO5 4YA
  Tel. 0703 629962

Skiing

The Ski Club of Great Britain
118 Eaton Square, London SW1W 9AF
  Tel. 071–245 1033
Ski Club skiing parties are grouped by level of proficiency and
by age. Most have an upper age limit of fifty-five but special
parties are organized for the over forty-fives and the over-
sixties. The club also runs pre-season courses on the artificial
slopes at Sandown Park, Hemel Hempstead, Gloucester and
Rossendale.

Swimming

Amateur Swimming Association
Harold Fern House, Derby Square, Loughborough, Leics
LE11 0AL
  Tel. 0509 230431

Table Tennis

English Table Tennis Association
3rd Floor, Queensbury House, Havelock Road, Hastings,
E Sussex TN34 1HF
  Tel. 0424 722525

The Veterans Table Tennis Society
Membership Secretary, 53 Solway, Hempstead Park,
Hailsham, E Sussex BN27 3HB
  Tel. 0323 845583

Tennis

Lawn Tennis Association
The Queen's Club, West Kensington, London W14 9EG
    Tel. 071–385 2366

Veterans' Lawn Tennis Association of Great Britain
c/o 3 Gainsborough Road, London W4 1NJ
    Tel. 081–994 3890

Walking

Ramblers' Association
1–5 Wandsworth Road, London SW8 2XX
    Tel. 071–582 6878
A voluntary organization established to protect rights of way,
to campaign for access to open country and to defend the
beauty of the countryside. The annual publication, *Rambler's
Yearbook*, has hints on safe walking, with separate sections on
long-distance paths, guided walks, public transport, maps for
walkers and shops that sell rambling gear, as well as an accommodation guide with two thousand bed-and-breakfast places.

Alternative Travel Group Ltd
1–3 George Street, Oxford OX1 2AZ
    Tel. 0865 251195
The company specializes in walking tours in this country and
abroad. The tours have been carefully researched, the main
aim being to combine comfortable night-time accommodation
with good food and daily walks amid spectacular scenery.
Trips are accompanied by a vehicle which provides the picnic
lunch and optional transportation. The groups consist of not
more than sixteen people of any age.

Teme Walk
Sunnyside, Knucklas, Knighton, Powys LD7 1PR
    Tel. 0547 520363
Offers more than three hundred guided walking holidays in
different areas of mid Wales. Walks are devised to suit the
requirements of each particular group.

Adventureline
  Tel. 0209 820847
All-year-round guided walking tours and holidays in Cornwall. Single people and children are welcome and walks are organized to cater for each group according to age, agility and preference.

Borders Ventures
  Tel. 091-565 7959
Escorted walking holidays in the Scottish Borders which include an all-female week led by experienced women experts. Groups are restricted in numbers and the pace is dictated by the slowest member of the party.

Countrywide Holidays
  Tel. 061-225 1000
Guided walking holidays at thirteen country houses throughout Britain. Walks are graded from very easy to strenuous.

English Wanderer
  Tel. 0740 653169
Offers walking holidays and weekends nationwide, including holidays in ten National Parks.

Footlines
  Tel. 081-686 0443
A walking-tour specialist offering unescorted tours for independent walkers. Itineraries are worked out according to individual requirements and accommodation is booked in advance. Baggage transfers are also arranged.

Ossian Guides
  Tel. 05403 402
The company organizes wilderness treks for three or seven days through the Highlands of Scotland, ranging in difficulty from easy to strenuous.

Windsurfing

Senior and Veteran Windsurfers' Association (Seavets)
Membership Secretary, 34 Nash Grove Lane, Wokingham,
Berkshire RG11 4HD
Tel. 0734 734634

Stamp Collecting

National Philatelic Society
107 Charterhouse Street, London ECIM 6PT
Tel. 071-251 5040

National Postal Museum
London Chief Post Office, King Edward Building, King
Edward Street, London ECIA ILP
Tel. 071-239 5420
Free admission to one of the world's finest philatelic collections, including the Phillips collection of British Victorian
stamps and the Post Office's own public-record collections of
the artwork, essays and registration sheets of all British stamps,
together with the Post Office's Universal Postal Union collection of world postage stamps since 1878.

Theatre

British Theatre Association
Cranbourn Mansions, Cranbourn Street, London WC2H 7AG
Tel. 071-734 1664
The BTA offers a variety of services to the theatre-goer and
amateur dramatist.

Society of West End Theatre
Bedford Chambers, The Piazza, Covent Garden, London
WC2E 8HQ
Tel. 071-836 3193
Offers tickets at a reduced rate to senior citizens.

Scottish Community Drama Association
5 York Place, Edinburgh EH1 3EB
  Tel. 031-557 5552
Offers information, help and advice to amateur dramatic societies in Scotland.

Theatre and Concert Travel Club
PO Box 1, St Albans, Herts AL1 4ED
  Tel. 0727 41115
Arranges theatre and concert bookings, rail travel at reduced prices and hotel accommodation.

Weather

Royal Meteorological Society, 104 Oxford Road, Reading, Berks RG1 1J
Members – both professionals and amateurs – receive the monthly magazine, *Weather*, and are invited to attend scientific meetings.

Wildlife
(See also Animals)

The Royal Society for the Protection of Birds (RSPB)
The Lodge, Sandy, Bedfordshire SG19 2DL
  Tel. 0767 80551
A charity that takes action for birds and the environment. Membership includes the quarterly *Birds* magazine, which includes news of RSPB activities, and free admission to most RSPB reserves. There are opportunities for involvement in voluntary work through the network of members' groups.

Holidays organized by the RSPB both at home and abroad are accompanied by guides who are experts.

Wildfowl and Wetlands Trust
Slimbridge, Gloucester GL2 7BT
  Tel. 0453 890 333

Worldwide Fund for Nature
Panda House, Wayside Park, Godalming, Surrey GU7 IQU
    Tel. 0483 426 444
WWF is the largest private international nature conservation organization. It exists to promote public awareness of conservation problems and raises funds for the protection of threatened species and environments.

Field Studies Council
Information Office, Preston Montford, Montford Bridge, Shrewsbury SY4 IHW
    Tel. 0743 850674
The council organizes a wide range of residential and day courses in Britain and abroad. Subjects include general interest, ecology and conservation, flowers and plants, birds and animals, landscape and climate, painting and drawing, photography and crafts, and stained glass in Paris and Chartres.

The British Butterfly Conservation Society (BBCS)
Tudor House, Quorn, Loughborough, Leics LE12 8AD
    Tel. 0509 412870
There are BBCS branches throughout the country and membership will involve you in field trips to observe and photograph butterflies; informal meetings and talks; working parties for practical conservation work and special events such as butterfly festivals.

Scottish Field Studies Association
Kindrogan Field Centre, Enochdhu, Blairgowrie, Perthshire PHIO 7PG
    Tel. 0250 81286
The association runs courses in natural history and the countryside, including botanical drawing and Highland walks.

Wine

English Vineyards Association
38 West Park, London SE9 4RH
  Tel. 081-857 0452

The association represents the interests of viticulture in England and Wales and can supply a list of English vineyards currently open to the public. The majority of people interested in planting vines with a view to commercial enterprise start in a small way, the average size of an English vineyard being just under four acres. No financial return can be expected until the fifth year, after the fourth year's fruit has been made into wine and sold. There are neither tax concessions nor government grants for the viticulturist and it will cost up to £6,000 an acre – *excluding* the price of the land – to establish a vineyard and well over £500 per annum for maintenance. The English Vineyards Association is able to offer general advice and to put a potential grower in touch with expert opinion and to forward lists of varieties and suppliers of vines and of vineyard and winery equipment. It publishes a bimonthly journal free of charge to members and associates.

The English Wine Centre
Drusilla's, Freepost (BR1 16), Alfriston, Polegate, E Sussex
BN26 5BR

As well as a restaurant, there is a small demonstration vineyard, wine cellars and a wine museum. The annual English Wine and Regional Food Festival takes place on the first weekend in September.

International Wine and Food Society
108 Old Brompton Road, London SW7
  Tel: 071-370 0909

Membership of the society brings together men and women who share an interest in gastronomy. All activities are designed to raise standards of selection, preparation and service of good food and wine. The society is organized into local branches which arrange regular events including dinners, tastings, lectures and gastronomic weekends and tours. There is an annual festival and the clubhouse (190 Queen's Gate, South

Kensington) offers members accommodation and *haute cuisine* in central London.

World Wine Tours Ltd
Drayton St Leonard, Oxfordshire OX10 7BH
   Tel. 0865 891919
Offers opportunities to visit the world's best known vineyards. All tours are led by wine experts.

Writing

The Royal Society of Authors
84 Drayton Gardens, London SW10 9SB
   Tel. 071–373 6642
Offers a wide range of services to professional writers, including legal advice and a special retirement benefits scheme which takes into account the fluctuating nature of an author's income.

The Poetry Society
21 Earl's Court Square, London SW5 9DE
   Tel. 071–373 7861
Anyone interested in writing, reading or listening to poetry will find the society a fund of information and activity. A criticism service is offered to those who would like to have their work assessed.

Reading

Below are just a few examples of the many books available on writing and publishing:

Michael Legat, *Writing for Pleasure and Profit*, Robert Hale, 1986

B. Turner, ed., *The Writer's Handbook*, Macmillan, 1990

The Writers' and Artists' Year Book, A. & C. Black, London, annual. An essential reference book.

S. Robinson, ed., *Guide to Literary Prizes, Grants and Awards in Britain and Ireland*, 6th ed., Book Trust, 1990

Reading and Criticism Service

For people who are interested in writing, the magazine *Writer's Monthly* (18–20 High Road, London N22 6DN; tel. 081–888 1242) has useful information and advice for the beginner and the experienced writer. It also offers a service whereby the aspiring writer can have work read and reviewed by a professional author. The cost of the service will depend on the nature of the manuscript, the length and the subject matter.

See also the Poetry Society, above.

THE VOLUNTARY SECTOR

Traditionally, the voluntary sector in Britain has been dominated by the middle-aged middle classes. Politically, too, it is regarded with hostility by the left who see it as a tool of Tory governments anxious to cut back on social spending. But now, with the increase in the numbers of active retired people who derive satisfaction from helping in their communities or from being involved in some kind of voluntary work which reflects their particular interests, this old portrait of the wealthy, idle, well-intentioned 'do-gooder' is rapidly changing. The opportunities for training and types of work available as a volunteer are almost limitless.

'Thanks', No Thanks!

'Thanklessness,' a spokeswoman at the Volunteer Centre told me, 'often makes volunteers drop out.' It is human nature to be discouraged by ingratitude: 'Is that all the thanks we get?', '. . . and after all I've done for her' are phrases which commonly express the hurt and disappointment of being let down by an ungrateful recipient. But the volunteer comes to recognize that reserve or even hostility from clients is usually a positive sign and more often than not means that a good job has been done. When people learn to cope on their own again, they do not always wish to be reminded of the times when they were forced to ask for help.

However, although the volunteer may not receive much in

the way of gratitude or congratulations, the job satisfaction and personal pleasure derived from helping and caring for others is usually reward enough for people who choose to give their skills and services free.

A Round Peg for a Round Hole

Finding the right job to suit your needs and interests is the most important criterion to consider when looking around for work in the voluntary sector. If the volunteer has a particular skill or professional training – in engineering, medicine or administration for example – then the search will probably be straightforward, but one of the pleasures of voluntary work is the opportunity which exists to train without cost for something entirely different or to become involved in a new occupation which requires no training at all.

In the first instance it is necessary to ask yourself where your main interests and abilities lie and how much time you have to devote to voluntary work on a regular basis. Contacts with the public happen in a variety of ways; do you enjoy close personal relationships with individuals or do you feel more comfortable keeping people at arm's length? Are you prepared to learn a specific skill or would you feel happier to be used as a volunteer in a more general way?

Initially at least, involvement is likely to be dictated by what is going on in your community and the distances you are prepared or are able to travel.

First Steps

Locally, there are a number of different routes you can take towards finding suitable work in the voluntary sector. The Yellow Pages or local phone book will have information under 'Volunteers' or 'Voluntary'. Councils for Voluntary Service or Rural Community Councils, Volunteer Bureaux (in some areas), Citizens Advice Bureaux, public libraries, Adult Education Centres and even Job Centres will all have information on the kind of voluntary work available in the area.

The organizations described below can help complete the picture with information on job opportunities nationally.

Voluntary Work – an Example

If, at a local level, you are unable to find voluntary work which interests you, there is always the chance of starting a new service yourself. The Beauty Care and Cosmetic Camouflage scheme operated by the British Red Cross is just one example of how the volunteer can become a pioneer. In this instance, volunteers are trained in beauty-care skill by experienced members of the Red Cross at a local branch or centre. If training is not possible locally, the welfare organizer will direct the volunteer to the nearest source. Once the training is complete, it is possible to initiate the scheme in your own area.

This is how Gillian Davis, chief organizer of the scheme, described the job:

Beauty care essentially means cleansing people's faces, using a little bit of make-up if they want it and looking after their hands. It's a free service which we take into residential homes, day centres, hospices, hospitals – anywhere it might be needed. It gives people pleasure and we hope makes them feel better. It works wonderfully well for the young disabled who care very much what they look like. Men who have been victims of a stroke and have perhaps lost the use of an arm are especially pleased with the hand-care service. It's not easy to cut your own nails on both hands under those circumstances. Older women with arthritis like the opportunity of choosing a nail varnish colour even if they end up by opting for their customary colourless version, but what they really enjoy is the hand massage. We have begun to train volunteers to teach the blind how to apply make-up. We've discovered various fairly foolproof ways in which they can apply blusher, eye make-up and lipstick. We give them a work-tape which they can stop and start according to directions.

Camouflage care is part of the same service but it is very different work and we only recruit trainees who have first become experienced in the hand-care and beauty treatment. They must have the personality, confidence and sensitivity to cope with almost any situation. It's too late to discover you can't stand the job when you are actually faced with the client. By using specially blended make-up, they must attempt to disguise the disfiguring effects of road-accident scars, birthmarks, burns after extensive skin grafting, facial cancers after mutilating surgery, and now increasingly, of Kaposi's sarcoma, the form of skin cancer associated with AIDS. Patients are referred to the Red Cross and in turn, the volunteer trains them to apply their own camouflage, which is actually available on an NHS prescription. The work is extraordinarily effective and very rewarding. It boosts people's self-image and allows them to go about their daily lives without the feeling that others are going to judge them by their appearance. In the case of an African woman with vitiligo, for example, in certain social settings it would immediately be concluded she had leprosy; and no man visiting his local pub wants to advertise the fact that he has AIDS.

No Need to be Out of Pocket

No one should be deterred from volunteering by lack of funds. A booklet, 'All Expenses Paid?', available from the Volunteer Centre (see below), describes the types of expenses and reimbursements which may be claimed by volunteers. These are perfectly legitimate and will not threaten benefit or give rise to any tax liability.

Voluntary Organizations

Below are some of the organizations which provide a useful starting-point for the reader interested in finding out about opportunities in the voluntary sector. It should also be noted that many of the agencies and organizations described in Part III are supported by volunteers.

The Volunteer Centre
29 Lower Kings Road, Berkhamsted, Herts HP4 2AB
  Tel. 04428 73311
The aim of the Volunteer Centre is to encourage volunteering for the benefit both of individuals and of the community as a whole. It provides information, training and support for people who work with volunteers, and offers guidance for those contemplating voluntary work. It is not a placement agency but the centre has ample information which gives the would-be volunteer some idea of the myriad opportunities which exist both in this country and overseas. Their information pack 'So you Want to be a Volunteer?' is especially useful.

International Voluntary Service (IVS)
162 Upper New Walk, Leicester LE4 0QG
  Tel. 0533 549430
IVS is the British branch of Service Civil International (SCI).
Membership is open to all ages. There are branches and
groups throughout western Europe, in Asia and north America
and in Africa. The Development Education and Exchange
Programme sends volunteers to work camps in Africa and
Asia. At home, camps include activities for people with physical
or mental disabilities and conservation or ecology work. The
placement of volunteers on work camps in Britain is handled
by field offices in Scotland and in the north and south of
England.

National Council for Voluntary Organizations (NCVO)
26 Bedford Square, London WC1B 3HU
  Tel. 071–636 4066
The council acts as the voice of the voluntary sector in England.
Members include the largest national voluntary organizations
and the network of 208 councils for voluntary service which
operate at the local level; it is constantly in touch with thousands
of smaller groups in every town and village in the country.
Their membership leaflet gives an indication of the huge range
of opportunities which exist for the volunteer.

British Red Cross
9 Grosvenor Crescent, London SW1X 7EJ
  Tel. 071–235 5454
There are ninety-six branches in the UK and 1,200 centres
serving local neighbourhoods. There are opportunities in ambu-
lance and first-aid work, nursing, transport, charity shops,
administration, community and residential care.

Voluntary Service Overseas
37 Putney Bridge Road, London SW15
  Tel. 081–780 2266
VSO places volunteers, usually between the ages of twenty-
one and sixty-five, in full-time jobs in Third World countries
for a minimum of two years. Technical skills or a professional
qualification are required, together with work experience in

relevant areas. A maintenance allowance is related to local salaries and there is an overseas travel and clothing allowance.

Charity Appointments
3 Spital Yard, Bishopsgate, London E1 6AQ
   Tel. 071–247 4502

Charity Recruitment
The Garden Studios, 11–15 Betterton Street, London WC2H 9BP
   Tel. 071–379 0344

Reading

Volunteer Work: A Comprehensive Guide to Medium- and Long-term Voluntary Service (1986) 4th ed., revised by Hilary Sewell, Central Bureau for Educational Visits and Exchanges, 1986

Working Holidays: A Comprehensive Annual Guide to Short-term Paid and Voluntary Vacation Jobs in Britain and Overseas, Central Bureau

Voluntary Agencies Directory, Bedford Square Press, 11th ed., 1989

BACK TO BUSINESS

Starting Your Own Business

High interest rates do not encourage new businesses and 1990 saw a sharp increase in the number of firms going broke. In that year, the policy-holders of the trade insurance group, Trade Indemnity, recorded 978 business failures between January and March as against 628 in 1989 – an increase of 56 per cent. By the end of August 1990, the total number of companies falling into receivership was 2,365 compared with the figure of 1,499 for the whole of 1989.

Cycling for Softies was started in 1981 by Roy and Susi Madron. Although this now highly successful business started to make a profit in its second year, at the end of the first year the company's losses totalled £14,000 and it took the Madrons the following nine months to persuade a bank to give them a loan. Their experience of their initial problems prompts Susi Madron to offer the following advice to anyone considering starting their own business:

There are two main points to consider, the idea and the accounts, and neither should be looked at separately. The idea may be brilliant, but without sufficient financial back-up it will be no more than an expensive dream. It is so easy to make the mistake of underestimating the capital needed, especially if you are offering a service. You must plan ahead and envisage the company in five years' time. Work out the sum you think is appropriate and treble it. There is always the temptation to rush off and buy a posh car when the loan comes through. We bought a bicycle! Energy, enthusiasm and commitment are the vital ingredients which will break through most barriers, including the bank, which eventually offered to support us. Health is an important consideration. Small businesses are very hard work, and illness can be a serious setback.

The Madrons began their cycle-touring company with an enormous advantage in that they are a husband-and-wife team and in the early days Roy was in full employment with a steady income, meaning that whatever happened to the company there was always money coming into the home to support the couple and their three children. When it comes to lending money, banks are ultra-conservative, and despite what they say in their advertisements, they neither 'listen' very attentively, nor are they particularly 'friendly' to single women who come to them for a loan, however sound their projects.

Rowena Paxton, winner of the 1990 Good Housekeeping/ National Westminster Bank Enterprising Women Award, founded Veterinary Employment Services on her own following the death of her husband. She was no exception to this rule of prejudice. She went to see her bank manager to inform him of her intention to start a business, but did not ask him for a loan at the time, preferring to wait until it was needed. In the event, the loan was not required. Some time later, the manager moved to a different branch and she met him again at a local social function. He told her that, at the time of her visit, he thought her business had no chance of success and would last about six months. Would he though have granted her a loan?

'He was like a politician', Mrs Paxton laughed. 'He wouldn't commit himself, but I felt he would only have done so if my father had guaranteed it.'

Mrs Paxton's experience of building a small business from scratch provides a useful example of the progress and pitfalls involved:

> As a vet my husband was self-employed, so apart from a £64 per week widow's pension which I received for six months, I had no income and two young children to support. Just before my husband died, we had sold our home in Scotland, so my first panic-stricken thoughts were 'where do I live and what am I going to do?' Fortunately, the proceeds from the house sale allowed me to take the first step and buy a roof over our heads. Under the circumstances, I thought it was most essential to provide stability for the children by finding some sort of work to do from home so that I could be there to look after them.
>
> My own work experience was rather limited. I had once had a job as an interviewer in an employment agency. Other than that, I had assisted my husband and knew my way round the veterinary world. We had travelled extensively in the Far East and Australia and had worked in a practice in Africa for a couple of years. We had often discussed the fact that there seemed to be a niche in the market for a veterinary locum agency, so when I was confronted with this awful situation, I remembered our conversations together and decided to look into the possibilities. The idea was unique at the time and I was excited by the fact that as a service it seemed to have great potential.
>
> My immediate need was a ready income for day-to-day living. I had no capital to invest and could not afford to take the risk of borrowing money. Huge overheads were out of the question. Everything had to be done on a shoestring. Working from home meant obtaining a Department of Employment licence

and permission from the council. My dad gave me an
old electric typewriter and an unwanted desk and my
bedroom doubled as the office for the first two years.
I splashed out on an answerphone, which was essential.

In the first place I had to sell the idea to veterinary
practices. I had to convince them to use an agency
when they wanted to find a locum. I did a direct-mail
shot to all the veterinary practices in the country. I
went to the library and photocopied seventy yellow
pages, shared them out amidst as many friends as I
could, who in turn hand-wrote all the envelopes and
stuck down two thousand stamps, because I wanted
them to be read. They had to look like personal mail
because vets get so much junk through the post, it
just gets thrown straight into the bin.

The next step was aimed at getting local vets on to
my books, so I advertised in the profession's weekly
paper, the *Veterinary Record*. This kind of advertising
costs very little. A short ad amounted to about £10–
15 a week. The response was tremendous. At this
stage, I would say my outgoings were about £700.
Postal costs were kept down with the help of the
government allowance to small businesses. Within
three months, I began to see a profit.

Most of our potential locums come over here from
Australia or New Zealand for a two-year working
holiday. I interview them at home and find them a job
with a vet who by now has probably come to know
me personally, since I try to visit as many practices
nationwide as possible. Now I employ a number of
part-time mums during the week and I am able to
take three weeks' holiday a year.

When I started out, there were no competitors;
now there are four. When I saw my first competitor's
advertisement in the *Veterinary Record*, it was like
a bullet to my stomach. I was devastated. But much
to my surprise, it has made no difference to my
business at all. In fact, it has been helpful, because I
had no guidelines as to what fees to charge. When I

discovered their charges were higher than mine, I thought that if the vets are prepared to pay more money for the service, then I should increase my fees. I think I was right to begin by keeping them low though; you can always put them up, but it looks like failure to reduce them suddenly. It is also a healthy situation for clients to have someone else with whom they can compare your services. In the end, you don't lose them. You just have to be the best.

Mrs Paxton agreed with Susi Madron that people who are thinking of starting a small business should make health an absolute priority. Obtaining a private health insurance was her first major investment. 'If anything goes wrong, you just don't have the time to join the National Health waiting-list, and if you're not insured against ill health, how are the bills going to be paid when you are off sick for a couple of months?' she said.

Both women agreed that it is not so important to have an original idea as to be quite certain there is a market for the product or service you are offering. It is also vital to enjoy the work involved and have tremendous enthusiasm for the project. Anything less will lead to lack of commitment and ultimately to failure.

To start any business it is necessary to be prepared to take certain calculated risks, but if these include plunging all the precious retirement savings into a new venture without the security of a regular income, it would be wise to shelve the idea unless alternative funding can be found.

One of the most accessible guides to starting your own business is Rosemary Brown's *Good Retirement Guide* (Bloomsbury Publishing, annual).

The *Guide*, updated each year, covers simply and concisely the following areas in the chapter on starting a business: the legal aspects of business; alternative ways of getting started; taxation; key budget changes affecting small businesses; national insurance; your responsibilities as an employer; employment legislation; trading regulations; finding suitable premises; insurance; marketing; raising finance; and sources of advice and training.

The Complete Guide to Managing Your Business (available from Christopher Stopford, 39 Osborne Villas, Hove, East Sussex, tel. 0273 821499) is more detailed but also more expensive. It offers comprehensive advice on all aspects of running a business and is updated throughout the year. The cost of the manual and the subscription are tax deductible.

'Starting and Running Your Own Business' and 'Services for Small Business' are available free from the Employment Department's Small Firms Service.

Organizations Which Can Help

The following list of organizations represent small business interests and offer a range of services from general help, training and low-cost consultancy to free advice on all aspects of starting a small business:

Small Firms Service at the Employment Department
Business and Enterprise Branch, Employment Department, Training Agency, Moorfoot, Sheffield S1 4PQ
    Tel. 0742 593231
The Scottish and Welsh Development Agencies provide the Small Firms Service in Scotland and Wales, and Northern Ireland is served by the Department of Enterprise Development. For further details, telephone Freefone Enterprise 0800 222 999.

Alliance of Small Firms and Self-Employed People Ltd
33 The Green, Calne, Wilts SN11 8DJ
    Tel. 0249 817003

Association of Independent Businesses
Independence House, 133 Copeland Road, London SE15 3SP
    Tel. 071-277 5158

Confederation of British Industry
Small Firms Division, Centre Point, 103 New Oxford Street, London WC1A 1DU
    Tel. 071-379 7400

Forum of Private Business
Ruskin Chambers, Drury Lane, Knutsford, Cheshire WA16 6HA
    Tel. 0565 4467

Institute of Directors
116 Pall Mall, London SWIY 5ED
   Tel. 071-839 1233

*National Federation for the Self Employed and Small
Businesses Ltd*
140 Lower Marsh, London SEI 7AE
   Tel. 071-928 9272

Rural Development Commission
141 Castle Street, Salisbury, Wilts SPI 3TP
   Tel. 0722 336 255

Women's Enterprise Development Agency (WEDA)
Aston Science Park, Love Lane, Aston Triangle, Birmingham
B7 4BJ
   Tel. 021-359 0178

A Few Suggestions

The following are just a few of the areas in which small
businesses thrive. Ideas will depend largely on personal interests and local facilities but again, as a starting-point, I would
recommend Rosemary Brown's *Good Retirement Guide*. As an
initial investment, it is well worth the modest price.

The A to Z of Self-employment by Sidney Bloch (Buchan &
Enright, 1989) is also useful.

Agriculture

Farm Shop and Pick-Your-Own Association
Agriculture House, Knightsbridge, London SWIX 7NJ
   Tel. 071-1235 5077

Agricultural Development and Advisory Service (ADAS)
Ministry of Agriculture, Fisheries and Food, Nobel House,
17 Smith Square, London SWIP 3JR
   Tel. 071-238 5745

Hotels and catering

Hotel Career Centre
43 Norwich Avenue West, Bournemouth, Dorset BH2 6AJ
   Tel. 0202 291877

Tourism

The addresses of the tourist boards will be found under Holidays, p. 201.

A New Career?

For specialist employment agencies and careers guidance turn to Part III, Careers in Retirement.

Pensions and National Insurance

It is possible to defer a pension for up to five years after retirement age. '*Your State Pension and Carrying On Working*' Age Concern's Factsheet No. 19, describes the current situation for people who wish to carry on working after sixty or sixty-five. (See also Chapter 4.)

6 Health: Taking Care of Yourself

In the second half of life it pays to be cautious about health. It is a fact, for example, that more women between the ages of forty and fifty-five die of breast cancer than from any other cause, so women over fifty, if they do not already do so, should begin to think about having regular check-ups (see p. 249). A quarter of all heart attacks occur in people under the age of sixty-five. A healthy heart pumps about as efficiently in late middle age as it does in a young adult; it is not age which causes damage but cardiovascular diseases, which in the majority of cases can be prevented by putting into practice an exercise and dietary regime designed to ward off the symptoms (see p. 259).

Stress is a major factor in the second half of life. For the first time we may be troubled by unfamiliar aches and pains. Lapses of memory can give rise to panic. It is likely that we will be forced to consider the problems of ill health as they affect our elderly parents, and there are few more stressful experiences than having to care for a parent or spouse with a terminal illness. Anxiety, depression and the distressing physical conditions which are often symptoms of stress can be hard to shake off without help.

Choosing a Doctor

Fear about one's own health drains both self-confidence and morale. The antidote is a doctor whose opinion we trust, who listens carefully to what we have to say about ourselves, who gives us an appropriate examination and who does not treat us as though we had the understanding and the brain of a gnat. Where and how do we find such a paragon? It is not always easy. The present system, which is supposed to encourage general practitioners to work more cost-effectively and efficiently, does not necessarily involve a happy relationship between patient and doctor. At large National Health Service clinics, a request to see the particular doctor under whom a patient is registered can often mean several days' wait before an appointment becomes available. In the more-than-likely event that the attention of a doctor is required immediately, it means that in the course of a year it is quite possible to see a different practitioner on every visit. This is all very fine if the complaints are relatively minor and the patient does not feel the need to be supported, but in middle and old age, when health becomes more vulnerable to attack, it is essential for both physical and mental well-being to feel the security of being cared for by a doctor who knows the patient as a person and not just as another anonymous ailment. It is even more essential if that patient happens to be living alone.

I asked a ninety-two-year-old woman what advice she would give to those in the process of changing their doctors: 'When it comes to choosing a doctor, always opt for the youngest one in the practice. He knows the latest things and hasn't had time to get bored with the job!' She warned: 'Some doctors don't like old people. You've got to find someone who's sympathetic and understands the problems which older people have.'

Her advice would seem to bear out the findings of Professor Anthea Tinker and her colleagues at the Institute of Gerontology. According to Professor Tinker, the service offered by general practitioners to their older patients is 'very patchy'. 'Teaching is a lot better in medical schools now and some doctors are very good; others are simply not interested in old people and these practitioners are still saying to patients, "Oh, it's your age", without bothering to listen to their problems.'

The unfairness of life is such that if a patient has enough money, the choice of a general practitioner in private practice in a large urban area is extremely wide. It is not that GPs in the private sector are better at their job than those working for the National Health Service: it is simply that they have more time to spend on each patient, and therefore more time to get to know them as individuals and to understand their particular needs. But their time costs money – up to £50 for half an hour's consultation.

Changing Your General Practitioner

The government's proposals for 'a new National Health Service' are already being put into operation throughout the country. One such proposal suggested in a leaflet produced by the Department of Health in 1989,[39] was supposed to give the patient greater freedom of choice and encourage general practitioners to offer a better service, 'because their pay will be increasingly related to the number of patients they attract'. In the early 1990s, stories are emerging of doctors turning patients away because their problems are too time-consuming and therefore not cost-effective. It is not a climate which is likely to encourage unhappy, dissatisfied patients to risk a move.

Patients' Rights

Patients have the right to complain about treatment from a doctor, dentist or optician. In the first instance, complaints should be made to the local Community Health Council (in England and Wales), the local Health Council (in Scotland) or the district committee of the area Health and Social Services Board (in Northern Ireland). The Citizens Advice Bureau is another source of help and advice. Telephone numbers and addresses are in local directories and libraries. It is important to pursue the matter as soon as possible after the event, because strict time-limits are involved.

The Health Service Ombudsman

Complaints against a health service authority for maladministration or for an improperly provided service which has resulted in hardship or injustice may be taken to the Health Service Ombudsman after first reporting the matter to the Health Authority or Family Practitioner Committee. For this initial procedure, advice and help may be obtained from the local Community Health Council.

The Health Service Ombudsman can be contacted at Church House, Great Smith Street, London SWIP 3BW (tel. 071-212 6271).

The Pharmacist

The more reliant a person becomes upon medication, the more important it is to shop around for a sympathetic pharmacist. It is one thing to drop a prescription for antibiotics into a chain-store pharmacy and collect it an hour or so later without communicating with anyone other than the sales assistant; it is quite another to hand it over to the man or woman personally responsible for making up the prescription, who knows you well and who will be able to ensure that you understand the instructions involved. Those who have to take a number of different drugs at regular intervals during the day will know how difficult it is on occasion to remember to take the right dosage at the right time. A telephone call to a familiar pharmacist will go a long way towards restoring confidence. In a crisis where, for example, a patient runs out of an urgently required medicine and is unable to visit the surgery, a pharmacist who knows you will be able to arrange a new prescription with your doctor over the telephone. If you are concerned about the effects of a particular drug or the dosage prescribed by your GP, the pharmacist is an obvious source of advice and information.

Prescription Charges

The NHS charge is £3·40 (1991), with total exemption for women over sixty years old and men over sixty-five. The charge has now become so high that it is possible to pay more for a medicine prescribed by a doctor than for the same medicine bought over the counter. Nevertheless, the prescription rate is still very cheap compared to the charges made for medication to private patients. A long-term condition like glaucoma, for example, can cost the private patient around £16 a month. Antibiotics, too, are particularly expensive.

Since most patients who visit a GP in private practice are already enrolled in the NHS, many – especially those on regular medication for chronic illness – solve the problem of expense by asking their private GP to forward details of the prescription to their NHS doctor. He in turn will then convert the prescription – but this assumes the willingness on both sides to cooperate. To date, there is no insurance plan which covers the service of GPs.

For people using the NHS who require multiple prescriptions over a period of time – more than five items in the next four months or fourteen items in the next year – money can be saved by applying for a season ticket in advance. Applications forms are available from the chemist. Help with prescription charges is available for patients suffering from some forms of chronic disease and for people on a low level of income or who are receiving income support. Leaflet P11, 'NHS Prescriptions', from the Post Office or doctor's surgery, will indicate whether you are entitled to exemptions.

Hospitals – Is There Really Freedom of Choice?

It is difficult to discuss matters concerning freedom of choice when in 1989 there were around 800,000 people waiting for hospital treatment but, in theory at least, a family doctor can now refer a patient to any NHS hospital or consultant in the land. The reality, however, is somewhat different. Apart from a few areas of the country – parts of East Anglia, Wessex and Birmingham for example – in which experiments in Health Service practices are being conducted, family doctors generally prefer to use the hospital facilities with which they are most familiar and the consultants whose quality and skills they trust. But there is another reason why the new referral system does not seem to be working. According to a report in the *Independent*,[40] growing numbers of hospitals are refusing to take patients from outside their catchment areas. (See also Part III, Health Services – the NHS, for details of the *Guide to Hospital Waiting Lists*, 1989.)

Private Health Insurance – Different Companies, Different Deals

The addresses of the two largest medical insurance companies in the UK, Private Patients Plan (PPP) and the British United Provident Association (BUPA), can be found in Part III, Health Services – The Private Sector. In both companies, the costs are age-related, with a great difference in monthly payments between the youngest and the oldest groups. The lowest rates for maximum coverage with PPP, for example, are for people up to the age of twenty-four – £32·10 per month – whereas the same coverage for an eighty-year-old man or woman costs up to £150 per month. The rates vary, however, according to the particular schemes available, and PPP does offer a Retirement Health Plan which has no upper age limit. BUPA has introduced a new scheme 'designed to offer the essential elements of private hospital cover to people on a budget'. Again age-related, it costs from around £8 to 27 per month and is not available to those over the age of seventy-five.

BUPA and PPP are only two examples of a massive industry which offers older subscribers a limited insurance coverage for very high prices. If private health care is being considered, it is essential to shop around and, before making a decision, make sure you know exactly what the insurance plan covers and *what it does not*. (See also Chapter 4, Finance.)

PHYSICAL WELL-BEING

An Annual Check-up

Preventive medicine is one of the great steps forward in the history of modern medicine, yet many people fear an annual check-up in case it reveals a health problem which they did not know existed. Discovered in their earliest stages, many forms of cancer are curable. Full blood tests and analysis of the urine can reveal signs of diabetes (a common illness in the second half of life) and a raised cholesterol level – usually controlled by a change in diet – can warn of the possible danger of stroke or heart disease. Newly developed ultrasound screening techniques harmlessly produce clear pictures of the pelvic organs. Why wait until it is too late?

Screening for breast cancer is to be made available through all local health authorities by 1991 for women between the ages of fifty and sixty-four. Screening for cancer of the cervix (cervical smear test) is available on the NHS to women of all ages but the organization of the programme is often rather cumbersome. One Midlands health authority, for example, summons a third of the women in its area each year over a period of three years. Thereafter, those women whose initial smear test is negative are offered an appointment every five years. The well-woman service which takes place at the same time as the cervical smear test is fairly rudimentary (urine test, blood pressure and brief check of heart and lung function by stethascope). As a service, it is better than nothing, but its limitations are obvious.

In contrast, an annual check-up in the private sector for a woman over thirty-five may include mammography, full blood tests, cervical smear tests, hearing and sight tests, checks on lung functioning, an electrocardiogram and consultations with both a physician and a gynaecologist. The cost for this service will be around £350.

Smoking

Coronary heart disease (CHD) is the leading cause of death in most developed countries and studies carried out by the Imperial Cancer Research Fund in Oxford have shown that one third of all deaths from CHD in middle-aged men and women are attributable to cigarette smoking. Diseases of the lung – cancer, emphysema and bronchitis – are unquestionably linked to smoking. Smoking is also known to cause loss of libido. However, research suggests that 'those who stop smoking before they have cancer or serious heart or lung disease can avoid much of the excess risk of death from smoking that they would have suffered if they had continued. The longer the period of cessation, the greater the diminution of risk.'[41]

Richard Peto, Director of the Imperial Cancer Research Fund, points to a distinction between pipe and cigar smoking and cigarettes: 'In the UK and the USA, cigarettes appear to have a far greater effect than pipe or cigar tobacco does, and so the switch earlier this century from pipes to cigarettes has produced vast increases in lung cancer rates. The reasons for this difference are not adequately known, especially as the smoke from pipes and cigars is about as carcinogenic for laboratory animals as that from cigarettes.'[42]

Suggestions as to why cigarettes should be more harmful

than pipes or tobacco include the fact that pipe and cigar smokers don't inhale to the same extent as cigarette smokers. Also thought to be significant are the differences involved in the curing processes of the two types of tobacco.

Giving up

For the addicted smoker, giving up the habit can seem an insurmountable task. It may not be possible to achieve without help. Part III, Addictions, lists a number of agencies which the reader can turn to for help and advice.

Alcohol

The more research unearths about the dangers of alcohol, the more depressing the news is for social drinkers. A woman who drinks two and a half glasses of wine with her evening meal daily would not normally be regarded as having an alcohol problem, neither would a man who drinks a couple of pints of beer at lunch each day and shares half a bottle of wine with dinner. Yet both drinkers are placing themselves at considerable risk. Their weekly intake is above the safe limit which is up to 21 units for men and up to 14 units for women. The *Sunday Times* Magazine of 19 February 1989 published an analysis, by Dr Ian Robertson, Principal Clinical Psychologist at Astley Ainslie Hospital, Edinburgh, of the effects of regular drinking. The table overleaf is based on their research.

Men drinking between 21 and 50 units and women drinking between 14 and 35 units of alcohol a week are steadily increasing their chances of suffering liver damage and greatly increasing their chances of suffering a stroke, especially if they binge.

Men who drink more than 50 units and women more than 35 units risk cancer of the oesophagus, high blood pressure, stroke, loss of libido and impaired memory function. If heavy drinking is combined with smoking there is more chance of developing cancers of the mouth and larynx. A man who drinks more than 10 units a day is 117 times more likely to suffer from cirrhosis of the liver than is a moderate drinker, while for a woman drinking over 50 units a week there is a fourteen-fold increase in the risk of liver damage; she is also more susceptible to cancer of the breast.

Table of Units of Alcohol

Amount	Units
1 glass low-strength table wine	1
1 glass sherry	1
1 glass port	1
1 pub measure of spirits ($\frac{1}{6}$ gill)*	1
1 glass champagne	$1\frac{1}{2}$
1 glass ordinary-strength table wine	$1\frac{1}{2}$
1 small home measure of spirits ($\frac{1}{4}$ gill)	$1\frac{1}{2}$
1 pint ordinary draught lager	2
1 pint ordinary-strength draught bitter	2
1 glass top-strength table wine	2
1 pint special draught bitter	3
1 can strong cider	3
1 can strong lager	4
1 bottle low-strength table wine	6
1 bottle champagne	9
1 bottle ordinary-strength table wine	9
1 bottle Martini	11
1 bottle sherry	13
1 bottle port	15

* 1 gill = $\frac{1}{4}$ pint.

Tolerance to alcohol decreases with age so that older people are more inclined to suffer from the physical effects of alcohol, ranging from hypothermia, incontinence, accidents, tremors and the shakes to poor digestion and interrupted sleep patterns. They are also more likely to be taking medication in old age, thereby risking the dangerous combination of alcohol and drugs. Alcohol Concern, in a pamphlet entitled 'Alcohol and Older People: Safer Drinking for the Over 60s', suggests that 'Older people who have been regular drinkers all their lives may need to cut down by at least half. For some older people with particular health problems, especially those on medication, it may be best not to drink at all.'

Social drinking is for so many of us one of life's great pleasures, and although one must be aware of the potentially harmful effects of alcohol, to eliminate it altogether, unless under doctor's orders, is generally unnecessary and may even be unwise: 'Sensible drinking is the norm and should be encouraged. It is important to remember that most people who drink alcohol enjoy it sensibly; the old lady who enjoys the occasional glass of sherry and the old gentleman whose daily treat is a well-nursed half-pint of beer are deriving benefit, rather than harm, from their little indulgence.'[43]

Although very little research has been conducted on the possible physical and psychological benefits of alcohol, an American study which set out to determine the effects of wine on elderly self-sufficient people, found that after one or two 3 oz servings of wine each evening, there was consistent improvement in the quality of sleep, with a trend towards a greater level of energy and accomplishment and signs of improvement in both mood and morale.[44]

Since alcohol in moderation increases the appetite, it is not unreasonable to suggest also that it might be beneficial for those who have lost their enthusiasm for food. One robust seventy-six-year-old widower learning to cope on his own after the death of his wife told me: 'I eat my main meal in the middle of the day, always preceded by a couple of gins and tonics, which I drink while I'm doing the cooking. I'm never hungry to start with, but by the time I've downed the gins, I could eat a horse!'

In the *Professional's Handbook on Geriatric Alcoholism* Deborah L. Sherouse reports that 'one half the American population is in need of treatment for alcohol-related illness'[45] and yet, according to Kathryn Graham of the Addiction Research Foundation at the University of Western Ontario, 'The existing data on prevalence of alcohol abuse among the elderly indicate that there is a very low rate of problems among this group compared to other age groups.'[46] It may be that many heavy drinkers in their fifties and sixties do not, because of the health risks involved, live long enough to stand and be counted among the numbers of elderly, or that alcohol users as they become older find the age-related intolerance to drink quite naturally forces them to cut down their consumption. The evidence is difficult to qualify. However, one does not need a PhD to be sensitive to the fact that the circumstances of some old people could make them especially susceptible to the comforts of the bottle. Alcohol Concern suggests five main reasons, listed below, why some people abuse alcohol in old age. Unfortunately, the elderly, with their increasing intolerance of alcohol, are especially vulnerable to its ill effects if they attempt to drown their sorrows.

Finance – managing on a reduced income can be difficult, especially with high winter fuel bills, and money worries may lead to drinking.

Cold – elderly people feeling the cold may believe a few drinks will warm them up. In fact, alcohol speeds up the loss of body heat.

Loneliness – feeling isolated and lonely, some may drink for comfort without realizing that alcohol is a depressant drug.

Pain/sleeplessness – people often use alcohol to get to sleep, especially if pain keeps them awake. Although alcohol can help to bring on sleep quickly, it usually leads to wakefulness in the night. Sleep patterns may be further upset, leading to more drinking. [But research indicates that sleep is positively enhanced by *moderate* drinking – see above.]

Bereavement – this is the most traumatic of a range of losses felt by older people. Loss of work, dignity, independence are others. Alcohol may be used to fill the gaps that are left.[47]

Drink and/or Drug Abuse: Early Warning Signs

The following symptoms, while they can also be the result of a variety of causes, are very often a sign of heavy drinking or of prescription drug overuse, or a combination of both.

Shakiness, trembling, confusion, loss of memory and incontinence are often associated with dementia, but they may also be signs of alcohol abuse. Restlessness, impaired concentration, fine body tremor and shaking hands could be the clues to an overdose of medication. Frequent falls and accidents can be the result of heavy drinking, as can bad temper, violence and depression. A shuffling gait can indicate drug overuse and/or alcohol abuse. The absence of expression may be the result of Alzheimer's disease – or it could be caused by prescription overuse. Uncontrolled salivation has two main causes – stroke and prescription overuse.

I talked to a group of fifteen men and women between the ages of seventy-one and eighty-four. They came from similar backgrounds, where alcohol consumption was part of a lifelong pattern of 'normal' social behaviour. Their incomes meant that they could all afford to buy as much alcohol as they wanted. To the extent that they depended on alcohol for the comfort and relaxation it brought them, they could be said to be at least psychologically dependent upon it. To them, alcohol was like an old friend, life-enhancing, greatly respected, always welcome, but never too intrusive.

Their doctors were aware of their regular drinking habits but they had not been advised to cut back on consumption unless they had been prescribed medication where alcohol was contraindicated. In one case, one member of the group was asked by her doctor how much she drank at night. 'Two large whiskies', she replied. 'That's fine, that's my nightly ration too,' responded her doctor. 'What brand do you drink?' She named her usual brand of scotch, which, it transpired, was the same as her doctor's. He seemed rather startled: 'But Mrs B.,' he said, 'I don't mean to be impertinent, but surely on your income, you can afford a better quality than that!' 'Now that's what I call an understanding doctor,' his patient added. 'He's right too. I immediately went off and bought a more upmarket blend, which goes down very nicely – much better for the digestion.'

Another member of the group, Mrs S.T., a widow aged eighty, normally drank two large vodkas on the rocks before supper and occasionally a vodka with lunch. She had had two frightening experiences of drunkenness through combining her usual daily alcohol intake with strong tranquillizers. When her doctor explained the dangers of taking the medication with alcohol, she chose to eliminate the tranquillizers and had no further trouble.

Apart from one member, who has drunk a litre of wine a day all his adult life, the group generally said they began to find it necessary to cut down on the consumption of alcohol during their sixties. They found three things in common – first, regularity in terms of the amount of alcohol consumed and the time of day, which tended to coincide with a meal; secondly, they could not take more than their usual amount without feeling adversely affected. (The individual allowances were generally considered satisfying and those who preferred spirits rarely had a glass of wine with their meal. None felt they could drink more than their usual intake without ill effect, even if they wanted to, tending on special occasions to accept soft drinks rather than exceed their daily limit.) Thirdly, all enjoyed the little ritual involved in pouring a drink at the right time and the right moment. It added a certain structure to a sometimes lonely day.

Alcohol Abuse in the Post-retirement Years

While the very limited research material currently available may suggest that alcohol abuse is relatively uncommon in the years from sixty-five onwards, carers of elderly people with drink problems are only too well aware of the realities. Since so many elderly people drink on their own, the true picture of alcohol abuse in this age group may be impossible to determine.

Mr M.B. is aged seventy-five, and has been a widower for five years. His daughter takes up his story:

> My father appeared to cope with the years immediately following my mother's death very well. He was lucky to have my unmarried brother living at home. He has learned to cook and has become quite expert. Apart from feeding himself well, cooking has helped him maintain an active social life.
>
> Dad's routine was to pour himself two pub measures of gin with tonic at lunchtime and three small whiskies in the evening. He had a light supper and took a fourth whisky to bed with him which, he said, helped him to sleep. This was his self-imposed daily allowance, and as far as I could see, he stuck to it rigorously and didn't seem to suffer any ill effects, although I realized that the amount he was drinking daily was well over the top. I was visiting him regularly – about twice a week – when I began to notice the differences in his mood. He was always pleased to see me but sometimes he would be happy and optimistic, while at others, he seemed depressed and irascible. I watched his drinking one lunch time and noticed that he gave himself three gins instead of his usual two and did not use his regular pub measure,

but poured the gin straight from the bottle. At that time in his life, several things had happened to tip the scales. His angina attacks had become more frequent and he was afraid his licence to drive would be revoked. An old friend with a similar history of angina had died eighteen months earlier after driving his car into a ditch during a severe attack. A year ago, two great friends of his youth, who meant a very great deal to him, died of carcinoma of the prostate. Following their deaths, his best friend and companion of years died of a stroke. In the week prior to my last visit, another old friend had died in hospital aged eighty-four. I realized my father was frightened. His pills, ailments and possible death from heart disease were the main topics of conversation. I felt so sorry for him, but how could I, his adult child, come between him and the death of which he was so afraid? It just didn't seem fair to deny him alcohol, which seemed to offer some comfort, however false.

After much discussion with my brother, we decided to inform the family doctor. Because my father's visits to the surgery are frequent, the GP will be able to keep a watchful eye on him and has promised us that if he thinks Dad is drinking too heavily, he will take steps to make sure he cuts down. The doctor is also careful to take his alcohol consumption into account when prescribing medication.

Not all those anxious about the drinking habits of a friend or relative can expect to receive such active cooperation from the patient's GP, however. Dr Keith Palmer, a general practitioner at the University Health Centre in Southampton, writing in the journal *Psychiatry in Practice*, notes:

GPs must also come to terms with their inexperience and lack of expertise in handling problem drinkers. The counselling skills needed to obtain an alcohol history from a patient have been neglected in training. There is no place for judgemental or critical appearances; any lack of empathy and sensitivity on the part of the GP will stifle sensitive disclosures by the patient ... GPs as a body perceive alcoholism as a 'can of worms' that they are loathe to uncover:

problems will be complex and demanding. There is a high level of pessimism regarding outcome, founded on the negative experience of dealing with the few severely dependent alcoholics known to every practice ... GPs take fewer alcohol histories than they should, partly because they do not believe that they will receive a reliable answer.[48]

Exercise

The overwhelming benefits of regular exercise cannot be stressed enough. The combination of the ageing process and reduced physical activity is thought to be largely responsible for a decline in muscle function which leads to the loss of bodily strength. In the United States, surveys have shown that after the age of seventy-four, 28 per cent of men and 66 per cent of women cannot lift objects weighing 10lb (4·5 kg) or over. It is not difficult to see the connection between loss of strength and loss of independence.

Research conducted by Dr William Evans and his team at Tufts University in Boston has revealed that, provided they adopt a regular exercise and weight-training programme, even people in their nineties can become stronger and build up the size of their muscles. Men between the ages of sixty and seventy-two were able to increase their muscle mass by 15 per cent and their strength by 200 per cent, while between the ages of eighty-six and ninety-six, the achievement for both men and women was only slightly less.[49]

It is not reasonable to expect that people in their seventies or eighties who have led very sedentary lives in retirement will suddenly exchange their armchair habitat for an exercise bike in the local gym. Yet two of the best ways to keep fit – walking and swimming – are within the range of almost anyone who is not very severely immobilized. A daily twenty-minute brisk walk has been shown to reduce the risks of heart attacks in both men and women, and steady, regular lengths of the swimming baths exercises and strengthens the muscles in a way suited to people of all ages; since the body is supported by the water, it is especially good for people who are overweight or who suffer from backache, stiffness or disability. Ideally, a regular exercise programme should be adopted in mid-life when it more readily becomes an enjoyable habit rather than a disagreeable daily chore quite likely to be relinquished at the first opportunity. Reluctant exercisers may find an acceptable way to keep fit and active in the variety of opportunities described in Chapter 5, Leisure and Working for Pleasure.

It is not usually necessary to consult the GP in cases where the exercise taken is regular yet fairly undemanding, but if there are any doubts about health, it would be wise to do so just to make sure the plan for action is appropriate.

Reading

The Medical Aspects of Exercise: Benefits and Risks, The Royal College of Physicians, 1991.

Protection against Heart Disease

The earlier a regime of regular exercise, no smoking, low-alcohol consumption and a healthy low-cholesterol diet is adopted, the greater will be the benefit in the long term.

The warning signs of heart disease include persistent high blood pressure (hypertension) and angina (a pain in the region of the heart which occurs when the organ is not being supplied with sufficient oxygenated blood). Since hypertension can be present without always making itself felt, regular blood-pressure checks are advisable, especially in late middle and old age when pressures tend to be slightly raised. People who are unused to exercise should always consult their doctor before embarking on a more demanding physical routine. A half-hour brisk walk daily is really all that is necessary to produce the right results.

Diet – Lowering the Levels of Cholesterol

Excess levels of cholesterol in the blood are known to cause damage to the heart but the fact that there are two kinds of cholesterol – HDL (high-density lipoprotein, which is made in the body and acts to protect the arteries by cleansing them) and LDL (which is artery-damaging and acquired in the diet) – makes the picture somewhat confusing, causing some researchers to suggest that cholesterol is not, after all, to blame for heart disease.

Cholesterol is a fatty alcohol – it is not the same as body fat. It is the highly saturated fats in the diet, such as those listed below, which can raise the blood cholesterol. Therefore, in order to control cholesterol levels, the *type* of fat included in the diet is all-important. Exercise on its own cannot undo the effects of a cholesterol-raising diet.

Egg yolks, offal – particularly liver and brain – red meat, sausages and sausage meats, ham, hard cheeses and cream cheese, butter, cream, lard, vegetable shortening, beef and poultry fat, coconut, palm-kernel and palm oils, and nuts are all high in cholesterol or saturated fat and can raise levels of cholesterol in the blood. You should try to substitute skimmed milk and low-fat dairy products, skinless poultry, lean meat and shellfish, olive oil and polyunsaturated vegetable oil and margarine, but even these should be eaten in moderation.

The following are foods which are beneficial and some of them can actually help to lower the levels of cholesterol in the blood: grains, especially oats and barley; fruits and vegetables, especially carrots, leafy green vegetables and garlic; dried peas and beans; and fish, especially oily fish such as herring, mackerel, trout and salmon.

In April 1990, a report from the British Regional Heart Study findings (directed by Professor Gerald Shaper of the department of clinical epidemiology at the Royal Free Hospital School of Medicine, London) showed that men whose weight increased in middle age, even though they were not necessarily deemed to be overweight, were at greater risk from heart attack and stroke. The study, which involved 7,735 men between the ages of forty and fifty-nine, showed that those who maintained a steady weight – a gain or loss of no more than half a stone over a nine-year period – had the lowest mortality rate.

In Part III, Diet, there is a list of publications which offer further information and suggestions. A sensible diet in combination with regular exercise will help to keep the weight down and the cholesterol levels low.

Skin

A feature of ageing skin is the small brown patches which occur most commonly on the surface skin of the hands and face. Seborrhoeic warts – slightly raised brown patches – may also appear in middle age; they can easily be removed by a dermatologist, who will painlessly 'freeze' them off. Brown patches which contain a small dark area like a black mole are known as lentigo maligna; although malignant, these are completely curable but need immediate treatment to stop them spreading.

Other facial lesions can easily be removed by cauterization – that is, they may be burnt off – provided they are not rooted below the surface of the skin. Moles, for example, require excision, and a dermatologist will usually refer a patient to a plastic surgeon if the mole is on the face, because the latter, with his specialist training, is likely to do the neatest job.

'On the whole, GPs are not keen to refer patients to dermatologists for what they regard as cosmetic work, and they may take some persuading,' one leading dermatologist told me. It is useful to know, however, that private medical insurance will usually pay for work carried out by a dermatologist, but it will not pay for cosmetic surgery except under special circumstances, as for instance in cases where scars are considered to be disfiguring.

Tretinoin (Retin-A)

Sales of this drug (used by acne sufferers for many years) have soared since research in America has shown that it has beneficial results in the treatment of ageing skin. The fine lines which appear on the face as a result of the ageing process are formed by the gradual loss of collagen and elastin. Retin-A stimulates the manufacture of these natural substances, while removing the top layer of skin (epidermis) and so leaving the face looking clean, shiny and smooth. Retin-A is not a cosmetic, it is a drug, and must be used with great caution. If tolerated, the success is quite remarkable and at under £10 for a tube of cream or a bottle of lotion, which should last up to three months if used sparingly, as the manufacturers recommend, it is not expensive. However, Retin-A can only be bought with a doctor's prescription and some unscrupulous British 'specialists' have been charging more than £200 for a course.

Some doctors may be reluctant to prescribe the drug for cosmetic purposes because of the possible side-effects.

Research sponsored by the manufacturers and conducted at the University of Michigan showed that more than nine out of ten patients were forced to stop using Retin-A for a few days after developing skin irritation. For over a quarter of the forty patients in the trial, this was so serious that they had to be given a powerful steroid drug. Three found the side-effects so intolerable that they had to withdraw from treatment altogether.

With Retin-A, the skin becomes photosensitive and must not be exposed to sunlight without maximum protection. The highest sunblock creams are mandatory but even with their use, the skin can become so hypersensitive that sunworshippers may no longer be able to enjoy their god. So why do so many women swear by the use of this drug? One 'fan' explained:

Despite the known side-effects of Retin-A, the evident benefits seemed too good not to give it a chance. My GP recommended using a lotion rather than the cream because it spreads more thinly and is less prone to be overused. He also suggested that I use it at night only rather than twice a day. If too much of the drug is applied, it will leave dry, scaly, red and raw patches. If applied to the lips, it will leave them dry and cracked. After the first week or so's trial, my skin became reddened, lumpy and painful. I stopped using it for a few days until the condition had settled down and then changed my usual cleansing and moisturizing routine, since the adverse effects of the drug suggested an allergic reaction. Using a hypoallergenic unscented soap and toner and a heavy moisturizing cream which combats dryness, together with a UVA sunscreen, my extremely fair, thin, sensitive skin now tolerates the drug very well, with rewarding results. However, it seemed wise not to apply the ultimate test – continued use during a week's skiing holiday in strong sunshine in the high Alps. After the first day, despite being covered in total sunblock, slight signs of facial irritation occurred and for the remainder of the week, I stopped applying Retin-A and continued using the sunblock cream with no ill effects. It was possible to resume treatment immediately following the end of the holiday. The moment my skin shows signs of intolerance – if it begins to feel a bit lumpy or spots appear – I stop using it for a while until it settles down.

In America a new form of the drug, Time-Release Retin-A, is being developed to eliminate or at least lessen its unpleasant side-effects. This involves a topical treatment which releases minute doses over a twenty-four-hour period. If approved, this could be available in 1992.

One of the problems of Retin-A would seem to be the dramatic nature of its success. For those who are able to use it with no ill effects, such success can actually make it addictive. If users feel that by withdrawing it they will begin gaining a few wrinkles, they may be reluctant to stop applying it even when circumstances are inappropriate.

Injectible collagen

Collagen is a natural protein which cushions and supports the skin. As time passes, it is gradually worn away, leaving the facial lines associated with ageing, against which no cosmetic cream however expensive and enticingly packaged is an effective weapon. Zyderm or Zyplast collagen derived from purified animal collagen is injected beneath the surface of the skin and acts like Polyfilla, filling in the lines and plumping out the skin. It is a very effective form of cosmetic treatment for ageing skin but it is expensive and lasts only for a few months before a 'top-up' becomes necessary.

Changes in Appearance: Cosmetic Surgery

To turn the clock back ten years by eliminating the more obvious signs of physical ageing with the help of plastic surgery is not everyone's idea of a viable alternative to the ageing process. In fact, the British attitude in general is to regard face-lifts and hair transplants (see p. 272) as not only laughable but also somewhat revolting. But all this is changing. Requests for various forms of cosmetic surgery are on the increase,

particularly among men who feel threatened in their careers by
their age. A cosmetic surgeon who sees almost as many male
patients as female, told me:

'The image of the successful business man is currently one
in which a man looks in his mid to late thirties. Some business
men feel that looking old loses certain advantages. Too many
lines and wrinkles, and people start suspecting them of going
downhill. It seems as though businessmen, unless they have
reached positions of considerable power and wealth, do not
trust middle age – it is regarded as a weakness.

'There are two categories of people who elect to have cosmetic surgery. The first includes those who are seeking reme-
dial surgery – that is, they want to have corrected something
which they perceive as a blemish – too large a nose, too small
breasts, etc. The second category is one in which people wish
to offset the evidence of ageing. Ten years ago, almost 100 per
cent were those belonging to the first category; now increasingly, they belong to the second. Ten years ago also, cosmetic
surgery was an option open only to the rich and famous. This
is simply not true any more. I am constantly surprised by the
cross-section and breadth of social groups who come to consult
us. Women wanting face-lifts, for example, no longer fit the
stereotypic image of the bored, rich woman with too much
time on her hands. She is more likely to be an ordinary
housewife who has made considerable sacrifices to finance the
operation, or she is likely to have a career in the business world
or the media. Stars like Joan Collins, Tina Turner and Elizabeth Taylor by their glamour, and Jane Fonda and Raquel
Welch with their emphasis on diet and exercise have been
enormously influential. They have demonstrated to women
everywhere that forty is not the time to give up looking great
and fifty is just another beginning.'

For anyone contemplating the use of cosmetic surgery as a
means of changing their appearance, the options are surprisingly wide. What is not wide, however, is the choice of highly
trained specialists to carry out the surgery involved. A market
in which a great deal of money can be made will always attract
its share of 'cowboys'. Even qualified and experienced plastic
surgeons are capable of turning enhancement to disfigurement.
While it must always be remembered that any form of surgery

carries with it an element of risk, that risk can be reduced by choosing the right specialist for the job.

The medical director of a London clinic specializing in cosmetic treatments describes the differences between cosmetic and plastic surgery: 'Plastic surgery is essentially a specific form of surgery concentrating on the skin. The plastic surgeon specializes in plastic and reconstructive surgery after serious trauma – burns or the disfigurement left as a result of major head and neck surgery, for example. As an adjunct to this kind of work, a plastic surgeon might do some cosmetic surgery in his private practice. A cosmetic surgeon has the same training and background as the hospital plastic surgeon, but because he has elected to specialize in cosmetic work, his experience in the particular surgery involved will obviously be greater, because he is performing cosmetic operations daily.

'There is also, I think, a difference in attitude. It's fair to say that some plastic surgeons look down on their colleagues working in the cosmetic field. I have more than once been criticized for doing something trivial, but I find the work immensely rewarding. Not only can cosmetic surgery improve a person's looks but it can also have a quite remarkable effect on their health. It relieves the distress which they might feel about certain aspects of their looks, and gives them a wonderful self-confidence which seems to produce a new lease of life. When I hire the services of a surgeon for cosmetic work, he must obviously be properly qualified but he must also be sympathetic and not seem to despise his patients just because they come to him for a face-lift or a new nose.

'If a patient goes to a plastic surgeon and says, "I should like to have the bags removed beneath my eyes", unless the "bags" appear especially disfiguring to the surgeon, he may be reluctant to perform an operation. He may tell the patient that there really isn't any need for surgery and suggest that he or she comes back in a couple of months so that he can review the case. Plastic surgeons tend to regard voluntary cosmetic operations as unnecessary. A cosmetic surgeon will view the situation somewhat differently. Provided the patient is a suitable candidate for a particular operation and is in good general health, he will point out the elements of risk involved and stress the fact that absolute perfection is impossible to achieve. He will perhaps more readily accept the patient's final decision without erecting barriers.'

If you are contemplating making changes to your appearance which will require cosmetic surgery, the first step must be to seek advice from your general practitioner, if only to make sure that your general health can stand the strain. The second step is to make absolutely certain you understand what the operation involves. Major cosmetic operations can be extremely painful for a week or so after the event, and there is often a good deal of temporary bruising and always some permanent scarring. Some GPs will be helpful and refer their patients to the appropriate consultant, but others will be hostile and will not encourage the idea. A surprising number will not immediately know the name of a plastic surgeon, but they might be persuaded to find out. The British Association of Aesthetic Plastic Surgeons has a list of members all fully qualified to carry out cosmetic surgery. It is essential to know the background and training of the surgeon involved. Some people who describe themselves as 'cosmetic surgeons' have a very dubious background indeed. If in doubt about the qualifications signified by the letters following the name of the consultant, ask your GP for advice and clarification.

Cosmetic operations, unlike the plastic and reconstructive surgery required after accidents or disease, are not available on the National Health Service. The fees are very high, despite the fact that, increasingly, operations are being performed in out-patient clinics, thereby cutting the cost of an overnight stay in hospital. Many patients have saved up for years. One woman told me:

> When I was forty, I decided that I would have a face-lift soon after my fiftieth birthday. I told my husband and children that this is what I was determined to do. They laughed at me of course, but nevertheless, I started saving. Each week, I'd put a little money aside. When I needed new cosmetics, instead of buying my usual expensive brand, I went for the cheapest, purest brand on the market and added the change to my savings. I worked out more or less what I spent on clothes for myself each year and cut

the budget by half, placing 50 per cent into my face-lift account. Occasionally the family would tease me and say things like 'How many wrinkles have you paid for now, Mum?' When the time came, I drew out the necessary £1,500 and had the operation. Everyone was a bit shocked at first, but you can't say I didn't warn them! I couldn't believe the results. It was a wonderful feeling to look into a mirror and not see an old person staring back at me. I looked as old and as cheerful as I felt inside. The operation didn't make me look twenty again, thank goodness, but it did make me look about ten years younger, to the point where my mind could happily accept my body. After a while, the family stopped noticing the difference. I was just 'Mum' again. I will say though that it has had a very positive effect on my husband. He has started taking an interest in me that he hasn't had for years. Our sex life has improved beyond belief.

This woman's experience highlights the positive aspects of cosmetic surgery; if a consultant on close questioning feels that someone wants to alter some aspect of their appearance for the wrong reasons – perhaps, for example, because they hope to save a failing relationship – he is likely to advise against surgery, and indeed refuse to perform it, on the grounds that it will not achieve the desired purpose and may induce psychological trauma in someone who is already distressed and anxious.

Reading

Denise Winn, *Cosmetic Surgery – A Consumer Guide*, Macdonald Optima, 1989

Joanna Gibbon, *The Independent Guide to Cosmetic Surgery*, Newspaper Publishing, 1989 (available from Reader Services Dept, Newspaper Publishing plc, 40 City Road, London EC1Y 2DB)

Hair

Alopecia is the general term used to describe hair loss. White Anglo-Saxon males have a 50 per cent chance of balding by the time they are thirty-five. Known as male-pattern baldness or androgenic alopecia, this quite natural loss is hereditary and is caused by the action of hormones on the hair follicles. Because hormones are involved, baldness is sometimes equated with a loss of libido. Women, although well aware of this myth, find male baldness completely acceptable and certainly do not regard it as unattractive. Most men, it is true, adjust to their changing hairline with wry good humour, but others can be deeply affected by hair loss. They feel that, as a result, they will lose face both in bed and in the office. Men's attempts to hide their baldness behind a toupee or remedy the loss by a hair transplant are often regarded as vain and ridiculous, but hair loss can cause great suffering. One man's mirth is another man's pain.

In the natural process of ageing in both men and women, each hair becomes thinner, that is to say, it actually shrinks in diameter. A woman's hairs are at their thickest around the age of twenty; by the time she is seventy, they may be as fine as they were when she was a baby.

In common, genetic alopecia, two main factors are involved: one is the normal level of the male hormone, androgen – which in menopausal women appears more pronounced because of the decline in oestrogen – and the other is the inherited genetic tendency.

Shock, stress, illness, high fever, surgery and certain drugs can cause heavy loss of hair in both men and women; so too can an inadequate diet and vitamin deficiency. Altered hormone levels during pregnancy and during the menopause can result in sudden, heavy loss of hair, and some women have found that the contraceptive pill similarly affects their hair. However, under all these conditions, the hair loss is usually only temporary and provided the cause is established, the symptoms can be remedied.

Alopecia areata is a different condition; the term is used to describe the sudden hair loss – which may be caused by a disease of the autoimmune system – which can affect men, women and children of all ages. There are three distinct degrees of the disease: 'areata' leaves patches of baldness; 'totalis' applies to sudden total hair loss on the head, and 'universalis' involves total hair loss on both the head and the body.

Although a woman's hair tends to recede at the forehead line and the temples in the same way as a man's as she become older, excessive female baldness is something which is not supposed to happen – but it sometimes does and with devastating results. My mother began to lose her hair at the age of forty when she developed alopecia areata. Typically her hair fell out in patches leaving shiny bald areas over her head. Sometimes it grew back, only to be replaced by a new patch of baldness. In her early fifties, she began to go more generally bald and at the time of her death at seventy, she had no hair at all. She could not bear to wear a wig – she said it made her hot and looked silly – but instead wore a headscarf outside and inside the house. In consequence, she withdrew from social life and was only happy with people who knew and accepted her as she was. As children, we too accepted her as she was but now I regard my own receding hairline with something close to panic.

Trichologist Glenn Lyons, who has specialized in hair for twenty-one years, told me: 'We are seeing a drastic increase in alopecia areata in women. The overwhelming majority of patients we treat lead stressful lives or are involved in stressful relationships or circumstances, and we are becoming more and more convinced that when it comes to looking at causes of the problem, the stress factor is in the foreground of the picture.'

Dr David Fenton at St Thomas' Hospital in London and Dr Rodney Dawber at the Slade Hospital in Oxford were, at the time of writing, the only two consultant dermatologists (skin specialists) in the UK who had chosen to specialize in hair. (Since there are only about 250 dermatologists in the entire country, this low figure is perhaps not so surprising.) Dr Fenton, who treats at least as many women as he does men, is less certain that stress is a factor in the cause of female baldness. 'There is a tremendous pressure on women to continue to look physically attractive as they grow older. They feel it is cosmetically disastrous to lose their hair, but whereas a few years ago they just had to accept the condition and hide it under a wig, now they want to know about the causes of their hair loss and they are more inclined to persuade their GPs to refer them to us for treatment.'

There is no absolute 'cure' for baldness but some of the treatments currently in use can be very successful in helping to promote regrowth in some cases, as those fortunate enough to benefit are only too delighted to testify.

Treatments for Hair Loss

Because of the many possible causes, the right diagnosis in the first instance saves anxiety and money. There are a number of options to explore, both privately and on the NHS. The family doctor can refer a patient to a dermatologist, who in turn will be able to suggest tests which will pick up or eliminate any medical causes for the hair loss. Experienced trichologists may also be able to diagnose the cause of baldness, but because they are not medically qualified they are unable to prescribe some of the drug treatments currently in use.

The two most widely used forms of treatment are anti-androgen hormone therapy and minoxidil. Concerning the external use of hormones, a consultant dermatologist stated: 'Topical anti-androgen therapy has not been shown to work. In theory it should work, but until results from clinical trials have been published, we cannot say it does.' However, in one London hair clinic, trichologists under the guidance of a hormone specialist have used the anti-androgen treatment orally in women with 'some very positive results'. A study of the use of anti-androgen therapy in hair loss is currently being conducted by Dr Rodney Dawber at the Churchill and Slade Hospitals in Oxford.

Minoxidil

This is a powerful drug which was originally prescribed for high blood pressure but was developed as a hair lotion (Regaine) after it was discovered that it caused hair to grow on the heads (and bodies) of balding men. It has been on the market as a hair product in this country since May 1988 and is available on prescription only. It must be used continuously –

that is, for life – or the new hair will fall out, although the resulting loss will be no worse than that which would occur naturally. Minoxidil is not available on the NHS and one month's supply costs around £30.

In cases of common baldness, minoxidil seems to work as well for women as it does for men, but to date official figures for women do not exist. The studies conducted on men showed overall about a 30 per cent response; the drug appeared to be most effective in younger men (under forty) with small areas of baldness of recent origin.

I talked to one man – a fifty-eight-year-old pharmacist who has the advantage of being able to concoct his own lotion free of charge. He described to me his response to minoxidil. 'The results have been quite dramatic,' he said. 'I started to go bald gradually like the rest of my family at about the age of forty-five. I decided to try the drug when it first came on the market. It took about four months for the results to show up but now my hairline is just as it always was when I was young and the hair on the crown of the head is as thick. In contrast, both my brothers have followed the family pattern and become more or less bald and my sister's hair is very thin and her hairline has receded.'

One woman I interviewed began to use minoxidil when she noticed a pronounced loss of hair around the forehead and temples. There was a family history of baldness and her mother had begun to lose her hair in her fifties and was almost totally bald at the age of sixty-five. She said: 'My GP was very sympathetic. He told me that there was no reason why a healthy woman should not use Regaine and after three months the results were astonishing. My hairline has been restored by a visible growth of new hair.'

Diphencyprone

This drug is still experimental and the company producing it does not claim that it is safe for human use. It is not used for common baldness but has been found to have some success in cases of extensive alopecia areata, totalis and universalis. The drug produces an allergic reaction with extreme sensitivity, which results in an eczematous rash through which the hair is seen to regrow.

PUVA

A plant extract called psoralens sensitizes the scalp to ultraviolet (UV) light; UVA is then applied, which can induce the hair to regrow. (This treatment is also used for psoriasis.)

Kevis

This is one of a number of hair products available from chemists without a prescription. It was developed by an Italian consultant in clinical dermopharmacology, Dr Renato Venafra, and aims to reduce hair loss in men and women by restoring natural nutrients in which the hair follicle has become deficient, so encouraging thicker growth. It does not actually restore hair but if used early enough it can help to prevent further loss. Two ten-week treatment periods are required each year and the four packs for each treatment cost just over £100.

Cosmetic Treatment for Thinning Hair

Careful hair tinting makes the hair look thicker. Gels and hair mousses also help to create an illusion of bulk.

Hair Transplant

For this operation, doctors advise their patients not to go to private cosmetic clinics which advertise in the press but to consult an accredited plastic surgeon attached to an NHS hospital. Hair transplants are not available on the NHS and are very expensive, and their success cannot be guaranteed. There are various complex techniques involved which allow the hair to retain its identity while eliminating baldness. A more natural hairline around the face is achieved, for example, by removing small individual plugs from the back of the head and scattering them in front but, according to one consultant, 'a lot of the success depends on the number of plugs you can afford; the more dense they are, the better the result. It's payment by plug, you might say.' The treatment has not been used extensively for women so far, but a dermatologist suggested to me that there is no reason why the transplant operation should not be as effective as it can be in men, except that women tend to have a more diffuse loss over the top of the head while retaining their frontal hairline which sometimes makes them less suitable candidates.

Because of unpleasant side-effects, some of the treatments in themselves can cause considerable suffering – but, according to Dr Fenton, many patients prefer to work through a series of treatments in order to be satisfied that they have tried everything possible to reverse their hair loss.

In 1990 came the exciting news that scientists at Cambridge University had managed to grow human hair in a test tube from follicles taken from pieces of skin left over after plastic surgery. The hair in the laboratory grew at a rate of 0·3 mm a day – exactly the same rate as hair which is produced on the scalp. This means that for the first time, it will not only be possible to understand what makes hair grow and what goes wrong when baldness occurs, but there will also be a simple and safe testing ground for new hair-growth drugs.

Where to Go for Help and Advice

Where there may be differences of opinion concerning the treatment of hair loss, when it comes to the amount of psychological stress which can be caused by baldness – particularly when the loss is sudden – doctors and trichologists alike agree that the victim's suffering is intense and in extreme cases may even result in suicide. The stress is often compounded by lack of sympathy from the GP. 'It is very important for GPs to know how serious the condition is,' Dr Fenton said. 'Thankfully, more and more are referring patients to us knowing that we might actually be able to do something to help, but I still see women who have been told "Don't worry, it's just your nerves" or, in the case of one male patient, "Go and consult your hairdresser. I'm here to treat people who are ill."'

Help and support for anyone distressed by hair loss is readily available through a national organization called Hairline (See Part III, Health – Hair Loss, for details). Dr Fenton's hair clinic at St Thomas' Hospital is a part of the National Health Service. He can be contacted direct and will send out a standard letter which requests approval and referral from a general practitioner.

Facial Hair

With changes in hormone activity, facial hair has a habit of sprouting in unexpected places as women become older. While we are well used to keeping unwanted hair under control from adolescence onwards, a practical difficulty arises when eyesight becomes less sharp. Quite simply, one often does not see the odd whiskers which grow defiantly in places which were hitherto barren ground. A once-a-month visit to a beautician is the most pleasant way to deal with the problem, but if the cost proves too high, then the eyes of a good friend with a bright light and a pair of tweezers will do the job just as well. If the facial hair growth becomes abnormally heavy, the general practitioner should be consulted in the first instance to determine the cause and treatment.

Feet

The feet are generally the most neglected part of the human body and are only noticed when they cause trouble. The root of the problem is often found to lie not in the feet themselves but in the lower back, hip and knee joints. If there is a defect in the hip joint, for example, this can cause excessive pressure to be placed on a foot joint, with subsequent distortion and pain. It is important to make sure the cause is established so that appropriate treatment can be recommended, which might include help from an osteopath or orthopaedic specialist.

Chiropodists are trained to treat and diagnose all foot disorders. *Podiatrists* are all state-registered chiropodists who are qualified to carry out limited surgical procedures including, in some cases, removal of bunions. Chiropody is available through the National Health Service but the waiting-lists are often very long. The Society of Chiropodists (see Part III, Health – Foot Care) has a list of practitioners in private practice. Since it is possible for anyone to set themselves up as a chiropodist, the client should first check that they are state registered and have the letters SRCh after their name.

Most podiatrists are in private practice. The Podiatry Association is not a statutory body but its qualifications are recognized by the Council for the Professions Supplementary to Medicine.

A very helpful booklet, *The Footcare Book: An A-Z of Fitter Feet*, by Judith Kemp, SRCh, is published by Age Concern England.

Teeth

The techniques of modern dentistry mean that it is now possible to retain almost any tooth for life provided the gums remain healthy. Advanced gum disease is difficult to treat and can cause the teeth to loosen. Adequate cleaning and regular visits to a hygienist should be sufficient care to prevent dental problems but 'adequate cleaning' is much more difficult than good general dental advice would have us believe. Apart from the correct use of dental floss, one of the most effective means of ensuring the gums are left free of plaque-building detritis is by using a Waterpik, which squirts jets of water at varying speeds through the gaps in the teeth and around the gumlines. It is astonishing how much this little gadget still manages to dislodge after the tooth brush and even dental floss have done their work.

The expense of dentistry is sadly too often a deterrent and means that too many people are unnecessarily having to cope with false teeth. National Health patients, including pensioners, unless they are receiving income support, are expected to pay 75 per cent of the costs. Because dentists are not obliged to take on everyone who applies to be a patient, it is sometimes difficult to find a practitioner – unless, of course, you happen to want private treatment. Where the ceiling for the cost of private dentistry is limitless, the most you can expect to pay for one complete course of treatment on the NHS is £200, but in either case an estimate should be obtained for the work required; since dentists often assume that a patient will want private dental care, it is important to make it clear from the outset which form of treatment is expected.

Most district health authorities have a District Dental Officer, whose job includes advising and helping patients find NHS dentistry. They also manage the Community Dental Service, which enables people who, through handicap or infirmity, cannot be treated in a general dental surgery. The service will also organize visits to the homes of housebound patients and offers information and advice on preventive dental health. (Details can be obtained from the local District Health Authority.)

Hearing

As a result of the natural wearing-down process inherent in ageing, a large proportion of people over sixty have impaired hearing. It is cruel that nature produces this loss at the same time that it also forces many of us into a less active, more peaceful lifestyle. Television, films, concerts and discussion rely on a good standard of hearing and it is depressing to find that one's enjoyment of these ordinary pleasures is marred by natural causes.

The British Association for the Hard of Hearing (BAHOH) (see Part III, Health – Hearing) specializes in helping people who become hard of hearing in the retirement years. The association has two hundred clubs throughout the country which offer companionship, understanding and encouragement. It will also give advice on hearing-aids or any other aid available to alleviate the problem. In cases of severe deafness, lip-reading, although not a substitute for hearing, can enable people to conduct a conversation in near-to-normal speech. BAHOH runs lip-speaker training courses, both as a professional skill and for deaf people and their families who would like to learn to communicate in this way.

Tinnitus

The dictionary describes this most distressing condition as 'a ringing in the ears', which seems rather a mild phrase to use for the constant, often terrifying noises experienced by sufferers in their ears or head. The mechanisms of tinnitus are not fully understood but the abnormal sounds it produces are thought to be generated by microscopic abnormalities in the cells of the inner ear. These may be brought about by a number of different factors, including the normal ageing process, certain drugs and environmental noise pollution. It is estimated that one in two hundred people, mostly over the age of forty, is a victim of tinnitus and there is currently no cure, although much can be done to alleviate the symptoms. A national helpline for victims of tinnitus has been set up by the Royal National Institute for the Deaf (see Part III, Health – Hearing).

Reading

Richard Hallam, *Living with Tinnitus*, Thorsons, 1989

Eyesight

Age is almost bound to produce some deterioration in the eyesight, and regular eye examination is particularly important in later life. Although magnifying spectacles bought over the counter may rectify the *effects* of the deterioration, it is also important to identify the exact *cause*, as it may be possible to prevent further damage. For example, glaucoma is caused by abnormally high pressure in the liquid in the eye; if this is not treated it will cause progressive damage which is irreversible and will eventually lead to blindness. The condition is quite common and the treatment is usually simple and effective. However, the problem will not normally be noticed at first unless the pressure is measured by an ophthalmologist (ophthalmic medical practitioner) or optometrist (ophthalmic optician) during a check-up.

A high-street optician will only be able to determine the correct lenses to wear; he cannot make a medical diagnosis, although if he suspects there may be a medical problem, he will send his client to an eye specialist. Sight is one of our most precious possessions. It makes sense to have it checked at the highest level, asking the GP for a referral to an ophthalmologist, a fully qualified doctor specializing in eyes and eye care. Only the ophthalmologist is trained to diagnose and treat all eye problems.

For further information, the *In Touch Handbook*, prepared by the team that produces the weekly BBC Radio 4 programme *In Touch*, includes an easy-to-follow explanation of the changes in the eye which lead to visual loss. It is also invaluable for anyone with little or no sight who needs help in overcoming the difficulties of everyday living.

The Royal National Institute for the Blind (see Part III, Health – Eye Care) provides a range of services, including residential care homes, special equipment, holidays and advisory services. They will also explain the advantages of registering as 'partially sighted'. The partial-sight register is for those who, though severely visually impaired, are not so disabled as to be registered as 'blind'. It is estimated that as many as two out of three people who are eligible to register as blind or partially sighted choose not to do so, but registration would enable them to gain easier access to special services provided by social services and national voluntary organizations and to qualify for certain financial benefits.

COMMON ILLNESSES AND HEALTH PROBLEMS ASSOCIATED WITH AGEING

Although there is clear evidence to show that both acute and chronic illnesses increase during the retirement years, ill health is by no means the constant companion of the elderly. On the other hand, the symptoms of arthritis, for example, which may have been felt as intermittent joint pain in mid-life are more likely in old age to become a permanent fixture. Eyesight alters quite dramatically in middle age, and even those who have never worn spectacles may at this time find themselves needing them for reading. In later years, the eyes may need treatment for glaucoma and cataracts. All these are conditions which occur as the body gradually wears down during the ageing process, but modern medicine is so effective that the quality of life in old age can be as high as it was in mid-life. The vast majority of illnesses and diseases experienced in later life now have as much chance of being cured as they had in the years before retirement. A study conducted by doctors at the Mayo Clinic in Rochester, Minnesota, showed that even the stress of surgery appears to be well tolerated by people in their nineties and hundreds. [50]

The common illnesses and health problems discussed below are those which tend to crop up after the age of forty rather than during the period of young adulthood. These ailments will not lead to dependency, but they may cause considerable distress for a time. The real problem is the fear we feel at either *being* ill (will we recover or is this the end of the line?) or *becoming* ill (will this stomach pain turn out to be cancer?). The GP is obviously the first port in a storm but further counselling and care is always available. (See Part III, Health.)

It is astonishing how effective reassurance and support from a respected and trusted professional can be in the treatment of aches and pains. The chest pain which was feared to be the onset of heart disease can mysteriously disappear the moment the door of the surgery or consulting-room is closed. A recurrent headache evaporates the instant a patient is shown X-rays which eliminate his fear of a brain tumour. Those who are not satisfied with the treatment received from their GP, however, may need to be persistent in their efforts to find appropriate help elsewhere.

Diabetes

Diabetes is a disorder in which the body produces an abnormally high level of sugar in the blood. There are two forms of diabetes – insulin-dependent diabetes (IDD) and the much more common non-insulin-dependent diabetes (NIDD). While the former tends to occur in younger people and needs to be treated from an early stage with insulin injections to preserve life and health, the latter is more likely to occur in middle and old age and is often associated with being overweight. In the first instance, NIDD is treated by diet or by diet and tablets, but about 20 per cent of sufferers will eventually need insulin injections to control their blood glucose.

Although the treatment is usually less demanding for non-insulin-dependent diabetics, the disease is none the less serious – if blood glucose levels are allowed to become too high, the patient will be very ill. NIDD can also lead to eye, nerve and foot complications. Disease of the large blood vessels is not uncommon and may lead to heart attacks, strokes or gangrene. There is no known cure for diabetes, yet, although the consequences of neglect are potentially very grave, once diagnosed, all types of the disorder can be treated and normal health restored.

The main symptoms in both insulin-dependent diabetes and non-insulin-dependent diabetes are similar:

Thirst and dry mouth
Passing large amounts of urine
Weight loss
Tiredness
Itching of the genital organs
Blurring of vision

Diabetic coma only occurs in insulin-dependent diabetes and the symptoms are likely to be less severe and develop more slowly in NIDD.

The following is the case history of a seventy-two-year-old man, in which he describes how he copes with his disorder:

> I enjoyed good health all my life until I developed diabetes about five years ago. Now, I have had to learn how to inject insulin. Unfortunately, I have had to give up alcohol, which makes me very unhappy. Although I wasn't a heavy drinker, I certainly enjoyed a drink, and particularly wine with meals. But if there's no way of getting out of a situation you just have to adapt and make the best of it. When you are an old man you have to get used to these things; so rather than making a great tragedy out of being a diabetic, I try to make rather a joke about it. I tease my friends and tell them I'm going to share my needles with them – that sort of silly thing. The incision is right here in this little black spot. I don't even feel it. It isn't a big deal. I look on it like just another boring thing, like shaving in the morning, cleaning your teeth, and that sort of thing. You just get used to it.

However, not all diabetics are obliged to give up alcohol, chocolate, cake or biscuits. Dietary advice will be tailored to suit individual needs, circumstances and preferences.

Shingles (Herpes Zoster)

This unpleasant condition, in which nerve endings become inflamed, seems to be more commonplace in later life. The following is a letter sent to my seventy-year-old father, who had spent a miserable few weeks suffering from shingles. The advice it contains is still worth taking:

> My dear old friend:
> So you have shingles! I know how you feel, for I had it many years ago. Back, front, ribs – a girdle of blisters. Mind you, I don't know how today's quacks treat it. This is how I was treated – a sort of homespun method by my granny.
> She covered the blisters with an old soft vest soaked in warm olive oil, repeating this until they grew smaller and carefully sponging them until they faded. Calamine lotion was used to cool the burning. Ever cheerful, she said, 'Now if the blisters meet in a circle round you, you will die – but we won't let that happen!' (I don't believe that shingles are more painful when they are getting better as long as friction from clothes is prevented.) In about ten days I was fit again, bless her! I'll back her treatment against any modern consultant. They don't make grannies like her any more! Apparently, my shingles, according to her, was caused by stealing too many birds' eggs! After that, you may believe I never stole another one.

Like his old friend, my father found much of the pain to be caused by the blisters rubbing against his clothes as he moved. A more modern version of the soft vest soaked in olive oil (wide pieces of gauze with one side covered in a soothing ointment) can be bought from a chemist. On the other hand, 'granny's treatment' is probably just as effective and costs next to nothing!

Arthritis and Rheumatism

Only one person in fifty will escape some form of rheumatic complaint in their lifetime. The term 'arthritis' means disease of or damage to the joints, while 'rheumatism' is more generally used to describe pain in the bones, muscles, joints and the tissues surrounding the joints; 'rheumatic diseases' refers to all types of arthritis and rheumatism. There are about two hundred different forms of the disease, for which, as yet, there is no absolute cure, although some – like gout, for example – can be effectively treated and joint replacement surgery in extreme cases is very successful. Rheumatic diseases account for one third of all severely disabled people in the UK but the Arthritis

and Rheumatism Council (ARC) (see Part III, Health –
Arthritis and Rheumatism) stresses that arthritis does not
inevitably become worse and that very few people with the
disease become crippled. In most cases, modern treatment
enables the sufferer to keep fit and active and can help to
prevent progressive joint damage. Pain, stiffness and disability
can always be lessened – by analgesics, by injections of local
anaesthetic and/or corticosteroids and, in extreme cases, by
surgery. There are a number of relatively minor operations
which can help osteoarthritic joints such as the big toes. Hip
replacement surgery offers great relief and there have been recent
advances in the techniques involved in knee-joint replacements.

'Prostate Trouble' – Benign Prostatic Hypertrophy (BPH)

It is very common for men over the age of fifty to suffer the
problems associated with an abnormal enlargement of the prostate gland. Although the causes are unknown, it is thought that
they may involve alterations in the hormonal balance associated
with ageing. The condition is not cancerous but the symptoms
are distressing and can lead to chronic infection and serious
kidney damage if untreated.

Because the outlet from the bladder is obstructed it is unable
to empty itself completely and rapidly refills, causing progressive urinary frequency and urgency both day and night. There
may also be hesitancy and intermittency, with decreased size
and force of the urinary stream and sensations of incomplete
emptying with terminal dribbling. In more extreme cases,
there may be almost continuous overflow incontinence or complete urinary retention. Bleeding may occur while the sufferer
is straining to empty his bladder; a burning sensation on
urination, fever and chills will indicate that there is a urinary
infection.

The doctor will perform a rectal examination which will
probably reveal that the prostate is enlarged, but the size can
be misleading and even if it feels relatively small, it may still
be large enough to cause urethral obstruction. While stabilizing
drugs may be prescribed in the first instance, the treatment is a
simple, highly successful surgical procedure which carries with

it almost no risks and, contrary to popular belief, the patient usually maintains his pre-operative sexual potency. More recently, a successful and highly efficient technique has been developed whereby a laser beam is used to deal with the problem.

Urinary Incontinence

Incontinence should not be regarded as a 'normal' part of ageing. It has a wide variety of causes and many types of incontinence can be treated or cured. At the very least, with good guidance and advice it is usually possible to reduce the effects by proper management.

The two most common forms are *urge* incontinence and *stress* incontinence. The former is characterized by an urgent desire to empty the bladder, which is then followed by an involuntary loss of urine. The underlying cause is identified and treated accordingly – usually with appropriate medication. The latter develops – especially in women – as a result of an inadequately functioning sphincter muscle, which causes loss of urine on coughing, straining, sneezing, lifting or any other form of activity which puts extra pressure on the abdomen. Mild cases of stress incontinence respond well to a specially developed exercise programme known as Kegel's exercises. More stubborn cases may require drug therapy or corrective surgery.

Incontinence is by no means confined to old age. It is estimated that one in three women, many in their teens, twenties and thirties suffer some degree of stress incontinence. Laughing or sneezing can produce dribbles of urine. The victim is often too mortified or embarrassed to confide in anyone, and gets round the problem by wearing a sanitary pad, particularly on social occasions where they might feel especially vulnerable.

Early advice is essential. In the first instance the GP must be consulted so that a proper diagnosis can be made. After that, there are a number of steps which can be taken. Some district health authorities have a continence adviser – usually a nurse who specializes in the problems of incontinence. Alternatively, a district nurse or health visitor is a good source of help and advice.

There is no doubt that incontinence in whatever capacity is a most miserable complaint. It is something we all very deeply fear might happen to us in old age if not before. If it does happen, then there is just one blessing, namely that we no longer have to dread the thought. It only remains for us to cope with the problem. Sympathetic help, advice and counselling are all readily available.

Write to the Incontinence Advisory Service at the Disabled Living Foundation (380–84 Harrow Road, London W9 2HU) for information and advice, whether for yourself, your family or someone for whom you are caring.

Disabled Living Centres (listed in the telephone directory) offer advice on managing incontinence. An appointment can be made to discuss the problem in person and view samples of equipment and special clothing.

The Age Concern Factsheet No. 23, 'Help with Incontinence', has an up-to-date list of advice services, helplines and publications. It also advises on how to buy or borrow equipment and obtain aids at reduced prices.

Readers in Scotland might prefer to contact Age Concern Scotland at 54a Fountainbridge, Edinburgh EH3 9PT (tel. 031–228 5656).

Medication – Different Ages, Differing Effects

The effects of prescription overuse, either alone or in combination with alcohol, have already been discussed. What has not been mentioned, however, is the fact that in older people, prescription drugs can have serious side-effects which do not usually occur in younger adults.

With age, the body's metabolism changes; after the age of fifty-five or so, people become more susceptible to the ill effects of drug interaction. Older bodies are less efficient at metabolizing and excreting drugs which can, without these natural methods of dilution, rise to harmful levels, even when the drug is taken at the prescribed dose.

Because they are likely to be taking medication for more than one problem at the same time, older people may find that one drug cancels the benefits of another, or may adversely strengthen the action of another. The effects of some drugs can also be dangerously increased by only limited amounts of alcohol. General practitioners, impatient with the complaints of their elderly patients, are often all too eager to dismiss them from the surgery with yet another prescription. Careless doctoring can cause unnecessary suffering and can even cost lives.

When Mrs M.B.'s father, acutely depressed, committed suicide on 8 July, he left behind, in his own handwriting, a list of the drugs prescribed by his doctor which he was taking daily. With Mrs M.B.'s permission, I sent the list to a pharmacologist for analysis and comment. He concluded:

Much of what this patient was taking (for angina and asthma) would seem appropriate. However, the dose of prednisolone might have altered his judgement. The dose is high, but in severe asthma this is often needed. However, in some people such a dose can induce a feeling of well-being, not to say overconfidence and even delusions. In such a context the drug could not be said to have 'caused' suicide, but it may have contributed, since it might have made him less cautious than he might otherwise have been.

The patient's notes suggest that he was taking Phyllocontin and aminophylline, and four tablets of each a day at that. This is most odd, since they are essentially the same medicine, and so one wonders whether he was being given double the intended dose. If a blood test were to show that the concentration was in the toxic range, it could have caused loss of consciousness since the unwanted effects of this group of drugs include falls in blood pressure, abnormalities of heart rhythm and sometimes convulsions.

This experience suggests to the carer that if he or she has any doubt about the effects of medication on an elderly friend or relative, it would be wise to check in the first instance with the family doctor responsible for the prescription. If no satisfactory answers are forthcoming, a letter enclosing the details could be sent to the consultant pharmacologist in the department of pharmacology at the nearest large teaching hospital.

Dr Brian S. Katcher, author of *Prescription Drugs: An Indispensable Guide for People Over Fifty*,[51] urges people to ask their doctor the following questions:

- What is the name of the drug and what is it supposed to do?
- How and when should it be taken, and for how long?
- What foods, drinks, other medication, or activities should be avoided while taking this drug?
- What side-effects could occur and what should be done about them?

Know Your Medicines by Pat Blair is an excellent guide to medicines for elderly people and those who help to care for them. It also explains how the body works and how it is affected by medicines. The book is available from Age Concern England. A more detailed guide is *Medicines – A Guide for Everybody* by Peter Parish (Penguin Books, 6th ed., 1989); it outlines the basic principles of the use of medication and the treatments of commonly occurring disorders and it has a comprehensive alphabetical list of medicines, giving uses, precautions, adverse effects and dosages.

Painful Periods – Hysterectomy

For women who no longer wish to bear children but are still brought low by increasingly heavy, painful or irregular periods in the years approaching the menopause, a hysterectomy can bring the most joyful relief. This major surgical procedure requires a general anaesthetic and a week or more in hospital, but there is now a simpler alternative: the new technique, known as transcervical resection of endometrium (TCRE), can be performed under a local anaesthetic and involves cutting away the lining of the womb (endometrium), thereby removing the source of bleeding. Much needless suffering can be prevented by asking the GP for a referral to a gynaecologist for advice or, alternatively, by a visit to the family planning clinic.

Cancer

Mastectomy versus Lumpectomy

Popular literature has tended to suggest that women with breast cancer now have the choice as to whether to opt for removal of the breast or simply of the malignant lump itself. Since the difference is considerable mutilation as opposed to a simple scar, the choice seems obvious, but Alan McKinna, consultant at the Royal Marsden Hospital and one of the country's leading experts in breast disease, stated in an interview that the surgical procedure depended entirely upon the nature of the lump. 'Of course one would rather perform a lumpectomy, but there are times when it would not be safe to do so. In cases of more advanced breast cancer, sometimes the only way forward is to remove the breast. Each patient requires an individual approach and the treatment must fit her needs precisely.'

Some women find that, after a mastectomy, they are able to cope well with a prosthesis properly fitted into a bra or swimsuit, but others feel more 'normal' with breast reconstruction. This can be done at the time of the operation or afterwards by a plastic surgeon. Careful counselling is necessary to ensure that all the ramifications of breast surgery are fully understood. Reconstruction may not live up to the patient's expectations (plastic surgery of any kind is rarely perfect) and the disappointment will only add to the trauma of the operation. (See also Part III, Health – Cancer.)

Cervical Cancer – Smear Tests for the Over-sixty-fives?

Concern was raised by an article in the *Lancet* on 12 January 1990 suggesting that women over sixty-five were dying unnecessarily from cervical cancer because they were being excluded from smear tests by their GPs, in accordance with guidelines laid down by the Department of Health.

At the moment, women up to the age of sixty-five are called for cervical smear tests every three to four years. After that time, they are not normally recalled provided the tests are clear and there are no signs of possible future complications.

According to a spokeswoman for Cancer Link, some family doctors under the present contract system are finding that it does not make economic sense to call up women over sixty-five for smear tests. Their decision is backed by the fact that there is no current research to show categorically whether or not it is safer for older women to be protected by early-warning checks. Yet if one considers the statistics available, it is difficult to see how women in the upper age group are less vulnerable. Figures from the Office of Population, Censuses and Surveys for England and Wales in 1988 show that 1,942 women died of cervical cancer. Of these, 975 were under sixty-five and 967 were over that age.

This is one of those instances in which, when confronting members of the medical profession, it pays to have a mind of one's own. If a woman feels she needs a cervical smear test as a precautionary measure, then she should be able to go to her family doctor and ask for one, regardless of her age. If, in the (hopefully) unlikely event, she is denied a test, then she should demand an appointment with a gynaecologist, or a 'well-woman' clinic or any other agency in her area qualified to give her the examination she wants.

Women and the Menopause

In much of the literature today, the menopause is labelled 'a myth', 'a figment of cultural imagination'. But there is a great multitude of women who passionately disagree. 'They do so much disservice because they don't acknowledge the fact of the menopause, but by God it's a fact!', one woman exclaimed.

> I felt absolutely devastated – not so much physically, but it was the mental state which so affected me. The swings of emotion from elation to depression were terrifying. Now my children say, 'Thank God you're over that awful period, Mum.' I was an absolute harridan – yelling and screaming at anything that moved. You go for a long, long time not realizing you're any different until people start to comment on your mood. They say things like 'You seem to be feeling a bit more yourself today'; or 'While you're

still approachable, maybe we can talk about so-and-so.' I remained unaware of my condition until I started to get hot flushes – then I realized that I was menopausal but it was still about six months before I went to my doctor for help. The main symptom at the time was a terrible tiredness. All I wanted to do was to sleep. I could have easily slept the whole day through. I didn't want to get up in the morning and I had no interest in anything. I began to realize too that my behaviour was quite uncharacteristic – I was emotionally disturbed by small, silly things which would normally have passed me by. Hormone replacement therapy has restored me to myself though and that horrible period of my life is over. I would be very, very frightened indeed to go back to it and the idea of coming off HRT and running the risk of feeling like that again is unthinkable.

The Facts of the Menopause

For several years, Dr Julia Montgomery, Senior Registrar in Obstetrics and Gynaecology at University College Hospital and Research Fellow of King's College, has been carrying out research into the menopause. She is especially interested in the psychological problems which patients present to gynaecologists – the overlap between gynaecology and psychiatry.

The menopause syndrome is a wide-ranging syndrome covering many aspects of women's systems, ranging from vascular and cardiovascular problems, to skeletal and psychological disorders. According to Dr Montgomery, 'evidence shows that the majority of women suffer menopausal symptoms, particularly hot flushes and memory loss'.

The meaning of the Greek word 'menopause' is 'the cessation of menses', but to gynaecologists the term carries with it a far wider meaning, the loss of periods being only one aspect of the menopausal syndrome. Dr Montgomery explained: 'We tend to see both the post-menopausal women, those who would once have been called menopausal, and more importantly, the perimenopausal women, who present three to four years before the cessation of periods with irregular periods and menopausal symptoms. The "climacteric" is the term we use more now to encompass this group of women. Perimenopausal women are often ignored when it comes to research and, more importantly, when it comes to treatment. Many are told by their GPs, "You are not menopausal; you are still getting your periods. Go away. I'm not interested."'

It is not always easy to diagnose this group of women because similar symptoms can be suffered for a variety of reasons other than climacteric changes, but the chances are that tests will show a slight change in the hormone levels at this time, although not to the same extent as in post-menopausal women. Hot flushes and night sweats, which can also occur as a result of emotional disturbance quite unrelated to the menopause, are not uncommonly associated with the premenstrual syndrome as well. On the other hand, it is possible to distinguish empirically between the stress-induced 'blush' and the 'hot flush' which arises as a result of oestrogen deficiency.

Some menopausal women also complain of tiredness, loss of short-term memory, loss of concentration and loss of confidence. The cause is felt to be due to the *fluctuation* of hormones, including oestrogen, rather than to low levels of oestrogen. (This also occurs in the postnatal and premenstrual syndromes.) Because of the psychological problems associated with the menopause, research is now concentrating on the neurotransmitters in the brain and the regulatory effect which oestrogen appears to have on those areas which are related to mood.

What makes it difficult for women to gain a proper picture of their physical and mental condition at the time of the menopause is that not only are they confronted with their individual metabolism and its own unique way of responding to what after all is an entirely natural process of change, but that doctors themselves disagree widely as to the cause of some symptoms and the appropriate forms of treatment. Whereas, for example, Dr Montgomery and her colleagues are convinced of the connection between psychiatric disturbances and the menopause, Dr Barbara Ballinger of the Royal Dundee Liff Hospital is adamant that hormonal changes at this time have little or no effect on mental well-being. Writing in the *British Journal of Psychiatry* (August 1990), she heavily criticized colleagues in the medical profession who would prescribe HRT as a treatment for anxiety and depression during the menopause rather than conventional drug therapy.

Because there seems to be such fundamental disagreement amongst the medical profession about 'the change of life', it seems finally to be up to women themselves, if they feel it necessary, to seek professional advice, weigh up the evidence and make their own choices.

Sexuality and the Menopause

Apart from the psychological disturbances felt particularly by perimenopausal women, the menopause can be a period of intense mourning. Although it is true that for many women the end of their periods is a time to rejoice, others are devastated by the thought that they can no longer bear children.

Women whom Dr Montgomery sees in her menopause clinic frequently complain of a loss of libido. 'A change, they say, from an active, fulfilling sexual life to one where they have lost all interest. They also complain of loss of orgasm, loss of clitoral sensation and an altered touch perception, where they may be sensitive to certain clothing or they might not like to be touched by their husband or their children or grandchildren.

'Many said their sexual problems rose from the male side, that the men were no longer interested in the cuddling side of a relationship, the foreplay or actual intercourse. Women come back to us feeling fantastic after their hormonal implants, asking if their husbands could have one!'

Hormone Replacement Therapy (HRT)

Hormone replacement therapy is currently subject to as many myths as the menopause itself. It is a treatment which has been around for many years but was usually administered to patients who underwent early menopause, either naturally or as the result of surgical removal of the ovaries, and was regarded with too much caution to be prescribed more widely for menopausal women.

HRT was brought into the political arena in 1987 by the

Member of Parliament for Billericay, Mrs Teresa Gorman. In her middle fifties, Mrs Gorman began to suffer severe pain in her wrists and ankles, and back pain which was so bad she had to roll out of bed on to the floor and heave herself up to a standing position by grabbing the side of the bed. She felt permanently tired and could not climb her stairs without having to stop halfway up to pause for breath, but, she remembered, 'the most frightening thing of all was the loss of memory and lack of concentration. I was afraid I would have to give up my job. After two weeks on the treatment, the pains disappeared and have never returned. My energy level is astounding, I never feel tired and my memory functions as well as it ever did.'

Mrs Gorman is indeed a wonderful example of the benefits of hormone replacement therapy. When I met her, she looked about fifteen years younger than her fifty-eight years. 'HRT is the greatest treasure of a middle-aged woman's life. I'm nearly sixty but feel twenty.'

Much of the hostility surrounding the use of HRT comes from some of the press coverage it has received. Writer and media personality Clare Rayner, for example, is perhaps one of its best-known opponents. Edwina Currie, as Junior Minister of Health, was convinced that the only cure for menopausal symptoms was yoghurt and jogging. Her condemnation of Mrs Gorman's efforts to promote more widespread use of HRT was scathing. Mrs Gorman's response: 'Edwina was only in her early forties then. Wait till she gets to fifty – she may well change her mind! I know women often find it difficult to assert themselves and we all have a tendency to be in awe of the doctor, but it's up to them to say what they want. Women need to say to themselves, "I know this treatment is out there; I feel lousy and I want to try it for myself." They mustn't be put off by anybody.'

There is insufficient evidence at the present time to suggest that any type of cancer may be related to HRT; the medical profession is gradually beginning to take a more optimistic view of the benefits of the therapy, at least in the short term. Certainly women who are receiving the treatment report a great sense of well-being and those who have experienced emotional turmoil associated with the menopause find their equilibrium restored. After the hot sweats and night flushes have run their course HRT treatment can be discontinued.

Dr Montgomery and her colleagues at King's College are in the forefront of those members of the medical profession who would like to see widespread changes in the care of women's health. As one doctor said, 'In the past, women's life expectancy did not extend much beyond the menopause. At fifty, they were old. Now they can expect to live into their eighties. Hormone replacement therapy has been shown to prevent strokes, heart disease and osteoporosis.' For the new generation of middle-aged and older women, HRT is seen not only as a life enhancer but, by many, as a life saver.

The treatment is available on the National Health but many general practitioners still feel it should be used with caution, and, rather than prescribe it to patients direct, will tend to refer them to a gynaecologist. Others refuse women who request a prescription on the grounds that not enough is known about the long-term effects of the treatment or, alternatively, they are refused because in the doctor's opinion they do not need the treatment. The current hospital appointment system often means long delays and a woman desperate for relief from her symptoms may wish to take matters into her own hands and seek advice elsewhere. (See Part III, Health – Menopause.)

Reading

Malcolm Whitehead and Teresa Gorman, *The Amarant Book of Hormone Replacement Therapy*, Pan Books, 1989

Rosetta Reitz, *Menopause: A Positive Approach*, Unwin, 1985. Very critical of HRT.

Wendy Cooper, *No Change – A Biological Revolution for Women*, Arrow, 1983. Full of praise for HRT.

Jill Rakusen, *The Menopause: A Guide for Women of All Ages*, National Extension College, 1989

Osteoporosis

A gradual thinning of the bones, with increased porosity –
osteopenia – is a natural part of the ageing process by which
both the male and female skeletons slowly become smaller.
A major cause of loss of height in both sexes is loss of elasticity
in the discs. Osteoporosis occurs with excessive bone loss,
causing bones to become brittle and easily fractured. Unfortunately for women, osteoporosis begins earlier in their lives and
progresses twice as fast as it does in men, especially during
the first five or six years following the menopause. In extreme cases, the spine collapses, forming a 'dowager's hump'
with a loss in height of several inches. At about sixty-five-
years old, a woman's bone loss will slow down to keep pace
with a man's but even by the age of fifty-five, she may have
lost as much bone as she gained during her growth phase as
an adolescent. Osteoporosis affects one in four women and
one in forty men.

According to Dr Morris Notelovitz, Director of the Climacteric Clinic in Gainesville, Florida, 25 per cent of women are
likely to be affected following a natural menopause. Up to 50
per cent of those whose menopause is precipitated by surgical
removal of the ovaries will develop problems associated with
osteoporosis if HRT is not prescribed. Yet the picture is not as
bleak as it once seemed because, although osteoporosis cannot
be cured, it can be prevented if evasive action is taken early
and continued for life.

*In Stand Tall! The Informed Woman's Guide to Preventing
Osteoporosis*, which he wrote together with a colleague, Marsha
Ware, Dr Notelovitz claims, 'Prevention strategies are simple:
proper nutrition, adequate exercise and, for some women,
hormone replacement therapy. To be most effective, these
measures must be undertaken before bone loss begins and be
continued for life.'

Dr Notelovitz stresses the importance of exercise in helping
to prevent osteoporosis: 'Exercise is believed to be the only
preventive or therapeutic measure that not only halts bone loss
but actually stimulates the formation of new bone. Some scientists believe that age-related bone loss is not inevitable but
instead relates to a decline in physical activity. To the extent

that decreased activity with ageing is inevitable, then bone loss is also inevitable.'[52]

However, not all doctors and specialists working in the field agree that exercise and calcium are useful in helping to prevent osteoporosis, although no one denies that they have their place and are generally beneficial to health. Dr Ignac Fogelman, director of the Osteoporosis Screening and Research Unit at Guy's Hospital in London, sees no evidence to support the thesis that calcium and exercise prevent the development of osteoporosis. He told me: 'I have just seen a patient who had an early menopause at forty and from the age of eighteen went through ten years without a period. Her bones are in a horrendous state yet she lifts weights, jogs and takes a lot of calcium in her diet. As in all cases, her problem is hormonal; the osteoporosis is caused by the overwhelming, overriding effect of insufficient oestrogen. My biggest concern is that women are being deluded into thinking they can protect themselves by exercising and taking calcium. The exercise and calcium must be relevant but their relevance is insignificant compared to the benefits of hormone replacement therapy.

'Ideally, I think every woman when she reaches the menopause should get a bone density measurement and take hormones if she needs them.'

Recent studies have shown greater frequency of spinal and femoral fractures and Dr Fogelman is concerned that osteoporosis appears to be on the increase (probably due to the fact that more people are living longer) and the problem, he thinks, will escalate unless something can be done about it. Unfortunately, there are no plans to effect a National Health Service screening programme in the foreseeable future. Currently, Guy's Hospital offers a limited service whereby GPs can send women for bone-density measurements. They will usually do so if there are early risk factors such as a strong family history of osteoporosis, an early menopause or if a patient is taking steroids or has had a history of back pain, but there is nothing to stop a woman requesting a referral from her family doctor if she feels she has reached a point at which tests might be appropriate.

As a treatment for osteoporosis, HRT must be continued for at least ten to fifteen years. While some doctors are concerned that not enough has been done on the study of long-term hormone replacement therapy, Dr Fogelman is one of many who feel that the benefits will be seen to far outweigh any adverse effects.

Clinics equipped with the technology to test bone density accurately (an ordinary X-ray provides too crude an indication of bone loss) are available in limited numbers nationwide. A list may be obtained from the National Osteoporosis Society (see Part III, Health – Osteoporosis, for details) for a small membership fee.

MENTAL WELL-BEING

Changes in Memory Function

'Oh, my God, I'm going senile!' is the often heard response to those lapses of memory which begin to manifest themselves in middle age and which come to many of us as a frightening reminder of the passage of time. These brief losses of memory are extremely rarely associated with the onset of disease but are almost always temporary and, more often than not, associated with stress. In women, memory loss – again temporary – can also be due to the effect of hormone changes on the brain at the time of the menopause (see p. 288). The psychiatrist, Anthony Clare, suggests that memory 'steadily declines' with age, but, he adds, 'well-learned facts, such as familiar events and well-practised skills, are retained well into old age – which is why so many elderly people continue to drive quite competently and are not over-represented in accident statistics'.[53]

Men and women who return to formal education in later years, especially those whose courses lead to examinations, find their memory is not as adept at rote learning or at storing facts for regurgitation in an exam answer. On the other hand, they discover that experience enables them to approach a subject in more diverse ways than younger students might do.

The historian Peter Laslett, in his book *A Fresh Map of Life, the Emergence of the Third Age*, describes the way in which older people learn:

As for intellectual grasp, capacity to learn afresh, to write, paint, fashion objects, concern about their gradual elimination with age is easily exaggerated, since experience and maturity may compensate, or more than compensate. Elderly learners, as we shall see, especially elderly learners from each other, are usually keener and fresher than their juniors. These are a self-selected group of course, but we should be delighted to hear that creativity is surprisingly independent of period of life. Even memory, for that which is of importance to their purposes, continues to be adequate to the ends of elderly people, much as they tend to reproach themselves about its fading ... It is now known that new skills, new items of information, especially when built upon those already possessed, can be acquired at any age – calendar, biological, social or personal age. Admittedly the time needed to learn gets longer, and the elderly would-be learner is often exasperated by the inadequacies of his memory. But this is what is to be expected, and one more instance of what we are all so marvellously equipped to do, to compensate for deficiencies as they occur. Final mastery of a novelty may be securer in older than in younger learners, and there are business administrators who are well aware that this is so.[54]

Dr H. B. Gibson, a retired clinical psychologist, leads a course in psychology for adults attending the University of the Third Age in Cambridge. He finds memory loss to be the subject which most concerns his older students: 'Most people have the idea that as you get older your memory goes. It is much more complex than that. Recent studies are beginning to show a rather different picture. In the past, research has tended to be carried out on a cross-sectional basis which means that if you take a number of men and women in their forties, fifties, sixties, seventies and eighties, the results you get are marginally conditioned by these people's backgrounds and life experience. People now in their eighties have had a very different education and lived in a very different world to those men and women currently in their forties. It is these differences which have led to a lot of misapprehension in psychology about the process of memory.

'For the past sixteen years researchers at Addenbrooke's Hospital in Cambridge have been running a longitudinal study following the same people as they grow older. Their results show that the expected deterioration in memory doesn't take place. Of course, there are certain disorders like Alzheimer's disease, arterial sclerosis, and Jakob Kreuzfeld's syndrome which account for total memory loss, but if people maintain their health, they don't lose their memories.

'One of the problems of memory – I know from my own experience – is that it is often a problem sheerly of overload. For example, if you had only twelve books in your house, you could locate any one book easily, but if like me you have thousands of books upstairs and downstairs, unless you have them all classified properly like a librarian, it becomes quite a problem to lay your hands on any one book; and that's what happens when you get older. The memory is so stuffed with data that there is a problem of retrieval.'

Stress

One in six women and one in nine men will suffer some form of mental breakdown during the course of their lives and the root cause of breakdown, either mental or physical (often in the form of a coronary heart attack), can usually be directly attributed to a prolonged period of stress.

Dr Joe Kearns, an occupational physician who for many years has specialized in stress management and stress counselling, explains that the state commonly described as 'stress' is 'the discrepancy between a person's ability and the demands being made upon them. Individuals can be as stressed by monotony as they can be by overwork; they can be overloaded or underloaded in quantity or quality.'

Dr Kearns pointed out that in the workplace people tend to be promoted to one stage above their level of competence, and it is something of which they should be aware. If they feel underqualified it should be possible to approach the organization and ask for help in making good the discrepancy by further training or resources. Unfortunately, however, the fear of losing the job or being demoted is such that employees often find they cannot trust members of their own medical department in case admitting their anxiety and lack of confidence should prejudice their careers. Although companies are becoming more aware of the effects of stress on members of their work-force, and are attempting to set up appropriate sources of help, there is evidence to suggest that this fear has some foundation.

Whether the symptoms of stress are caused by conditions at home or at work, they are much as described in the following paragraph. Other factors can also include a lack of personal efficiency – of putting off a complicated programme or being unable to make decisions; an inability to concentrate or a loss of *joie de vivre*, where social events become a burden and are dropped in order to rest, lie down or vegetate in front of the television.

Depression/Anxiety State

There is a sharp distinction between ordinary bad moods and depression serious enough to require treatment, even though the irrational thoughts experienced in both conditions are much the same. Just about everyone suffers from bad moods from time to time, but the normal feelings of sadness, irritability, hopelessness and anxiety typically clear up in a matter of minutes, hours or days. If, however, the moods persist for more than a few weeks and are accompanied by other symptoms, such as insomnia, loss of appetite, lethargy or a withdrawal from normal activities, it is time to ask for help. The kind of help so frequently meted out by the family doctor in the form of a prescription for tranquillizers or antidepressant drugs is not necessarily an appropriate response to the problem. Overcoming serious depression needs skilful and perhaps prolonged specialist treatment or professional counselling.

The Art of Counselling
(See also Part III, Counselling)

Patients who visit their doctor with complaints due solely to physical causes are in the minority. The major part of a general practitioner's workload consists of patients who are suffering some kind of psychological stress. It is not that doctors are unaware that patients need their time, but people find it so difficult to discuss their emotional concerns that very often it is not until they are about to leave the surgery that they will suddenly pluck up the courage to talk about what is really troubling them, and by then it is time for the doctor to try to meet another patient's demands. Many GPs are now employing counsellors in order to cope with the psychological needs of their patients.

How does counselling work? Dr Kearns described it in this way:

'The most important objective is to help a person maintain self-esteem. Anyone suffering from the effects of stress or who has experienced a nervous breakdown thinks they are the only ones to whom it has ever happened. They are afraid they might be defective in some way; so when they are persuaded that their problem is very commonplace, they no longer feel they are suffering in isolation and are comforted; their condition becomes less threatening. They can then begin to put things in perspective and try to work out for themselves what they see to be the cause of their suffering. A counsellor or doctor, or even a friend, just by listening is doing some good, simply because the sufferer has been forced to make his thoughts coherent in order to describe how he feels. In sound counselling, nobody suggests to you what you ought to do or tells you to "go away and pull yourself together". If a counsellor encourages the person under stress to discipline the mind in order to structure the problem, a solution frequently presents itself. For example, if you are told to go to the boss and complain that you are overworked, your mind is being forced to take more strain. Instead, you yourself might decide to take a holiday or a rest, or resolve to see a doctor, thereby erecting a whole series of your own options to suit your own circumstances. Each problem is virtually unique and it is really up to the individual to examine it in their own terms and construct their own solution.'

Choosing the Best Therapist

The decision to turn to someone for help in a crisis is the hardest step to take, but once taken, usually brings great relief. Choice of therapist is dictated by three main considerations: money, time and availability. Sessions with a psychiatrist or psychotherapist are about an hour in length and, depending on the nature of the problem, more than one session a week may be required. Although fees vary, at around £35 an hour, professional help in private practice is a great luxury. Psychotherapy is available on the National Health but choice and accessibility are more limited. Even those able to take advantage of help privately may feel that after the first encounter they have made a terrible mistake. The therapist they have chosen is not at all the kind of person with whom they feel secure and confident. It is very difficult then to persuade a vulnerable and anxious person not to give up, yet persistence will eventually provide what so many people come to describe as 'a life-line'.

Robin Skynner (*Weekend Guardian*, 21–2 September 1991) stresses the importance of the therapist's training, knowledge and experience, but he suggests that, in order to establish a basis for a collaborative relationship, the 'quality of the therapist as a person is more important still'. He adds, 'I also believe that the most committed and effective therapist is one who is more healthy than the patient though not so much more healthy that they cannot remember what it was like to be at that stage of development themselves, or how they got out of it.'

Psychotherapy is all about helping people to help themselves and an alternative to expensive therapy is to contact the British Association for Counselling (see p. 366) for advice about counselling services which are often provided free of charge; or to choose a local self-help group which seems likely to offer the right kind of sympathy and support. Fairly new to this country and rapidly gaining in popularity is an organization called Co-Dependents Anonymous (CoDA), a fellowship of men and women whose low self-esteem and lack of self-reliance makes it difficult for them to maintain functional relationships. The only requirement for membership is a desire for healthy and fulfilling relationships with others and for positive self-respect.

Loneliness

Loneliness is something that everyone experiences at certain times in their lives; it is part of the human condition, yet it is a condition we all dread because, in its more extreme forms, it goes against all our natural instincts. Man is a social animal, deeply reliant on his fellow creatures for pleasure, interaction and, perhaps most importantly, his self-esteem. It is by communicating with others that he receives a sense of his own worth. Loneliness will cause a person to lack self-confidence and motivation: 'Nobody cares whether I live or die, so what's the point of caring about myself?' 'Why bother with anyone if nobody bothers with me?'

Living alone does not automatically mean that a person is lonely. On the contrary, thousands of men and women of all ages live happily on their own surrounded by friends and family, enjoying an active and fulfilled life. Loneliness is by no means exclusive to old age. It is a feeling as familiar to teenagers as it is to single parents bringing up young children or to elderly widows or widowers alone for the first time in their adult lives; but in old age, the condition is rendered more acute when it is associated with ill health and disability. The fear that cries for help in an emergency would bring no response is terrifyingly real.

What is it then that turns 'aloneness' into one of the unhappiest and most destructive of all human conditions? In the first instance, loneliness can be created externally – as by a bereavement, where the loss of a partner or loved one can form such a devastating vacuum that, by comparison, a desert island would seem a haven of friendliness. Externally created loneliness can also be experienced in a relationship or environment in which a person may find that he or she has suddenly become 'the odd one out'. This situation may produce attacks of extreme panic in which sufferers find themselves wanting to run away from whoever or whatever is causing their feeling of isolation. Both these conditions are usually temporary and, given time, victims will gather the momentum needed to reshape their lives – unless that is, they also suffer from the second, more insidious cause of loneliness, namely an isolation which has been created internally, by their own thoughts, beliefs and attitudes. What makes this form of loneliness difficult to deal with is that it can become established as part of the personality. The more withdrawn people become, the more they will appear to repel all offers of friendship. If they are unable to recognize loneliness as *their* problem they will be unable to bring about changes in their way of life, in their approach and even their appearance – all of which would help to remedy their isolation.

How Can Loneliness be Overcome?

Each person's experience of loneliness is unique to their situation, and there are no easy answers, but there is a great deal of help available provided the sufferer is willing to reach out for it. The very act of looking for help and deciding which might be most appropriate for their needs is an act of involvement which in itself will go halfway towards solving the problem.

Friendship is discussed in Chapter 1, Retirement and the Rewards of Early Planning, and useful names and addresses can be found in Part III, Friendships.

Reading

Val Marriott and Terry Tiblick, *Loneliness – How to Overcome it*, Age Concern England

SEX AND SEXUALITY

In a lecture given at the Institute of Obstetrics and Gynaecology, Professor Alex Comfort, gerontologist and author of *The Joy of Sex*, condemned the 'outrageous folklore' and 'misinformation' which cloud the issues concerning ageing and sexuality:

People, particularly the young, still think of sexual activity as a wasting asset which has no particular interest to anyone over sixty. In all periods of history, people over the age of sixty could tell them that wasn't true, but they tended to keep quiet about it simply because of the flack the sexually active elderly were liable to encounter. Until recently, no one took case histories from older people because older people were assumed not to have an active sex life and they were assumed not to be active because nobody had bothered to ask them.

With all the variations, it is quite impossible to draw any conclusions, but statistical studies are beginning to show that old people have always remained sexually active, although frequencies do vary quite a lot within marriage. People don't always decline in interest. Some people show an increase and some people a decrease in sexual activity in age. Ageing abolishes neither the need nor the capacity for enjoying sex. It may, though, limit the opportunity, especially since women are in the majority in the older age groups.

There is an enormous variation in people's interest in sex. We all know people for whom sexuality is very unimportant and other people who think about virtually nothing else. Most people come between the two. Those who rate sexual urges in youth as strong tend to rate them as moderate in old age, and those who describe their sexual feelings as weak to moderate in youth tend to describe themselves as being without sexual feelings in old age.

Gerontologists are very familiar with the discrepancy between the common perception of what old age is like and what it's actually like when you get there. It feels remarkably little different from youth. What is different is other people's attitudes. Apart from sex, older people have been hocused out of many other areas of activity such as learning new skills simply by popular misinformation. I have known people who thought it wasn't worth going to college because if they were old they couldn't learn. Thomas Jefferson worried about this when he was an old man but it didn't stop him learning. There are a lot of women who have looked forward to the post-menopausal years as a period of enforced asexuality because they will be no longer desirable and a great many men have been certain they will be impotent as a result of the passage of time.

It is true that ageing does induce some changes in physiology. In the male, orgasm becomes less frequent and requires physical stimulation to produce it. There are some other minor changes, in that the carrying angle of the erect penis becomes lower and the reflex does not retract the testes during orgasm, but these are very unimportant and by no means impair function. Women undergo a more spectacular change in the menopause, which does terminate fertility but it in no way terminates sexuality; on the contrary, nowadays very commonly, it tends to release it. Compared therefore with age changes in other systems, such as the focusing of the eye or the vital capacity, these changes are really quite minimal. People are agreeably surprised and perhaps a little guilty to find themselves still functional when everybody else tells them they shouldn't be. Sexual function judged by intercourse, not by reproduction, holds up very much better than most other similar functions. When it does fail, it fails for a very wide variety of reasons which can range from general ill health to opting out. There are, of course, people who have found sexuality unsatisfactory or anxiety-making and they may be relieved at having the excuse as they get older to lay down an anxious and embarrassing function.[55]

Dr Comfort emphasized the need for close communication between the patient and the GP. Doctors failed to draw the right conclusions from patients' histories, partly because they were afraid to cause embarrassment and partly because the patients themselves find difficulty in finding the words to describe their symptoms.

Sexual Dysfunction

It is extremely important for doctors to establish the cause of sexual dysfunction. Impotence, especially in men who have previously managed to have sex without any difficulty, can be an important indication of early disease – diabetes, renal disease, vascular disease, for example. In the past, it was thought that the main reason for sexual dysfunction in men was psychogenic; thus, in the first instance, impotence was generally treated with some form of psychotherapy. Women who failed to achieve orgasm were taught how to 'get in touch with themselves'. However, it is now estimated that about 50 per cent of male dysfunction at the performance level is wholly or partially physical in origin and this proportion increases considerably with age. Dr Comfort explained that although impotence in the previously potent can be psychogenic, and that impotence following illness or local surgery is much more common in people who have a past history of dysfunction, there is a great range of physical causes, which include circulatory changes, a laxity of the penile ligaments, leakage from the veins, undiagnosed depression and undiagnosed diabetes. Alcohol and numerous drugs, including beta blockers and most of the drugs used in psychiatry, also inhibit potency.

In concluding his lecture, Professor Comfort offered the following advice which, although aimed more towards general practitioners in the audience, provided some useful information for the rest of us:

If the patient doesn't respond in the first instance to counselling, then he or she should be sent to a specialist sexual disorders unit at least until general practitioner training and equipment catches up with the new knowledge.

We now know it's possible to produce useful erection in virtually anyone, but to do so, you have to inject a drug into the body of the penis. You can produce about an hour's erection but if you overdo it, you produce priapism. But there is a simple antidote for this. Papaverine is a drug which has produced erection in diabetics who have been unable to perform for long periods. The interesting thing is that after a few shots of the drug, some people have been able to continue normal function without the help of the drug.

Other cases are correctible either by vascular surgery or by medication. In most cases of late-life male dysfunction, you can now give some useful forms of treatment which should be administered exactly as it might be with any other physiological problem arising from the ageing process, although this is not easy in the GP's office because family doctors do not generally have the time or the necessary equipment.

On the other hand there are forms of impotence which can be helped with judicial counselling by the general practitioner. Widower's impotence is loss of sexual function due to a mixture of guilt and relief over the partner's death, getting out of the habit and then performance anxiety with a new partner. Then there is menopausal impotence: when a woman receives her hormone supplement at the menopause, lubrication goes sharply up just at the time when her partner requires more friction; he, of course, thinks he's running out of steam. These are all perfectly simple things to be dealt with.

The immediate job in hand is to persuade the patient not to suffer in silence or to fail to report drug effects for fear of embarrassing the doctor. You very often find that if somebody is put on an anti-hypertensive and fails to achieve an erection, he doesn't tell the doctor – he just stops taking the drug.[56]

Another view of sexuality after forty was put forward by Dr H. B. Gibson (see p. 297): 'A woman's sexual function doesn't alter much through the whole of her life span. A man's does. His sexual function gradually diminishes. There are of course men in their nineties who are still sexually active, but a woman can fall in love in her sixties and have a more passionate expression of love than she has ever had in her life before. This is an extraordinary thing, and when it happens to people, they are utterly amazed that their love can be expressed with such physical passion. Although the cultural pattern is for men to marry younger women, it would be far better if things were different and men were to marry women older than themselves, since not only do women maintain their sex drive, but they generally outlive men.

'It isn't as true as you might think that women need necessarily to look young and beautiful in order to be sexually attractive to men. The Starr-Weiner Report, an American research project which was published in 1981, asked eight hundred men and women over sixty to describe their ideal partner. The surprising thing was that most of them described somebody not much different to themselves in age. It rather gave the lie to the fact that older men wanted women in their twenties. But what makes a person attractive is very complex. As we get older, it is the character as expressed in the face and the body and the total body movement which impresses and attracts rather than the youthful desire for perfect body contours and a lovely face.'

The following brief histories express the passion and the sadness of romance in later life.

> My husband died when I was sixty. Five years later I fell in love with a man whom I should have liked to marry but it wouldn't have worked out. He was American and I felt I couldn't make the move across the Atlantic. The passion I felt for him was not much different to that which I had felt in my youth for my husband – it was at least as emotionally intense. The main difference, I think, was understanding that we were both, at our time of life, more independent. I should not have minded being on my own as much as I did when I was young.

> I met my future husband when I was seventy-five and was determined to marry him before I was eighty. In fact, we got married on my eightieth birthday. It was the second marriage for both of us. My two daughters were very disapproving at first, but we are so happy together and my husband takes such good care of me that one of the girls is now truly delighted but the other, sadly, still refuses to see her stepfather and consequently I almost never see her.

Relatively little research data is available on the sexuality of women but their sex lives are often enhanced after the menopause, especially since hormone replacement therapy has become an option (see p. 291). Although statistics conclude that in general women's interest and involvement in sex declines considerably more than men's after the age of fifty, what these same statistics do not show are the reasons for this decline. It is thought, however, that the discrepancy has more to do with lack of opportunity than anything else. In the older age groups, there are just not enough men to go round.

Attitudes of the Medical Profession

Doctors, whether they are general practitioners or hospital consultants, can still be extraordinarily insensitive about sex, surely

the most sensitive and intimate area in the whole of our biological and psychological make-up – where sex is concerned,
some doctors regard middle and old age as another country. The
following is one man's experience of an all-too-common attitude:

> I went to my doctor with prostate trouble and was
> told that at some stage in the not too far distant
> future, I would need an operation. The first thing that
> came into my head was 'My God, what about my sex
> life?' But when I asked the GP whether he thought I
> would be adversely affected by surgery, he just
> laughed at me and said 'You're surely not worried
> about such things at your age!' 'But, Doctor,' I said,
> 'I'm only fifty-five.'

Another man showed me a booklet which a consultant had
handed to him after he had been referred to a hospital out-
patient clinic for sexual dysfunction. The pamphlet described a
'user-friendly vacuum pump for impotence management'. 'Go
home and talk this over with your wife,' he was told. The very
sensitive nature of sexuality and sexual function means that the
introduction of mechanical or surgical aids to help performance
must be handled with the greatest delicacy and tact if they are
to have any value at all between couples. It is no good offering
a man a useful aid if his partner is going to turn away in
disgust. Again, careful counselling and communication at every
level can be the greatest source of help.

Younger doctors are only reflecting in their surgeries what
the great majority of us have been conditioned to think in the
past, namely that we can have sex, we sometimes believe our
children can, but we have great difficulty in accepting that
older generations do. Lodged in the back of our minds, we all
perhaps carry with us into adulthood the strong childish belief
that our parents, if they 'did it' at all, only had sex together as
many times as there are children in the family.

Specialists working in the field are convinced of the need to
re-educate both the young and the old about sex in middle and
old age. One psychologist stated:

'Young people through popular magazines and literature are
bombarded with information about sex, whether it be from
magazine articles or from letters to agony aunts. Yet the people

who really need sex education are in their mid-sixties because they are still living with the stereotypes of the past, when one did not talk freely about sexual concerns. Now, it's all right for couples not to talk about sex when things are going well, but if problems arise and they are too shy to communicate with each other, a couple might just drop lovemaking as it were by mutual consent, each one of them thinking, "I'd like to continue, but obviously my partner doesn't." This lack of communication can have devastating results. For example, occasional bouts of impotence can affect men at all ages. If this is not understood and discussed between partners, barriers will be set up which could lead to the collapse of their marriage. If a man, convinced of his impotence, meets another woman who restores his sexual confidence, he will see his future with her rather than with his wife. Conversely, the dissatisfied and bewildered wife, feeling she is no longer desired, may well turn to another man, thereby dealing her husband a blow from which he may never fully recover.'

In 1990, the Association of Retired Persons (ARP) published the results of a sex survey of men and women between the ages of fifty and eighty.[57] The survey showed that enthusiasm for lovemaking for 72 per cent of men and 75 per cent of women is as strong as ever and that reaching a climax is just as essential after the age of fifty as before. It also indicated that 45 per cent of the survey's respondents had sex at least once a week, and a quarter more often than that. Asked if they had ever wanted to be unfaithful in the past five years, 25 per cent of the women and 30 per cent of the men said yes. These percentages go up to 33 per cent for women in their sixties and 40 per cent for men in their fifties. According to the ARP survey, the findings suggest that overall, people's sexual needs and interest change very little with the passing years.

CHECK LIST: HEALTH'S DO'S AND DON'T'S

Do

Take care of yourself and avoid health problems
Get prompt medical attention

Understand your body and personal medical needs
Eat a healthy, balanced diet
Exercise daily, strenuously three times a week
See ageing as partly inevitable and partly alterable
Slow down and relax
Keep up appearances
Take pride in your age
Make a commitment to healthy living
Look after your partner
Maintain your stamina, mobility and strength

Don't

Smoke or drink too much
Overeat or eat the wrong food
Ignore warning signs
Use crash diets
Become inactive
Sleep too much
Let yourself go

7   Caring for Others

Adapting to the losses of mobility, hearing or sight, or learning to come to terms with illness and pain, requires an inner resourcefulness which is hard to acquire unless it is backed up by a strong support system, and for most people that means a reliance on their family. It is one thing to rely on someone else for help from time to time, but quite another to be completely dependent. Dependence is a state which is universally feared. 'I don't ever want to be a burden to the children' is a sentence uttered by every parent who feels the touch of age upon them, but in the end it is usually 'the children' who are the first to express concern and the first to offer support. 'I say to my mother when she worries about being a burden, "You've spent most of your life giving; now you've got to be prepared to take"' was one typically caring response.

But however great the love and the desire to help may be, the burden of looking after a dependent relative can be very heavy indeed. The disruption to family life, the physical strain and mental anguish push to the limit the women – for it is usually women – upon whose shoulders the weight rests. This chapter looks at some of the problems involved and suggests ways in which carers can themselves find support.

CONDITIONS WHICH CAN LEAD TO DEPENDENCE

Parkinson's Disease

Parkinson's is a disorder affecting the area of the brain which coordinates voluntary body movement. It usually affects people over fifty and its progression is often fairly rapid.

At the moment, the most successful drug used in the treatment of Parkinson's has been L-dopa, which relieves rather than prevents the disease, but after a year or so the drug loses its effectiveness, even when given in increased doses.

In August 1989, *Science* magazine published the optimistic findings of researchers Dr James W. Tetrud and Dr J. William Langston of the California Parkinson's Foundation in San José. Animal studies showed that a new drug, deprenyl, actually prevents the death of brain cells, without any obvious side-effects. The results of a small-scale study of twenty-seven patients was optimistic but could not, mostly because of its size, be described as conclusive. Currently, however, the US government has sponsored a study of eight hundred patients, which compares deprenyl alone against the drug in combination with vitamin E and against a placebo. The study will be completed in November 1991.[58]

Dementia and Alzheimer's Disease

According to Dr John Kellett, consultant psychogeriatrician at St George's Hospital in London, 'dementia' (or the now rather old-fashioned term 'senility') 'is not a diagnosis'. He said, 'I always liken the word to a chest physician telling a patient he has a cough. You wouldn't be too impressed with the doctor if that was all he could come up with.'

Degenerative diseases of the brain which impair memory, thinking and behaviour in older people are in the main caused either by Alzheimer's disease or by damage to the arteries which supply blood to the brain. When these arteries break down, the result is a series of small strokes.

We tend to fear becoming demented in old age more than we fear death itself, but dementia must be put in perspective. As Dr Kellett reminds us, 'If you take the figure which generally shows that 20 per cent of people over the age of eighty are demented, it means that 80 per cent of people over eighty are not'. He is currently involved in conducting trials with a new drug to combat the effects of Alzheimer's disease. This debilitating and progressive disease affects only a small number of people in their sixties, although the chance of it developing increases with age and rises sharply among those aged over eighty-five – about 20 per cent of over-eighty-fives are affected by it.[59]

The results of the trial at St George's have so far been optimistic. Dr Kellett commented: 'I am very impressed with [the new drug]. It does, I think, improve the memory of people who suffer from Alzheimer's. If we assume that 50 per cent of dementia is caused by Alzheimer's disease and the drug I am talking about works, that is a 50 per cent improvement over all. The other 50 per cent of patients who become demented have even greater chances of improvement because the problem is often caused by high blood pressure, arteritis or other blood abnormalities – all of which can be treated and should be treated in the early stages.

'People over the age of eighty ought to have some form of clinical assessment once a year in order to catch these things before they start to damage the brain. The most important thing to check is the blood pressure, because high blood pressure damages the arteries so that the flow of blood to the brain becomes inadequate. In general vascular disease, you can get narrowing of the brachial artery on the one side and not on the other, so the blood pressure should be tested in both arms because, while it might be found to be normal in the left arm, it could be grossly raised in the right. A further check can be made by manually testing the pressure in the carotid arteries of the neck since the pressure in both arms may be an underestimate of the blood pressure to the brain.'

In Dr Kellett's experience, general practitioners don't always take the precaution of including both arms in blood-pressure tests and older patients should insist upon their doing so.

Case Histories

It was two years after his death from Alzheimer's before Carla could bring herself to discuss the problems surrounding her father's illness. Her difficulties are similar to those experienced by many carers who have been brought face to face with the daily realities of the disease. Sharing her experience may prove helpful:

> Looking back, I first realized there was something wrong with my father about ten years before he died.

Just after his retirement, we felt that he was behaving in an eccentric and extremely irritating way. We, my two sisters and I, were very unsympathetic at this stage. We tried to get him to take a part-time job. I tried to persuade him to take a course studying antiques at the local college of higher education, but he was hostile to any suggestions. We thought he was probably upset about his retirement and the phase would pass. Then he started to hoard things. We discovered piles of banknotes behind a bookcase in his bedroom. One of the things he liked very much was to come down to Sunday lunch with my daughter and me. He suddenly started to forget and I became very angry with him.

It's difficult to know exactly when I realized that the forgetfulness was a symptom of something more serious. He developed a rheumy-eyed look – almost as if there was a gap in the brain. He lost interest in eating properly and lost a lot of weight. It was all very gradual. He complained of feeling dizzy in his brain and sometimes looked completely bewildered.

After about five or six years, I went to his GP and said I was very worried about him. The GP suggested that he and a psychogeriatrician would make a home visit to assess his condition. We could have gone to a hospital for the same thing, but I was afraid my father would have been upset by the atmosphere there. The home assessment took about two hours, and a diagnosis of Alzheimer's was made. I found it difficult to tell my father that he was ill at this stage because he wouldn't have understood what I was talking about.

I felt absolutely devastated when I learned what Alzheimer's really involved. The idea of my father becoming doubly incontinent was the hardest of all to come to terms with.

I immediately contacted the Social Services to get him a home help. We all felt he should be at home for as long as possible. There was a long wait before a home help became available and I had to keep badgering the Social Services. They first of all wanted to deliver frozen meals to him either every day, or sometimes a week's supply, but I had to explain to them that he was incapable of cooking the food properly and could not tell the difference between the deep freeze compartment and the refrigerator. Eventually we were sent an extremely efficient and very kind home help, Mary, who spent about an hour to an hour and a half with Dad each day, cooked for him and did the shopping. The only thing she didn't do was to give him a bath; it wasn't her job to do so. The District Nurse would have had to do it. I tried a couple of times but it was too much for me. Sometimes Mary would wash him all over. She was wonderful with him. She never patronized him. She came five days a week and I took care of him at the weekends. We also had incredible support from the neighbours. If it hadn't been for their help, he would have had to go into a nursing home at this stage. I noticed particularly if he didn't want to do something, he became violent.

Things went on like this for about three years until they got so bad I began to be frightened for him. First of all, Dad smoked and there were cigarette burns all over the place. Secondly, I thought there was too much stress on the neighbours. There was almost an explosion with the gas cooker. We had to have the cooker and the gas fire dismantled. He was becoming very thin. He began wandering off in the middle of the night. He usually made his way home, but sometimes he'd dart out into the street. We knew it was only a matter of time before something terrible would happen to him. I was worried twenty-four hours a day for his safety.

He came to stay with us a couple of times but it was a disaster. He couldn't bear to be out of his own little world or routine. After he had been ill in hospital for ten days, I brought him home, but it was impossible. He became completely disorientated and when I tried to take his arm to lead him to the hairdresser's, he lashed out and knocked me down. He had been roughly treated in hospital. Because he kept wandering about and climbing into other men's beds, the nurses had become fed up with him.

Once he was back in his own home with Mary looking after him during the day, he settled down and we were able to keep him there for a while, but he was just too much danger to himself. When we finally put him in the home, the feelings of guilt were terrible. Many people have their parents living with them in their own home at this stage. I just couldn't manage it. In a big Victorian household with an extended family and plenty of help, he would have been perfectly happy just to be left in his old chair by the fireside and would have fitted in as 'dear old grandad'. But it's quite impossible to have someone living at home who is so helpless if you have to be out to work all day.

A friend once said to me, 'At least you don't need to worry that your father feels unhappy because he really doesn't know what's going on.' I honestly don't think this is true. He had great fears. A lot of the time he seemed deeply unhappy and embarrassed. Sometimes he would try to describe feelings of persecution, but his vocabulary was very limited. At these times, I know he felt terrified. Oddly enough, even in the last few months of his living at home, he could understand a little conversation on the telephone. He could almost always recognize my voice, although sometimes, towards the end, not even mine. He even managed at quite an advanced stage to ring me. I took advantage of his ability to focus on the telephone by placing beside it notes with numbers and little pieces of simple information.

Seeing my father's disintegration was totally annihilating. I had to treat him like a little child. It was a terrible role reversal. The grandchildren could't cope. It was very distressing for my daughter when he came to stay although she was wonderful to him.

Being in the home proved very traumatic for him. He deteriorated after six weeks or so even though it was a marvellous place. The matron, one of the most exceptional women I have ever met, told us that it seemed to be a pattern that if patients settled down quickly and appeared happy to begin with, they soon deteriorated. On the other hand, patients who settled down more slowly did better on the whole. They appeared to benefit from a more gradual acceptance of their new way of life, but perhaps it was just an indication that their disease was not quite so far advanced. At first Dad liked the home but soon sank into a gloom. He became incontinent and spent a lot of time in bed.

When he was in the home, someone had to take absolute control of his business affairs. I had taken over his financial dealings for some years with the cooperation of his bank manager and solicitor. His bills were always sent to me and I used to take the cheques for him to sign. When he was unable to write his signature, I took over power of attorney. It is a difficult business because of course the patient must be protected. The situation is obviously open to terrible abuse. My father would have signed anything.

Since Carla regarded the nursing home in such a favourable light, I asked her how she came to decide upon that particular home for her father. She replied:

We were lucky to find it. We looked at twenty-two others before making a final choice. It was a pleasant house, Victorian and rambling – very like the house which we had grown up in, and I think Dad identified with it. Then again, I liked the atmosphere. It's a bit like looking at schools for your children. You can sense the kind of place it is as soon as you walk in the door. The matron, of course, was the most important factor and there was a high proportion of staff to patients. We did not want a house which was too isolated in the country. Some homes did not offer a single room, only a dormitory. Dad had been living on his own for ten years or so, and we thought he would prefer his own little room. Some homes did not have carpets on the floor and seemed so cold. This home had a special bathroom with pulleys which enabled patients to have showers. We also liked the fact that the staff believed in talking to the patients. They didn't believe in tranquillizing them. They took them out on trips in little minibuses. They took them shopping and down to the pub every day before lunch. They were the only place we saw that did that. My father was allowed to take as much of his own furniture and pictures as the room would hold. He took a couple of cushions, his favourite chair, and about sixteen of his pictures decorated the walls. We could visit any time of the day or night.

When we first started applying for homes, we found the local authority could not help. As far as they were concerned, he wasn't bad enough for them to take over. That meant they refused to have him because he was not doubly incontinent and hadn't yet been run over. Attendance allowance covers a daily help or twenty-four-hour help. I applied for attendance allowance for someone who needed twenty-four-hour supervision. We were turned down the first time but eventually we were given the full allowance. I would advise anyone in the same situation, knowing things can only get worse, to apply for attendance allowance well in advance. The procedure takes such a long time.

Morlais Price has been a carer for thirteen years. He is vice-chairman of his local branch of the Carers National Association and the area contact for the Alzheimer's Disease Society. He works tirelessly on behalf of both organizations with the same energy and enthusiasm which he devoted to teaching, a job he still misses since, at the age of sixty-one, he gave up the headship of a large urban junior school to look after his wife Peggy when it became evident she was afflicted by Alzheimer's. 'For me,' he said, 'there simply was no choice.'

When I first met Mrs Price, I was struck by how physically

robust she was. She looked somewhat younger than her seventy-three years and I was astonished how anyone so entirely helpless could be maintained in such apparent good health. It seemed to me miraculous that her husband, without her physical or mental cooperation, could persuade his wife to take in enough food to keep her so well-nourished and to exercise her limbs to the extent that they seemed to be in such good condition. I asked Mr Price whether he felt the success and quality of care depended on the quality of the love felt by the carer. He said that, in his case, he thought it did and explained:

I've always been a one-woman man. We got on very, very well together. We met fifty-two years ago at college when we were both training to be teachers and we've been together ever since. She taught for forty years, but towards the end the headmistress noticed she was becoming a bit absent-minded, which is something she never was. She was the most efficient person with an eye for detail. She was an italic-script writer, and you could see the lines beginning to wobble when she was doing her class notes, whereas these had always been immaculate. I began to be rather worried about her and asked her if she felt all right. 'Sometimes I get a bit bothered,' she said. I suggested she give up teaching but she wanted to continue. In the following year, she began to lose a terrible amount of weight and it turned out she had tuberculosis in one lung. While she was having tests and hospital treatment, it was discovered that there was a malfunction in the brain. Her memory by this time was going and the diagnosis of Alzheimer's was made. She was in hospital for two months, during which time I gave in my notice at school. When she came out of hospital, there was a definite change and from that time on, although she is completely over the TB, there has been a steady deterioration in her condition and it has been a downhill struggle all the way. First, she used to lose her bearings when she became disorientated and kept blanking out. She constantly had to ask people where she was. At that stage, she was still more or less aware of her surroundings and could just about cope with feeding herself and going to the toilet, and she was still able to communicate, but I had to be with her all the time. I thought to myself, 'we must get away', so I bought a mobile home in France, a country which we had always loved and had often visited. We lived down there five months of the year for five years until ultimately Peggy's condition became impossible and we couldn't maintain it.

She then became terribly depressed because she realized something was wrong with her but couldn't understand what was happening. Then came the frustration when she used to become very violent and hit me, often so hard that I would fall under the blows. She was always sorry afterwards but she got herself into such a panic that she'd turn and lash out at me. Then she began running away. She was physically fit and she'd run away for miles and miles, all over the place. I spent half my life tracking her down by car. I was always terrified she'd find water because she was a wonderful swimmer, but of course without me beside her, she would lose her bearings. We swam regularly until about four years ago when she became incontinent. It was wonderful exercise for her. I think she could probably still manage to keep herself afloat, but I can't get hydrotherapy for her in her present condition.

By this time, Peg had so deteriorated that I couldn't manage to look after her at home. The house was just too big. I wasn't well myself then – physically and mentally at a very low ebb. I decided to sell the house and move into sheltered accommodation. Although I find this little flat claustrophobic, it has certainly made things much easier for me and my own health has vastly improved. It's meant I can organize my life. It cost me about £7,000 to equip the place with the hoist, the bath lift, electric chair and bed, but it has been worth every penny. I have even changed the car for a specially designed van.

Mr Price took down a photograph of his wife from the bookshelf. The hair on the pretty young woman in the frame was piled on top of her head in carefully dressed curls. It was a style she wore throughout her life and which her husband lovingly keeps up for her. He said, 'I feel it is good for my morale and for all our friends to see her looking like she always did. It's silly sentiment, I suppose, but despite the terrible changes, my memories of her as she used to be are very strong and you see, there are still times when she recognizes me.' He turned to his wife, 'You do know me, don't you, Peg?' Lifting up the lolling, lifeless head, he gently patted her cheek. Her eyes opened, looked at his face and for a fraction of a second, the position of her mouth altered slightly. It might almost have been a smile.

Yet even in these darkest days, when her disease has reached the final stages of helplessness, there have been moments of more positive recognition. Every three months, Mr Price is able to take a break from his carer's role when Peggy is placed in a local nursing home for a fortnight and he uses the time to travel abroad. 'Only once when I returned has she failed to recognize me. On that occasion, she didn't know me for a whole week, then one morning, she just woke up and put her arms out to me. When I came back from Italy after my last break, I went to collect her and said, "Come on, Peg, we're going home." She turned round and as soon as she saw me she just smiled and smiled.'

I asked Mr Price, from his many years of experience as a carer, what advice he might have for people who find themselves in the same position. He said:

> You must find time for yourself and your family. It is so easy to neglect the children when you are looking after someone who needs your attention twenty-four hours a day. My daughter found it especially difficult to get over the fact that her mother no longer recognized her. It was a terrible time for her and she needed a lot of support and reassurance from me, but now she can take pleasure in the fact that apart from myself, Peggy seems to recognize her four-year-old grandson. My granddaughter on the other hand is

rather afraid of her grandmother, but the little boy just climbs on her knee and strokes her face and she responds by sometimes just focusing on him and sometimes smiling.

You cannot struggle along on your own. Accept the fact that you need help as a carer and you must take regular breaks from the job. Counselling is especially important. I know that sooner or later, I won't be able to feed Peggy and I won't be able to care for her and then I will have to take the decision to have her live out the rest of her days in a nursing home. Now my daughter has grown up, it is relatively easy for me. I have only myself and my wife to consider, but where there are conflicting loyalties, the difficulties are greatly increased. I really do feel, though, that the decision should always come down on the side of the 'living'. It is in nobody's interest for carers to allow families to break up because they feel they must devote all their time and attention to a patient who will ultimately become impossible to look after at home.

Despite her total dependence upon him, Mr Price has never treated his wife as a child. There are very rare moments when Peggy utters familiar phrases which remind him that she is still, somewhere deep within herself, the person he knew so well. On one occasion, she called out 'Certainly not' in what he described as 'her best classroom voice', adding, 'and you could see them cringing in the back row!' Their closeness as a couple has helped him to perform the intimate services necessary for her care and even in the days when Peggy was still aware of her dependence, she did not resent his attention.

Mr Price is concerned that people in his position do not become consumed by their duties. They should always retain a sense of proportion and develop interests outside the home. 'They must never fall into the trap of thinking that no one else can do the job as well as they can themselves. Be prepared to let others take the strain.'

(See also Part III, Mental Health.)

Cancer

Many types of cancers are now curable, but because certain forms of the disease need long-term care and may lead to terminal illness, it seems appropriate to mention it here. Cancer is responsible for 25 per cent of deaths in this country each year. About one third of patients die at home and the remainder in hospitals and hospices.

Cancer often forces radical changes upon patients and their partners. It is a family affair, in which the most important source of comfort and support is the spouse. A study of women conducted by the Dutch gynaecologist, Dr Bos-Branolte, in 1989, indicated that while the majority of patients felt they were both practically and emotionally supported by their husbands, many found it difficult to talk to them about their feelings, about the nature of the disease and the future. Many of the women interviewed were concerned that their partners needed an emotional support which they were not receiving.

In gynaecological cancers, where the pattern of a couple's sex life might be quite dramatically altered, Dr Bos-Branolte stressed that a positive partner relationship appeared to be determined more by intimacy, emotional support and open communication than by sexuality. In a lecture delivered at the Institute of Obstetrics and Gynaecology, she warned:

Not everybody is able to cope with the consequences. While for some problems begin in the hospital, others suffer after they get back home. Psychological problems are more likely to manifest themselves six to twelve months after the operation. In the first few months, while families are so involved with the treatment and after-care, there is not much time for reflection. Patients who cope well in the beginning may collapse later on. A husband may no longer be able to bear the burden of his wife's illness. In a state of fear, worry, and grief, he may commonly develop alcohol problems and even symptoms of heart disease. At the same time, the patient can become seriously anxious and depressed. She worries about her body image, loses self-esteem and feels that the partner relationship is threatened.

Dr Bos-Branolte's report emphasizes the need for counselling for both husband and wife at a time when serious illness puts so much strain on them both as individuals and upon their marriage partnership. The children's anxieties too can be relieved by counselling. Talking to a trained impartial outsider is of immense benefit during this critical period. Experienced counsellors, if they cannot be recommended by the GP, can be found by telephoning Relate or the British Association for Counselling (see Part III, Counselling), *not* by answering advertisements in newspapers or magazines.

Counselling is particularly valuable when the surgery required is mutilating. One of the most tragic stories was recalled by a counsellor in the Midlands: 'A patient was referred to me by her family doctor following a radical mastectomy for breast cancer. He had been horrified when she first came to him in an obviously advanced stage of the disease. "But why on earth didn't you come to me before when you first discovered the lump?" he asked her. She replied, "Because when I told my husband, he said he would leave me if I had to have my breast cut off. I have only come to you now because he has just asked me for a divorce to go off with someone else."'

Help

The stress of serious illness should not be borne alone whether by the sufferer or the carer. See Part III, Health – Cancer.

Stroke

A stroke occurs when an artery in the brain becomes blocked off or bleeds. In Britain, about a hundred thousand people annually suffer from strokes, which usually develop without warning and kill about a third of their victims. If symptoms do occur, they are likely to be in the form of a transient ischaemic attack. Lasting a few minutes, this can involve loss of speech or visual disturbances, or perhaps a one-sided weakness with tingling or numbness. These symptoms should never be ignored and can be effectively treated.

At the time of writing, the only place in Britain where stroke victims can receive the long-term speech rehabilitation which they so desperately need is run by the City Dysphasics Group

(City University, St John's Street, London ECI; tel. 071–608 0080). Research conducted by the group over a period of twenty years has revealed that people do not begin to make progress towards regaining their speech until a period of at least six months after the stroke has occurred. Sufferers do not lose their intelligence, but their powers of communication must be completely relearned. It is a long and arduous process and can take years to produce results. Under the present system of care, patients are generally returned to their uncomprehending families after hospitalization and a six-month course of speech therapy of perhaps one hour a week. The City Dysphasics Group insists upon two full days a week for just as long as it takes to learn to talk again.

Incontinence

See p. 283.

COPING WITH DEPENDENCY

Caring for Someone at Home

When a parent or relative can no longer manage to look after themselves, they will need to be cared for, either at home or in the home of a family member or a friend. Under these circumstances, outside help is likely to be required, whether they remain in their own home or are accommodated by a family, whose members may all be in full-time employment. The decisions involved can bring great stress and anxiety to those who consider themselves responsible for providing the necessary care, and as the following case history suggests, caring for the dying can be a very lonely business:

> At first, I could only be glad he was at rest because he had been very ill with cancer. I often think of what I did when first he died. My son was just nineteen at the time and he was a wonderful help. But instead of being very sorrowful at first, I was being horribly practical – paying bills and making plans – but then

of course, later on it sank in. I regretted that I hadn't
done a lot of things when Ed was still alive. I looked
at myself in the mirror one day as I came in through
the doorway of his bedroom and I thought, 'Oh my
God, he had to see me looking so awful all these
months and months. Why didn't I do something about
myself?' Ed had to have nursing care round the clock
just before he died, but for most of his illness, I had
looked after him on my own and I just didn't have
time for myself, I suppose. He was alert enough then
to remark about it and said 'It really seems pretty
awful we don't have someone to help at this stage of
the game.'

Age Concern receives an enormous number of inquiries
about help in the home, living-in help and companions. The
requests may concern light domestic help for two or three
hours a week, or round-the-clock care. They may come from a
carer who needs a break or who needs time to deal with an
emergency elsewhere. Their Factsheet No. 6 suggests possible
sources of help and ways of advertising for companions, reviews
some of the benefits which may assist in paying for help and
lists some agencies which offer different kinds of home care
services. (See also Part III, Benefits and Rights.)

'Someone Needs to Care for the Carer'

A senior social worker involved in the care of older men and
women in extreme need expressed his compassion for the
carer:

In cases of long-term care where families and spouses
are involved in looking after relatives in ill health,
serious problems can arise when the carer becomes
burnt out. They become exhausted and worn down
by incessant giving. Feelings can change from love to
hatred, from kindness to cruelty; from care to neglect.
It is a time when someone needs to care for the
carer.

One of my regulars is a woman aged sixty-nine

who is having to learn how to live again. She looked after a chronically sick mother for five years before her death; no sooner had her mother died than my client had to take care of her husband following a stroke. The affliction changed his personality. He became extremely difficult and abused her verbally and physically. She lost her job and her self-worth. She had also lost touch with her family. She has two sons, both married with children, who live within a few miles of her. They had apparently found their father so impossible to deal with that they had cut themselves off from the family home, leaving their mother isolated. We helped her to get in touch with the sons and encouraged her to help take care of the grandchildren. We tried to teach her to have fun again. When she became emotionally stronger, we introduced her to one or two groups of people her own age and now she is beginning to enjoy a little social life.

More often than not, those who care for elderly and infirm people living in their own homes are women. They may be professional carers or they may be women within the family who become responsible for the day-to-day care of their own parents or their husbands' parents. Because women generally outlive men, they inevitably form the largest group of dependent elderly people, a large section of whom will be cared for by their daughters. As a mother, I enjoy a warm and happy relationship with my daughter and was therefore much saddened to learn from Dr John Kellett, Consultant Psychogeriatrician at St George's Hospital, London, that 'mothers and daughters just don't make for a very good pair'. He explained: 'What I see in many caring situations is either the mother dominating her daughter or a daughter dominating her mother. It is tragic that in so many cases the carers are the people who get on least well with their mothers. So often you find mothers who ignore their caring daughters and talk non-stop about their sons, whom they may not have seen for two years and who probably live far away.

'Yet there is something about the strength of this strange

relationship which keeps it together and makes it continue to work long after most people would have given up and arranged some form of residential care for their parent. Whether it's a question of guilt or whether it's a last desperate attempt to win the battle for their mother's affection, I don't know. If a daughter's major life experience has been lack of her mother's love, even if she still does not receive the love she longs for, at least she now has her mother's attention and is in control. It is a cruel kind of benefit but I think it means a lot to people who have been deprived of love in childhood.

'As a psychogeriatrican, I am very dependent on carers, but I'm afraid I spend more of my time trying to persuade them to give up than I do to continue. I see people whose marriages have come apart and children who have been discriminated against because a daughter has devoted herself to caring for her mother. My first message to them is that life for the next twenty or thirty years will revolve round their husband, and children. Their own family must come first. It seems harsh, but support of this kind can come as a great relief because the burden of making such a decision is taken out of their hands.

'Sometimes men do help their wives with the caring and things are a little easier, but I'm sad to say about my own sex that men are far less tolerant of other people living in their house than women are. On the other hand, when men do the caring, although they may not do such a good job as women do, they are far less neurotic about it. They set limits very easily whereas women find it very difficult to do so. Some of the male carers I have seen are extraordinarily callous about the care they give, but nevertheless they cope with it and can go on coping for the rest of their lives if necessary.'

Residential Care
(See also Chapter 3, The Gains and Losses of Old Age)

In the UK, about 5 per cent of people over the age of sixty-five do not live in private households but are cared for in hospitals, homes or residential care. Carla's experience in looking for a home in which to place her father, a victim of Alzheimer's disease (p. 313), highlights some of the problems of choosing the right kind of residential care.

Committing an elderly, helpless parent to a home is a terrible
burden of responsibility for the adult child. Most people as
they embark on the ordeal are well aware of the possibilities of
subjecting their parent to a life of misery and abuse. The
British Geriatrics Society's report published in May 1989,
*Abuse of Elderly People: An Unnecessary and Preventable Prob-
lem*, presented a bleak picture. It suggested that half a million
elderly people in Britain living at home or in institutions may
be at risk of abuse at the hands of their carers.

For any resident, no matter how dependent or independent
they are, a residential home is an alien environment and the
move to it is a severe shock to the system. The only way to
soften the blow is to choose humane, caring, stimulating surroundings which insist upon the maintenance of human dignity
and self-respect no matter what the circumstances.

The following are a series of questions and considerations
which will help determine the quality of a residential home:

Both cleanliness and smiles can mask inhumanity and
cruelty. Do not be impressed simply by outward appearances,
either in terms of the home itself or of the smiling faces of the
staff. Look beneath the surface. Talk to other residents. Find
out how much chance they have of being in **contact with the
outside world**. Do they go to the pub? Do they visit the local
shops? Are they just told they may do so or are they actively
encouraged to go out, accompanied by staff to make their trips
safer and easier? Does the home have its own transport – a
minibus, for example? Are the residents taken on outings? If
so, how often?

Apathy quickly takes over if an elderly person is lonely and
neglected. What steps does the home take to combat apathy in
its residents? If they sit around all day in one room watching
television, the answer is – none. Are there games, activities,
hobbies? Are professionals available to help residents find new
skills and cope with losses? Are they encouraged to communicate with each other? How do staff respond to their queries
and requests?

Communication amongst residents and between residents
and staff is of the most important aspects of life in a residential
home. Why should we expect our parents or relatives to create
instant friendships in this alien world? They are much more

likely to withdraw into themselves and suffer feelings of unbearable isolation. Some homes have trained therapists with the skills to help regain the confidence and self-worth of an elderly man or woman who may feel rejected and lost.

Are **families** positively encouraged to visit their parent or relative? Are there facilities for joining them at mealtimes. Is there freedom for residents to make cups of tea or coffee for themselves or visitors? May families visit the home unannounced or must they telephone to make an appointment?

What kind of **accommodation** is available – a single room or a shared room or dormitory? In the family's view, does the accommodation suit the needs and temperament of the prospective resident? Are items of personal furnishing permitted? Is the place warm, comfortable and carpeted? Is the atmosphere homely and friendly?

Are **drugs** regularly used to sedate residents? Who has access to medicines? How are they administered? How often does a physician check on patients? A survey conducted by the British Geriatrics Society of 351 patients in private nursing homes in Weston-super-Mare, Avon, found that one fifth of the nursing home residents in the town had never been seen by a doctor. Half were sedated at night and one in ten were given their drugs at the discretion of the nursing staff.

The wide range of homes available makes it essential to shop around before committing a loved parent or relative to someone else's care. The list of names and addresses and publications in Part III, Housing – Residential Care, provides a starting-point. It is also important to contact the general practitioner, who should be helpful in recommending the most appropriate care for his patient. The doctor will also have details of residential homes within the local community.

The final and perhaps most important consideration is whether you yourself would be willing to live in the home.

Planning for Dependency

Many old people living on their own independently make arrangements with a particular residence to take them in when the time comes that they can no longer look after themselves. Mrs R.B., aged eighty-four, told me why she had made her own particular choice:

At the moment, I can perfectly well look after myself, but when it is no longer possible, I shall go to the 'hospital for the old' down the road. I've had my name down there for about five years now. I've known quite a few people who've ended their days there and there is an old lady there now who I visit from time to time. It's rather depressing though. She doesn't really know what she's talking about and her condition is a bit catching. There's not much wrong with my memory normally, but after I've spent a couple of hours in the home trying to talk to her and other people there, I come out quite the worse for wear. My thinking is definitely affected. On the other hand, I've come to know the staff very well and they are wonderful. I have complete confidence that when my turn comes they will look after me kindly and well and allow me to die with dignity.

Abuse of the Elderly

The ways in which elderly dependent people can be abused are as varied as the reasons for the abuse. What ordinarily caring, loving mother has not at some time during her child's babyhood, when under pressure from stress, anger and frustration, come close to seriously abusing her infant? While most parents manage to suppress their violence, some do not. The dependency of one human being upon another can be a joy or an unbearably heavy burden – a duty to be performed without love. Babies and young children are generally loved and wanted; their dependency is expected and does not last for ever. The relationship between adult children and their elderly parents or relatives is complicated, by no means always loving or close, and dependency is resented.

Dr James O'Brien, an Irishman now at Michigan State University, began his specialist training in geriatric medicine after experiencing what he describes as 'a very dramatic personal case' which provided him with the incentive to research into the area of abuse of older adults. He tells the story thus: 'An elderly woman in her late seventies came to our emergency clinic. She had a severe headache. Her blood pressure was out of control. She was run down, dishevelled and unkempt. I admitted her to hospital and co-managed her with one of our residents. We wondered about her being the victim of some form of neglect but when her son came to visit her, we noticed that he was equally unkempt so we thought it was probably the norm for that particular family. The son was the sole carer of his mother.

'In the next twenty-four hours, we cleaned her up and managed to lower her blood pressure. When we talked about discharging her, she became very distressed and said she was going to die. We explained that her medical condition was not life-threatening and she was well enough to go home, but she just continued to insist she was going to die. The psychiatrist saw her. She was not suicidal and he could find no psychological reason why she felt her death was imminent. We subsequently discharged her with plans to follow her up carefully in the out-patients' clinic. Two days later, we had a phone call from the coroner to say she was dead. She had been found with a plastic bag over her head which had been secured with a piece of string tied in a neat bow. The coroner was suspicious that the son had murdered her. The conditions in which they lived were found to be quite incredibly squalid. There was also some suggestion that he had been physically, psychologically and sexually abusing her.

'We have another case of an elderly dependent mother, more or less bedridden, being cared for by her two sons. One son lives with her; the other lives forty miles away but visits every weekend. He is quite well off and leaves enough money for the two to manage for a week. The brother supposedly taking care of his mother badly neglects her. Sometimes he will respond to her calls for attention; sometimes he won't. Sometimes he feeds her; sometimes he doesn't. Often he allows her to lie in her own excrement for days. When we talked to the son, it transpired that as a child he was also badly neglected. As a punishment he would be locked in his room unable to get out and go to the toilet when he wanted to. Now in adulthood, his response is to treat his mother in the same way as she treated him – not necessarily for revenge, although perhaps that does come into it somewhere – but because if you were trained in certain ways as a child then you are not unlikely to fall back on that training as an adult. Hence the family pattern repeats itself.

'It is not unusual to find that the adult children abusing their parents were themselves victims of child abuse. It is also true that it is often the weakest, least able – therefore least appropriate – member of the family who is persuaded by stronger siblings to accept the burden of care.'

Despite the cases quoted, Dr O'Brien insists that the problem of abuse of the elderly should be put into perspective. He told me: 'Most abuse is perpetrated by a family member. The vast majority of people don't abuse their elders; the vast majority provide on-going caring support. Usually, elders choose to live independently but close to their adult children. Most live within thirty minutes' travel time away. Most families keep in touch with ageing parents. Those whom I encounter in the course of my work tend to have either seen their parent or parents the previous week or talked to them on the telephone.'

He went on to describe the common pattern of abuse of the elderly: 'The typically abused older person is female, aged seventy-five or older, white and middle-class. She is typically dependent on the abuser, who is most usually a middle-aged daughter or son living with the victim. It seems that about nine years of care-giving have passed before abuse takes place and then it tends to take the form of neglect rather than physical abuse. Often the care-giver has reached the stage when he or she just can't cope any more with the demands placed upon them. As care-giver, they have grown older, weaker and less energetic, while their dependent relative is likely to have become increasingly demanding.'

Detecting Abuse in the Elderly

Abuse of elderly people is often difficult to detect. The British Geriatrics Society reports that their 1989 figure of half a million cases of abuse may be an underestimate.

Neglect is the most frequently encountered type of abuse, followed by psychological and physical abuse. Other categories of abuse include material abuse – that is, abuse of personal property and/or money – and the violation of rights whereby an elderly person is placed prematurely into a home against his or her will. It is very uncommon for the victim to report being abused. It is not easy to make serious allegations against a son or daughter, who may be the only means by which they remain free of an institutional life which they may fear more than the abuse from which they are suffering.

Research in the United States suggests that there may be a fairly high incidence of spouse abuse. Dr O'Brien recalled a case which illustrates the difficulties of detecting the problem. It came to light almost by chance.

'An elderly gentleman in his seventies was admitted to hospital with a chronic form of leukemia from which he was certainly going to die. He came in regularly for a blood transfusion which pepped him up for a while and was sent home generally feeling better. His condition involved the loss not only of blood cells but of some of the clotting component as well so that he was prone to bruising, weakness and exhaustion. We were on our rounds one morning, and as I sat him up in bed to examine him (he needed my help at the time because he had an intravenous drip running), I noticed that his back looked like a Christmas tree with almost regular lines of herring-bone bruises from top to bottom. The last thing we thought of when we saw his back was abuse. In fact one of the house physicians came up with the idea that he might have fallen against some sort of grid.

'That afternoon, the patient's wife arrived to see him. She was somewhat dependent and was carrying a cane. I took a bit of a chance and asked her about the bruises on her husband's back. She came out with the answer immediately. It transpired that when he was stronger following his blood transfusions, he would be physically violent with her and the only way she could defend herself was to beat him with her cane. However, as the leukemia took hold and he became more exhausted and weaker again, he would leave her alone.'

Men who have been aggressive and domineering throughout their married lives are unlikely to change their pattern of behaviour in old age, yet whereas they may remain as verbally abusive as ever, physically they may have become very feeble.

DEATH AND BEREAVEMENT

'Good general advice for the bereaved, particularly in countries whose traditions derive from Britain, is "Don't try to be too wonderful. Let other people help you."' This advice is offered by Dr Richard Lamerton, Medical Director of the Macmillan Service, a home care service for dying patients and their families in the East End of London. He continues:

During the period of numbness and also during the early phase of the acute pangs of grief, bereaved people need help with almost everything, and especially with decisions. They need mothering ... The helpers should do nothing which will discourage the expression of appropriate grief. They should make it clear to the grieving person that they do not mind if he weeps. Over the next few weeks visits from friends will be appreciated, even if they are awkward occasions. The friends may find that they have to share some of the pain, to reassure the grieving person that his disorganization is normal and not a sign that he is going mad. Any mention of suicide, however, should be taken seriously and is an indication for referral to a psychiatrist or skilled social worker for help.'[60]

One of the organizations most experienced in helping the bereaved is Cruse, whose chief aim is to assist widows and their children by direct counselling on a local or national level. According to Dr Lamerton, only 6 per cent of women who are widowed between twenty and fifty years of age will eventually remarry. 'They are a potentially very lonely group,' he writes.[61] Dr Colin Parkes, in *Bereavement*, observes that 'Substitutes for a missing husband are not readily acceptable ... Reasons such as age and the difficulty of finding an eligible suitor were given for this lack of interest in remarriage, but many of the widows still seemed to regard themselves as married to their dead husband and remarriage would have been a form of infidelity.'[62]

It is generally believed that a period of intense grieving following the death of a beloved spouse, child, friend or relative is natural and, what is more, that failure to have such feelings of great distress or depression is thought to be a somewhat unhealthy sign – an indication that the psychological adjustment following the loss could be problematic. However, an article which appeared in the July 1989 issue of the *Journal of Clinical and Consulting Psychology* suggests that the response to grief is very much wider. In five different studies of widows and widowers, for example, research showed that more than a quarter of the mourners involved were not greatly distressed. The study, conducted by Dr Camille Wortman, of the University of Michigan, and Dr Roxane Cohen Silver, of the University of California at Los Angeles, brings considerable comfort to those mourners who feel guilty that their less-than-overwhelming sense of grief may not be an adequate response to their loss.

On the other hand, Dr Wortman and her colleagues also showed that sudden, unexpected and violent losses were likely to cause prolonged depression and anxiety. They concluded that those who were most affected at the time of bereavement were most at risk psychologically, while those who bore their grief lightly were more likely to be spared long-term problems. I asked Dr Wortman if she could suggest the circumstances in which a sufferer should consider help or be persuaded to ask for it. 'Counselling was more likely to be needed if the relationship to the deceased was one of conflict,' she said, and continued: 'Sometimes, people are unable to accept the reality of their loss. I have a patient at the moment who came to me for help when she realized that the only way she could cope with life was to pretend that her son (who had been killed in a car crash) was alive. She regularly told friends and neighbours alike that he was away on holiday and was "expected back any day now".

'There are occasions when a person becomes so wrapped up in caring for an ailing spouse that they lose sight of themselves. Their self-esteem becomes so low that when they are finally left on their own they become seriously depressed.

'In cases where people find it very difficult to adjust after bereavement, I would always recommend that they be referred to an experienced psychologist or social worker or, in cases where drugs are required, a psychiatrist. It is a very sensitive area and requires a high degree of professional skill.'

Suicide

A study of elderly suicide commissioned by the American Association of Retired Persons in 1989 revealed that white males aged sixty-five and over have a suicide rate which is nearly four times the national average. The ratio of male to female suicides in the age range of sixty-five to sixty-nine is 4 to 1 but gradually increases to 12 to 1 by the age of eighty-five. The report states: 'Important high-risk indicators for suicide among the elderly include social isolation and loneliness. Other factors include a history of recent losses, illnesses and intractable pain, and changes in status related to income, employment and independence ... fear of institutionalization in a nursing home and the anticipated loss of independence is a major precipitating event in elderly suicide.'[63]

In the United Kingdom, the Samaritans report that although the suicide rate among young people is high, accounting for 11 per cent of the total, the highest suicide rates are found among the elderly, in particular those aged between seventy-five and eighty-four: 124 in every million, as compared with the national rate of approximately 100 per million.

The death of a parent by suicide, particularly if there is no note left behind to explain a motive, creates a terrible dilemma for the shocked and grieving family. Coming to terms with the death is made more difficult because questions arise for which there will probably never be answers. Did he or she consciously and rationally decide to end their own life; or was the 'suicide' a tragic accident brought about when the 'balance of the mind was disturbed' – perhaps by medication or disease? And then the most despairing question of all: 'Surely we could have done something to prevent it happening?'

Case Histories

Mr G.B. was taken into a private hospital suffering from a bad bout of asthma and angina. He was also acutely depressed. The nurse at his GP's clinic had refused to renew a prescription for laxatives as she could not find a doctor to sign the document. Mr G.B. had undergone a repair for an anal fissure some time previously and explained that it was essential for him to have the laxatives because any undue straining would open up the fissure. The prescription was denied and the fissure reopened, which caused bleeding and considerable pain. After the distressing period of asthma attacks and angina, the recurrence of the anal fissure was the final straw. Mr G.B. told his daughter he felt 'suicidal' and could not wait 'for someone to come and carry him away in a box'. After the first two days in hospital, however, there were no more bouts of angina and his breathing was almost normal. He was eating well, looked generally better and seemed more cheerful. On the fourth day, friends visited him in the morning, and the afternoon was spent in the company of his son; for about an hour and a half they watched horse racing on television together and Mr G.B. made various requests for newspapers and clean pyjamas to be brought to him the next day. After his son left, Mr G.B. received a visit from two old friends who remained with him for half an hour, leaving the hospital at 5 p.m. At 5·15 p.m. he was found lying seriously injured on the ground beneath his hospital window. Two hours later, he died from his injuries. According to the police report, the low table which had been dragged to the window to enable him to climb up on to the high sill above was a clear indication that he intended to kill himself. No one who saw Mr G.B. that day had any inkling of his distraught state of mind. On the contrary, they all agreed that he had seemed better in every way. His daughter was devastated. 'But he told me he felt suicidal,' she cried, 'and I just thought he was in one of his low periods like he always was when things were not going right for him. I should have done something about it. If only I had realized how seriously depressed he was, maybe he would not have killed himself.'

The response of Mr G.B.'s daughter was fairly typical in the aftermath of the suicide of a family member. There was no real justification for her feeling of guilt and yet how could she not in some way blame herself?

Mrs M.T. was forty-five when her father committed suicide. She had five teenage children and a husband who spent much of his time working from home. Her father lived seventy miles away. She suggested he join her family and move into a small, previously converted flat adjacent to the house, but he refused to leave the large family home in which he had lived for fifty years. At the age of seventy-eight, he took his own life by swallowing a massive overdose of carefully stored sleeping tablets. His daughter's sense of guilt and loss was profound.

You can pretend to someone that you love them and be thoroughly convincing, but you can't pretend to yourself. I didn't love my father but I didn't try hard enough not to show it. I was his favourite child and I suppose he expected a great deal from me. The trouble was that I did not get to know him until I was in my teens and by then it was too late. I saw a side to him that I neither liked nor respected. I didn't love him when he was in healthy, vigorous middle age, and I couldn't grow to love him when he was old and cross. He treated my mother very badly and she was unhappy for much of her married life. He had very little to do with us when we were children and I was sent to boarding-school when I was six. During all my years away at school, he never came to see me, not even when I was the star in the school play. I suppose he just wasn't interested. His death was still a terrible blow though. If I had spent more time looking after him and nursed him through his gloomy periods – those times when he became so angry, frustrated, bad-tempered and ungrateful; horrible in fact – he would probably still be alive. He needed to know that someone cared enough for him to continue living and I failed him.

The Threat of Suicide

The following account illustrates the terrible bewilderment and helplessness of a man of sixty who, during a regular visit to his parents, was informed by his eighty-year-old father that he intended to commit suicide:

Mum was in the kitchen at the time and I was just sitting with Dad when he suddenly turned to me and said, 'I'm near the end, son.' He's a very fit man for his age and I couldn't understand what he was talking about. He said, 'I'm going to kill myself.' I couldn't believe what he was saying. I asked, 'How are you going to do it?' 'I'm going to put a tube over the exhaust pipe.' So I said, 'Well, that's a bit silly, isn't it?' 'No,' he said; 'I've made up my mind; but there's just one thing, your mother's going on holiday to Malta in June. I want you to see she goes.' So I said, 'She won't go if you do it now. You had better wait till she has been on holiday.' So he agreed to wait. I was terribly shocked. If Dad had been very ill, it would have been more understandable but he doesn't even have arthritis. He retired long ago but he didn't really have anything he wanted to do and so what's happened is that his armchair has become his prison and he hasn't got any way of escaping now. He's lost his spark. He has become rather strange in some ways. He has phobias. He won't allow anyone to see him eat which means he won't even come to Christmas dinner. He's a very complex person and although, on the surface, you'd think he was a tremendous extrovert, in actual fact it's the opposite. It was all a kind of bluff and gradually in old age his true nature has come out; the bluff has gone and he's become very introverted.

If there is any suggestion that a friend or relative might be contemplating suicide, it is essential to seek help and advice. Whereas this will not in itself prevent it happening – and many feel passionately that it is their right to take their own life if they are determined to do so – for those left behind to cope with the grief and anguish and the guilt involved in the suicide of a loved one it will be reassuring to know that they did everything within their power to forestall the act.

If there seems to be no obvious source of help available – for example, a sympathetic family doctor – the organization which has most experience of suicide is the Samaritans. Their telephone number will be in the local phone book, or they can be reached through the telephone operator.

Hospice Care for the Dying

The hospice movement provides some of the best care for the dying available and in the knowledge and treatment of pain it is second to none. St Joseph's Hospice in Hackney, East London, founded in 1900, is one of the country's oldest hospices. Although independent of the National Health Service – 30 per cent of its income is derived from charitable donations – it has contractual arrangements to care for NHS patients. There are about 140 hospices around the country, with more being planned. Because they tend to respond to the needs of the local community there are individual differences but, overall, hospices exist to support families and offer special care for patients directed towards improving the quality of the life which remains to them.

Most hospice patients are suffering from terminal cancer, although the service can also include care of the chronically sick, the physically handicapped and day care for patients who are still able to travel. Many hospices offer a home care service, caring for patients with terminal illness in their homes; but the extent of the hospice role will depend on local requirements.

St Joseph's cares for over six hundred patients with advanced cancer annually, the average length of stay being twenty days. Criteria for admission are that the patient is no longer receiving curative treatment and the prognosis, in so far as it can be assessed, is less than three months.

The kind of care hospices can offer a dying patient differs from hospitals in a number of ways. Hospitals are committed to keeping patients alive; nursing and easing the suffering of the dying is not a first priority, neither is concern for the bereaved. Hospice staff are all experts in dealing with death and they have the time and resources to ensure that the patient is free of pain, relaxed and comfortable, and suffers neither anxiety nor depression. The patient's needs and those of the family are carefully and constantly assessed by an interdisciplinary team which includes a doctor, nurse, physiotherapist, social worker, psychotherapist and spiritual adviser.

The main aim of the hospice staff is to keep a patient free of the symptoms which are common in terminal illness: pain, nausea and vomiting, anorexia, dysphagia, thirst, dry mouth, sore mouth, constipation, diarrhoea, micturition problems, bleeding, discharge, fistulae, pressure sores, skin troubles, itching, fungating lesions, smell, weakness, immobility, paralysis, oedema, ascites, dyspnoea, cough, hiccough, emotional problems, confusion, insomnia, disfigurement.

'An Alternative to Euthanasia'

Dr J. F. Hanratty was, before his retirement, the Medical Director of St Joseph's Hospice. In a small pamphlet (available from the hospice), he writes:

The humanitarian and emotional reactions aroused in those observing someone severely disabled, diseased or dying are understandably distressing – particularly for the family. Not knowing what to do or what to say to alleviate apparent suffering leads to frustrating helplessness. Some people go away saying, 'I can't bear to see him like this.' The suffering in so many cases is on the part of the beholder and not the patient. It is a dreadful indictment of our medical services that one of the main arguments in favour of euthanasia is that so many people do die in physical and mental distress. But surely we do not have to kill the patient in order to kill the distress ... we have got the wherewithal, in medications and various therapies, to give our patients significant and in most cases complete relief from pain and discomfort.

A CHECK-LIST FOR CARERS

- Money – claim all benefits and allowances. Control income, investments, property and all assets. Be aware that if the person concerned is moved to residential care the DHSS will use the capital assets to pay for the care and support.
- Carers – assistance for carers is available in the form of day centres, respite homes and information. Support organizations include Crossroads, Age Concern, Help the Aged and many others.
- Services – Social Services and the local council provide meals, home helps, day centres and incontinence service and equipment.
- Medical care – provided by the NHS or private healthcare organizations. A good doctor you can rely on is essential, with specialists and hospital provision as required. The health centres provide nurses, therapists and health visitors as part of the service.

- Nursing – qualified and specialist geriatric nursing is available from the NHS and privately. The carer is responsible for nursing care for most of the time. The voluntary organizations are helpful for resolving problems and alleviate suffering.
- Housing – if the person who needs care lives within range of the medical and support facilities, with free transport provided, there will be fewer problems and costs. The house should be adapted to suit the disability and the needs of the individual. Assistance and grants are available for this purpose.
- Disability aids – Social Services have disability-aid centres which display a wide range of equipment for disabled people. Voluntary organizations, such as Remap, design special equipment to deal with particular problems. Specialist advice and funds are provided for the purchase of this equipment. Wheelchairs and other basic items are available on loan from the support organizations. These special aids and devices can restore a person's self-reliance. In this way they are able to look after themselves without help from other people.
- Diet – advice from a clinical dietitian is an important and often neglected part of medical care. Decisions on special dietary needs should be made by professionals. The adverse effects of the wrong foods are well known. Some shops package food in small quantities and there is no shortage of advice on cooking. Above all, eating is a social occasion and food is to be enjoyed.

Part III
**Where to Go for Help and Advice
An A to Z of Contacts and
Information**

The information in this A to Z is arranged under the following headings

Hair loss
Hearing
Heart and stroke
Incontinence
Keep fit
Menopause
Menopause: HRT
Osteoporosis
Teeth
Health services
    NHS
    Private sector
Housing
    Residential care
    Sheltered accommodation
    General
The law and legal aid
Mental health
    Depressions
    Phobias
    Stress
    Stress – ways to relax
Relationships
    Marriage
    Family
    Grandparents
    Step-family
Retirement
    Planning
    General
Sexual problems

Addresses and information on leisure pursuits and holidays will be found in Chapter 5, Leisure and Working for Pleasure.

Addictions

Alcohol

Al-Anon Family Groups UK and Eire
61 Great Dover Street, London SE1 4YF
    Tel. 071–403 0888 (line open 24 hours a day)

Help for relatives and friends of problem drinkers (whether still drinking or in recovery) through confidential group meetings. Contact this main office for details of the nearest local group.

Accept
724 Fulham Road, London sw6 5se
   Tel. 071–371 7477 (Open 10 a.m. – 6 p.m. every day and
   by appointment.)
Offers individual and group counselling, group therapy and activities, job and career planning for problem drinkers and their families. Operates the Drinkwatchers Network.

Aquarius
Aquarius Centre, Pebblemill House, 263 Bristol Road,
Birmingham, b5
   Tel. 021–471 1361
Voluntary agency linked to the Alcoholic Rehabilitation Research Group at Birmingham University. Offers day and residential counselling to people of all ages with different kinds of drinking problems.

Alcohol Concern
305 Grays Inn Road, London wc1x 8qf
   Tel. 071–833 3471
Offers advice and help to those with drinking problems. It also works with professionals, employers and trade unions, produces information material and provides an information service.

Scottish Council on Alcohol
137–45 Sauchiehall Street, Glasgow g2 3ew
   Tel. 041–333 9677
Deals with all alcohol use and abuse, and has twenty-five affiliated local councils throughout Scotland offering help to problem drinkers and their families.

Northern Ireland Council on Alcoholism
40 Elmswood Avenue, Belfast bt9 6az
   Tel. 0232 664434
Offers a confidential counselling service and information and advice on alcohol problems.

Alcoholics Anonymous
PO Box 1, Stonebow House, Stonebow, York YO1 2NJ
    Tel. 0904 644026/7/8/9
A self-help fellowship with nearly two thousand groups meeting throughout the country. AA is run exclusively by ex-alco-
holics and is open to all people of all ages and all religions; the
only entry requirement is a firm desire to stop drinking. There
is no professional counselling service and apart from following
a suggested programme of recovery, which involves twelve
spiritual and practical steps, the help and support derives from
sharing experiences at regular meetings with others in the
same predicament. Those members of AA who have learned to
live without alcohol hope that their particular path to sobriety
will be of use to other members who are still struggling with
their alcoholic illness. See local telephone book or contact the
office above for free literature and advice.

Drinkwatchers,
200 Seagrave Road, London SW6 1RQ
    Tel. 071–381 3155
An organization which aims to help those who are concerned
to limit their consumption of alcohol rather than cut it out altogether.

Antabuse

This is a drug prescribed for alcoholics which causes nausea,
headache, irregular heart beat, and tightness of the chest if taken
in combination with alcohol. Its great advantage is that it can
be used as a treatment in the home, but because the effects are
so unpleasant, it is difficult to persuade an alcoholic to take the
medication, especially if they are living alone with their problem. It is considered particularly effective, however, in helping
people to stay off alcohol once they have 'dried out'.

The Minnesota Method and Narcotics Anonymous

Narcotics Anonymous
   Tel. 071–351 6066/7 (daytime); 071–351 6794 (emergency)
This organization, directly modelled on Alcoholics Anonymous, was founded in Britain in 1980. It regards alcoholism and
drug addiction as progressive illnesses for which the only cure
is total abstinence. Minnesota Method projects refer clients to
both NA and AA as part of the essential follow-up treatment.

   The treatment offered by the Minnesota Method involves
assessment and admission to one of the four residential centres
in the UK for a period of six to eight weeks, after which the
patient progresses to an intensive programme of aftercare attending regular AA and/or NA meetings. On admission, each
patient is placed in the care of a counsellor, who will often be
an alcoholic or drug addict 'in recovery'. Apart from recovered
alcoholics and drug addicts, staff at the centres include physicians, social workers, psychologists, nurses and clergy reflecting the comprehensive, multi-professional approach to the
treatment of addictions.

   The results of the Minnesota Method have been encouraging. Dr Christopher C.H. Cook, writing in the *British Journal
of Addiction* in 1988, concludes, 'Despite exaggerated claims of
success, it appears to have a genuinely impressive "track
record" with as many as two thirds of its patients achieving a
"good" outcome at one year after discharge.'[64]

TREATMENT CENTRES: Broadreach House, Clouds House,
Broadway Lodge and Promise.
FUNDING: Some centres offer private treatment only and can cost
between £700 and £1,500 per week. Others are charitable trusts
registered as nursing homes where 'assisted' places are available.

Drug Abuse

SCODA (Standing Conference on Drug Abuse)
1–4 Hatton Place, Hatton Garden, London ECIN 8ND
   Tel. 071–430 2341
The national coordinating organization for groups helping
people with drug problems. They can supply up-to-date

information concerning drug centres throughout the country and are the most reliable first stepping-stone towards further advice and treatment.

Families Anonymous
Room 8, 650 Holloway Road, London N19 3NU
    Tel. 071–281 8889
Aims to provide support groups for families and friends of those with drug problems.

ADFAM International
82 Old Brompton Road, London SW7 3LQ
    Tel. helpline 071–823 9313 (10 a.m. – 4 p.m., Monday to
    Friday, plus a 24-hour answerphone)
Adfam is a voluntary organization working with and for the families and friends of drug users. The organization also acts as a training and advice resource for people setting up local family support projects, helplines, befriending networks and groups. The helpline provides information and support.

Gambling

Gamblers Anonymous and Gam-Anon
17–23 Blantyre Street, Cheyne Walk, London SW10 0DT
    Tel. 081–741 4181
A self-help fellowship of people with a gambling problem which also offers friendship and practical help to families of compulsive gamblers.

Smoking

ASH (Action on Smoking and Health)
109 Gloucester Place, London W1H 3PH
    Tel. 071–935 3519
Offers information on the risks of smoking and advice on how to give up the habit.

Quit (National Society of Non-Smokers)
102 Gloucester Place, London W1H 3DA
    Tel. 071–487 2858

A registered charity dedicated to helping smokers who want to give up the habit.

The Smokers' Quitline
A telephone service offering advice on giving up smoking, counselling and referral to local Stop-Smoking services.
Tel: 071-487 3000

Tranquillizers

Tranx
25a Masons Avenue, Harrow, Middlesex HA3 5AH
Advice and information for people who are dependent on minor tranquillizers, and are suffering from physical or psychological withdrawal symptoms.

Reading

Allen Carr, *Allen Carr's Easy Way to Stop Smoking*, Penguin Books, 1991. 'So You Want to Cut Down on Your Drinking', the Scottish Health Education Group Guide, is available from HE6, Woodburn House, Canaan Lane, Edinburgh. An expanded version is available from the British Psychological Society, St Andrews House, Princess Road East, Leicester

Peter Tyrer, *How to Stop Taking Tranquillizers*, Sheldon Press, 1986

Celia Haddon, *Women and Tranquillizers*, Sheldon Press, 1984

William R. Miller and Ricardo F. Munoz, *How to Control Your Drinking*, Sheldon Press, 1983.

Advice

National Association of Citizens Advice Bureaux Central Office (NACAB)
Myddelton House, 115–23 Pentonville Road, London N1 9LZ
   Tel. 071-833 2181 (or consult your local telephone directory)
Provides free advice and information on every subject from Social Security, taxation, debt counselling, housing and unemployment to family and personal problems and the law.

Northern Ireland Association of CABx (NIACAB)
New Forge Lane, Belfast BT9 5NW
   Tel. 0232 681117

Citizens Advice Scotland
26 George Square, Edinburgh EH8 9LD
   Tel. 031–667 0156
(The Scottish association is a separate body from NACAB.)

Community Development Projects Foundation
60 Highbury Grove, London N5 2AG
   Tel. 071–226 5375
A national community development agency which helps organizations to develop and support community initiatives.

Office of Fair Trading
Room 306, Field House, Breams Buildings, London EC4A
1PR
   Tel. 071–269 8977 (general inquiries); 071–269 8890
   (orders only)
Offers help and guidance to the consumer on a wide range of topics, including shopping rights, personal finance, misleading advertisements and home improvements.

Reading

Alex Comfort, *A Good Age*, Mitchell Beazley, 1989
Ann Spokes Symonds, ed., *Celebrating Age – an Anthology*,
   Age Concern, 1990
David Hobman, *Coming of Age – a Positive Guide to Growing
   Old*, Age Concern, 1990
Leslie Kenton, *Ageless Ageing: the Natural Way to Stay Young*,
   Arrow Books, London, 1985
Nancy Tuft, *Looking Good, Feeling Good*, Age Concern
   England, 1990

Ageing

Age Concern England (National Council on Ageing)
Astral House, 1268 London Road, London SW16 4EJ
Tel. 081–679 8000 (Open during office hours.)
A national organization which offers help, advice, support and
information on all aspects of ageing.

Age Concern Northern Ireland
128 Victoria Street, Belfast BT2 7BG
Tel. 0232 245729 (Open during office hours.)

Age Concern Scotland
54a Fountainbridge, Edinburgh EH3 9PT
Tel. 031–228 5656

Age Concern Wales
1 Park Grove, Cardiff CF1 3BJ
Tel. 0222 371 566 (Open during office hours.)

Age in Distress
54 London Road, Morden, Surrey SM4 5BE
Tel. 081–640 5523 (Open during office hours.)
Help and advice for the over-sixties.

Age Concern Institute of Gerontology
King's College London, University of London, Cornwall
House Annexe, Waterloo Road, London SE1 8TX
Tel. 071–836 5454
The only institute of its kind in the country. It offers a multi-
discipline degree course (MSc) in gerontology which looks at
older people from every perspective.

Help the Aged
116–18 St James' Walk, London EC1R 0BE
Tel. 071–253 0253
Dedicated to improving the quality of life of elderly people in
need of help in the UK and overseas. Their aim is pursued by

raising and granting funds towards community-based projects, housing and overseas aid.

ADVICE LINE: 071–250 3399. An advice and information service for elderly people, their friends, carers and relatives.

Counsel and Care for the Elderly
Twyman House, 16 Bonny Street, London NW1 9PG
   Tel. 071–485 1550
Offers a comprehensive free advisory service to all elderly people and to professionals. Some financial help is available. Inspects all registered private residential homes in Greater London annually.

Research into Ageing
49 Queen Victoria Street, London EC4N 4SA
   Tel. 071–236 4365

Centre for Policy on Ageing
25–31 Ironmonger Row, London EC1V 3QP
   Tel. 071–253 1787

Benefits and rights

(The information in this section has been compiled with the help of Age Concern England, Astral House, 1268 London Road, London SW16 4EJ; tel. 081–679 8000.)

Free Advice

Free advice on all Social Security benefits can be obtained by telephoning Freeline Social Security – 0800 666 555. In Northern Ireland, phone 0800 616 757. Local authority Social Services Departments are also an important source of help and advice. For further information contact the local Citizens Advice Bureau or Age Concern group.

Reading

'Which Benefit?' This is a free booklet (FB2) published by the DSS available at your local DSS office. It gives details of all benefits and explains how to apply for them.

'Looking After Someone at Home' (NP27) is also available from the DSS.

Sally West, *Your Rights: A Guide to Money Benefits for Older People, 1990–91*, Age Concern England, 1990. Information about Social Security benefits and other sources of financial help for older people. Includes sections on retirement pensions, income-related benefits and disability benefits.

The benefits to which you may be entitled

Income Support. Replaced supplementary benefit in April 1988, when changes also took place in the rules governing housing benefit. Income support provides help with basic living expenses and is available to people on a low income with no more than £8,000 savings.

The Social Fund. This scheme replaces the system of grants to people who were receiving supplementary benefit before April 1988. The fund makes loans and grants available mainly to those who receive income support. Unfortunately, the awards are discretionary so there is no guarantee that the extra money will be made available, but the following benefits are theoretically allowed for people on income support:

Free dental treatment
Help with spectacles
Grants for insulation and draught-proofing
Crisis loans
Community-care grants
Cold-weather payments
Help with funeral costs

Housing Benefit. Helps people with their rent and available to those on a low income with no more than £16,000 savings.

Community Charge (Poll Tax) Benefit. For those on a low income who need help to pay their poll tax.

Attendance Allowance. For severely disabled people needing constant care. The allowance is paid regardless of age or income and is tax-free. Further information and an application form are available in leaflet NI 205, available from post offices and local offices of the DSS.

Invalid Care Allowance. For a carer under retirement age who spends thirty-five hours or more each week looking after someone who is entitled to an Attendance Allowance.

Independent Living Fund. Grant for severely disabled people who need help to pay for a carer.

Mobility Allowance (DSS leaflets NI 211 and HB 5 will explain this more fully). The allowance helps severely disabled people to become more mobile and may be used in ways which are most suited to individual needs.

Higher Rate Personal Allowance. A tax allowance for people aged seventy-five and over. (See Inland Revenue leaflet IR81, 'Independent Taxation – a Guide for Pensioners'.)

Higher Rate Married Couple's Allowance. A tax allowance for married couples one of whom is seventy-five or over. (See Inland Revenue leaflet IR80: 'Independent Taxation – A Guide for Married Couples'.)

Reading

The following Fact Sheets from Age Concern, which are constantly updated, will help to make the benefits system clear:

'Income Support and Housing Benefit: Income and Capital (Savings)' (No. 16), April 1989

'Income Support and the Social Fund' (No. 25), April 1991

'Income Support for Residential and Nursing Homes' (No. 11), August 1991

'Housing Benefit and Community Charge Benefit' (No. 17), December 1990

'Help with Telephones' (No. 28), July 1991

'Help with Heating' (No. 1), July 1991

'Television Licence Concessions' (No. 3), October 1990

'Older Home Owners – Financial Help with Repairs' (No. 13), April 1991
'Arranging a Funeral' (No. 27), December 1990
'Companions and Help in the Home' (No. 6), September 1991

Bereavement and Death

Cruse
Head office: Cruse House, 126 Sheen Road, Richmond,
Surrey TW9 1UR
  Tel. 081–940 4818
Cruse offers counselling, advice and support for all bereaved
people through the national office and over 130 local branches.
It also runs training courses for professional and lay people
involved with the dying and bereaved.

Help the Hospices
34–44 Britannia Street, London WC1
  Tel. 071–278 5668
Funds specific projects, equipment, education and research in
the field of terminal care. It runs or supports management
policy, counselling and family-therapy workshops and clinical
courses in this field.

Hospice Information Service
St Christopher's Hospice, 51 Lawrie Park Road, Sydenham,
London SE26 6DZ
  Tel. 081–778 9252
A resource and link for members of the public and health-care
professionals. Telephone and written inquiries welcomed.

Marie Curie Memorial Foundation
Head Office, 28 Belgrave Square, London SW1X 8QG
  Tel. 071–235 3325

Scottish Office
21 Rutland Square, Edinburgh EH1 2AH
  Tel. 031–229 8332
The foundation provides eleven homes, 44,000 part-time Marie Curie nurses who nurse patients in their own homes, a research institute and a teaching institute. Referral for the homes is normally by hospital consultant or the patient's GP. The Marie Curie Nursing Service can be requested through the District Nursing Officer responsible for Community Nursing Services.

Lisa Sainsbury Foundation
8–10 Crown Hill, Croydon, Surrey CRO 1RY
  Tel. 081–686 8808
Provides publications, computerized information and educational help by means of workshops to carers working with the terminally ill.

The Voluntary Euthanasia Society
13 Prince of Wales Terrace, London W8 5PG
  Tel. 071–937 7770
Vice-presidents include Ludovic Kennedy, Dr Jonathan Miller and The Rev Lord (Donald) Soper. The principal object of the society is to make it legal for an adult person who is suffering severe distress from an incurable illness to receive medical help to die at their own considered request. This is already possible in the Netherlands but is still unlawful in the UK.

Age Concern
See under Ageing. Some local groups set up to provide services for elderly people offer bereavement counselling

National Association of Widows
5 Chell Road, Stafford ST16 5QA
  Tel. 0785 45465
Runs an advice service and local support groups for widows and widowers, which includes help with money problems.

National Council for One Parent Families
255 Kentish Town Road, London NW5 2LX
   Tel. 071–267 1361
Campaigns on behalf of all types of one-parent families; offers
advice and literature.

Gay Bereavement Project
Unitarian Rooms, Hoop Lane, London NW11 8BS
   Tel. 081–455 8894
A telephone help and support service for people bereaved by
the death of a same-sex life partner.

Reading

'Understanding Bereavement' (National Association for Mental
   Health (available from Mind Mail Order Service, 4th floor,
   24–32 Stephenson Way, London NW1 2HD)

Rosemary Dinnage, *The Ruffian on the Stair: Reflections on
   Death*, Viking, 1990

Peter Noll, *In the Face of Death*, Penguin Books, 1991

Richard Lamerton, *Care of the Dying*, Penguin Books, 1980

Colin Murray Parkes, *Bereavement: Studies of Grief in Adult
   Life*, Penguin Books, 1986

June Hemer, *Survival Guide for Widows*, Age Concern England.

'Arranging a Funeral', Age Concern (Fact Sheet No. 27), December 1990. A factsheet with help for those who have to
   arrange a funeral or wish to make plans for their own.

'Help when Someone Dies'. Free booklet, FB 29, from all
   DSS offices; a guide to Social Security benefits and state
   pensions

'What to Do after Death' (D49), DSS

'What Happens when Someone Dies' (IR45). Covers all
   aspects of taxation. (Free leaflet from all Inland Revenue
   offices.)

'Income Tax and Widows' (IR23). A guide to claiming allowances. (Free leaflet from all Inland Revenue offices.)

Joy Robbins, ed., *Caring for the Dying Patient and the Family*,
2nd ed., Harper & Row (Lippingcot Nursing Series), 1989

Lily Pincus, *Death and the Family*, Faber, 1981

Tony Lake, *Living with Grief*, Sheldon Press, 1984

What to Do When Someone Dies, Consumers' Association and
Hodder & Stoughton, 1986

Careers in Retirement
(See also Chapter 5)

N.B. Pensions and National Insurance: It is possible to defer a
pension for up to five years after retirement age. 'Your State
Pension and Carrying on Working', Age Concern's Factsheet
No. 19, April 1990, describes the current situation for people
who wish to carry on working after sixty or sixty-five. See also
Chapter 4.

Age Works – ARP/o5o
Parnell House, 19 Wilton Road, Victoria, London SW1V 1LW
The joint Association of Retired Persons and the Over 50s
Group (ARP/o5o) have combined with the French-owned
employment agency ECCO to launch Age Works in order to
meet the employment needs of the over-fifties. The agency
specializes in identifying skills and talents and finding a temporary, permanent or flexible job to suit the individual. There is
a large number of local offices in the UK offering local employment opportunities.

Success after Sixty
40–41 Old Bond Street, London W1X 3AF
    Tel. 071–629 0672
and 33 George Street, Croydon CR0 1LB
    Tel. 081–680 0858
An employment agency in the London area which helps people
over sixty to continue in active work if they do not want to
retire.

Age Endeavour (formerly the Employment Fellowship)
Willowthorpe, High Street, Stanstead Abbotts, Ware, Herts
SG12 8AS
   Tel. 0920 870158

The fellowship is a registered charitable organization. Current
activities include a programme aimed at providing visiting and
neighbourhood support for the housebound and less mobile
elderly, and Buretire, employment bureaux that set out to find
suitable paid and voluntary jobs, usually part-time or temporary, for fit and active retired people who would like to continue
to use those skills acquired during a lifetime of work. The
organization also offers many opportunities for the volunteer.

Women's Job Change
Birmingham Settlement, 318 Summer Lane, Newtown,
Birmingham B19 3RL
   Tel. 021–359 3562
The centre is funded by the Economic Development Unit. It
offers help and advice on job search, self-employment and
training, individual counselling and life and career planning.
Courses for non-waged women are completely free and on-site
child care is available.

Grey Matters
Prestage Street, Old Trafford, Manchester M16 9LH
   Tel. 061–226 6966
An agency operating nationwide which specializes in finding
executive, professional and clerical appointments for individu-
als over the age of forty-five.

London Careers Counselling Services

The following are details of some of the counselling services in
the London area. In local areas throughout the country, Job-
centres and Citizens Advice Bureaux Yellow Pages will give
advice free of charge; the Yellow Pages of the telephone directory provide another starting-point. The price for careers
advice and guidance offered by private organizations varies, as
indicated below; you may or may not consider it a worthwhile
investment.

The Careers Advisory Service
Education Guardian, 119 Farringdon Road, London
ECIR 3ER

Career Analysts
Career House, 90 Gloucester Place, London WIH 4BL
   Tel. 071–935 5452
Concerned with helping people of all ages discover the education, training and career opportunities best suited to their needs. Fees £250 plus VAT.

Careers for Women
4th Floor, 2 Valentine Place, London SEI 8QH
   Tel. 071–401 2280
Advice and information on careers and training. (About £50.)

Career Counselling Services
46 Ferry Road, London SWI3 9PW
   Tel. 081–741 0335
Help with career choice and preparation of curriculum vitae. The company aims to provide a flexible, comprehensive and personal service for clients. Fees £250 plus VAT.

Career Guidance Ltd
20 Bloomsbury Square, London WCIA 2NS
   Tel. 071–631 3149/1209
Provides advice on choice of careers for people of all ages. (Fee £205 inc. VAT.)

Centre for Professional Employment Counselling (CEPEC)
67 Jermyn Street, London SWIY 6NY
   Tel. 071–930 0322
For managers with work-related problems who are sponsored by their employer. Fees from about £500.

REACH (Retired Executives Action Clearing House)
89 Southwark Street, London SEI OHD
   Tel. 081–928 0452
Aims to promote the provision of voluntary assistance by retired executives to community groups, charities, etc.

Reading

Kenneth Lysons, *Earning Money in Retirement*, Age Concern
England, 1991

Carers

Carers National Association (Carers)
29 Chilworth Mews, London W2 3RG
Tel. 071–724 7776

This is a membership organization which aims to encourage
carers to recognize their own needs, to develop appropriate
support for carers, to provide information and advice and to
bring carers' needs to the attention of government and other
policy-makers. Members are sent a regular journal which
brings them up to date with information and keeps them in
touch with each other and the organization.

Care Alternatives
Head Office, 206 Worple Road, Wimbledon, London SW20 8PN
Tel. 081–946 8202

This is run by a team of professional people dedicated to
helping elderly or disabled people to stay in their own homes
as long as possible. Carers are happy to undertake domestic
tasks – shopping, cooking, etc., and provide companionship.
Arrangements can be made for full-time live-in help, overnight
care or care for short periods during the day. Professional
nursing staff are also available. The telephone line is almost
always open to deal with emergencies and the company is
usually able to supply staff at short notice. At the moment, the
team is confined to the London and south and west areas but
further afield one of the associated branches might be able to
help. Their service which includes the provision of escorts for
holidays or travel is available nationally. Rates are supplied on
request and advice given on how to apply for financial aid.

Reading

Jenny Pulling, *The Caring Trap*, Fontana, 1987. Information
for carers looking after elderly or disabled dependants.

Jill Pitkeathley, *It's My Duty Isn't It?*, Souvenir Press, 1989.
Ms. Pitkeathley is Director of the Carers' National Association.

Jenyth Worsley, *Taking Good Care – A Handbook for Care Assistants*, Age Concern England, 1990

Counselling

British Association for Counselling
1 Regent Place, Rugby, Warwickshire CV21 2PJ
Tel. 0788 587328
The association can put callers in touch with counselling organizations and individual counsellors throughout the country.

CoDA (Co-Dependents Anonymous UK)
PO Box 1292, London N4 2XX
Tel. 071–409 0029
A self-help group which works on the same lines as Alcoholics Anonymous. See also p. 301.

Northern Ireland Association for Counselling
Bryson House, 28 Bedford Street, Belfast BT2 7FE
Tel. 0232 32583

Relate
Herbert Gray College, Little Church Street, Rugby,
Warwickshire CV21 3AP
Tel. 0788 573241

East Region
46 Crowndale Road, London NW1 1TR
Tel. 071–380 1463

Midland Region
131/141 North Walls, Stafford ST16 3AD
Tel. 0785 42779
or Bishopsgate House, 5 Bishopsgate Street, Birmingham
B15 1ET
Tel. 021–643 1638

North-east Region
25 Micklegate, York YO1 1JH
  Tel. 0904 644916

North-west Region
93 Bewsey Street, Warrington, Cheshire WA3 7JQ
  Tel. 0925 572410

South Region
42 Holmesdale Road, Reigate, Surrey RH2 0BX
  Tel. 07372 21511

West Region
16 Clare Street, Bristol BS1 1XY
  Tel. 0272 214643

In 1988, the National Marriage Guidance Council changed its
name to Relate. The organization is committed to sustaining
family life by working with people of all ages and at all stages
of their marriage. It offers counselling in the workplace, counselling clients with relationship problems and offering marital
sexual therapy. Other services include work with the elderly,
step-parents, couples preparing for marriage, parents of teenagers and young mothers.

The Association for Sexual and Marital Therapy
Box 62, Sheffield 10

Forum for Occupational Counselling and Unemployment
Services Ltd (FOCUS)
Northside House, Mount Pleasant, Barnet, Herts EN4 9EB
  Tel. 081–441 9300
FOCUS was the first company in the United Kingdom to offer
counselling and advice services for unemployed men and women,
especially those whose lives have been interrupted and transformed by the problems of redundancy. These services have
now been extended under the organization's Employee Assistance Programme to help people with problems in the workplace, whether the difficulties are family- or work-related. (See
also p.24.)

Reading

Because many people find it embarrassing to order self-help books in shops and because many titles are difficult to obtain, Relate offer a book-sales service which lists up-to-date publications on: sex and sexual problems, marriage and relationships, divorce and remarriage, grief and bereavement, fertility, pregnancy, birth and adoption, depression, fears and phobias, stress and relaxation, children and teenagers, women's health and growing older.

Design for Independent Living

Keep Able
Fleming Close, Park Farm, Wellingborough, Northants
NN8 3UF
  Telephone advice line 0933 679426
Keep Able's designs enable people to maintain independence and help to promote greater comfort and safety in the home. Designs cover everything from specially fitted kitchens and bathrooms, motorized vehicles, garden tools and leisure ideas to gadgets which take into account different forms of handicap and solutions to the incontinence problem. A comprehensive catalogue is available free.

Keep Able Centre
Capital Interchange Way, Brentford, Middlesex TW8 0EX
  Tel. 081–742 2181
The centre displays rooms fitted out in a variety of ways to cope with individual needs. Their huge range of equipment can be demonstrated and tried out. Home demonstrations can be arranged. The centre is open on Monday to Friday, 9–5, and on Saturday, 10–4. Advice is on hand at all times, if required, as there are a number of professional therapists working in the centre, able to help visitors choose the correct products for each individual need.

Disabled Living Foundation (DLF)
See under Disability.

The Helen Hamlyn Foundation
1 Lower Wardown, Petersfield, Hants GU31 4NY
Aims to support elderly people in need of care within their own homes with the help of specially designed aids and with day centres where they can receive daily attention but return to the familiarity of their own homes at night.

Mobility International
228 Borough High Street, London SE1 1JX
  Tel. 071-403 5688
Aims to foster integration into mainstream society of disabled people through international exchange and travel.

Mobility Trust
4 Hughes Mews, 143a Chatham Road, London SW11 6HJ
  Tel. 071-924 3597
Aims to give practical support and information to disabled people about mobility aids. Runs seminars and day courses.

Reading

New Design for Old: Function, Style and Older People, Centre for Policy on Ageing, 1988

Diet

Weight Watchers UK Ltd
Kidwells Park House, Kidwells Park Drive, Maidenhead,
Berks SL6 8YT
  Tel. 0628 777077

Women's Nutritional Advisory Service
PO Box 268, Hove, E Sussex BN31 1RW
  Tel. 0273 771366
The service runs clinics in London and Sussex for health-conscious women interested in their diet. It is also an organization dedicated to the idea that diet can overcome problems of the menopause. A four-month postal course costs £86; for attendance at the clinic the charge is £50, with a £25 fee for subsequent visits.

Reading

Jonathan Brostoff and Linda Gamlin, *The Complete Guide to Food Allergy and Intolerance*, Bloomsbury, 1989

Louise Davies, *Easy Cooking for One or Two*, Penguin Books, 1979

Norman Parkinson and Lisa Ackerley, *Your Food*, Age Concern England, 1991

Eating Well on a Budget, Age Concern England, 1990

Rosemary Nicol, *The Irritable Bowel Diet Book*, Sheldon Press, 1990

Les Snowdon and Maggie Humphries, *The Walking Diet Book*, Mainstream Publishing, 1991

Earl Mindell, *The Vitamin Bible*, available from Alphavite Publications Ltd, 20 Potters Lane, Kiln Farm, Milton Keynes MK11 3HF

Disability

DIAL UK
The National Association of Disablement Information and Advice Services
Park Lodge, St Catherine's Hospital, Tickhill Road, Balby, Doncaster DN4 8QN
   Tel. 0302 310123
The national information and advice network on all aspects of disability. It acts as a forum for the network of over eighty Local Disabled Information and Advice Lines (DIALs) throughout the UK, providing support and information and representing DIALs at a national level.

Royal Association for Disability and Rehabilitation (RADAR)
25 Mortimer Street, London WIN 8AB
   Tel. 071–637 5400
RADAR is a key organization for people with disabilities. They offer advice and help on almost every aspect of disability and they publish *The Directory for Disabled People* (see below).

Disabled Living Foundation (DLF)
380–84 Harrow Road, London W9 2HU
  Tel. 071–289 6111
The DLF is a national charity providing practical, up-to-date advice and information on all aspects of living with disability for disabled people and their carers. Their services include a clothing and footwear advisory service, an incontinence advisory service, an equipment centre, a reference library and a wide range of publications.

Disability Alliance Educational Research Association
1st Floor East, Universal House, 88–94 Wentworth Street, London E1 7SA
  Tel. 071–247 8776 (general inquiries); 071–247 8763 (rights advice)
An umbrella organization concerned with the welfare of disabled people with a particular interest in the relationship between poverty and disability.
  The Disability Alliance Educational Research Association publishes the *Disability Rights Handbook*, a complete guide to rights, benefits and services for all people with disabilities.

Disability Scotland
Princes House, 5 Shandwick Place, Edinburgh EH2 4RG
  Tel: 031–229 8632
A voluntary organization offering help and advice to disabled people in Scotland.

Northern Ireland Council on Disability
2 Annadale Avenue, Belfast BT7 3JR
  Tel. 0232 491011
Practical help, information and advice to disabled people in Northern Ireland.

Wales Council for the Disabled
Information Service, Llys Ifor, Crescent Road, Caerphilly, Mid Glamorgan CF8 1XL
  Tel. 0222 887325
Help, information and advice to disabled people in Wales.

Greater London Association for Disabled People
36 Brixton Road, London SW9 7AA
  Tel. 071–274 0107

Disablement Income Group
Millmead Business Centre, Millmead Road, London N17 9QU
  Tel. 081–801 8013

Motability
Information Services Dept, Gate House, West Gate, Harlow,
Essex CM20 1HR
  Tel. 0279 635666

Reading

Out and About, Age Concern England, 1990. A comprehensive
    source of information on travel and transport for older
    people and others with limited mobility.

Ann Darnbrough and Derek Kinrade, eds., *Directory for Dis-
    abled People. A Handbook of Information and Opportunities
    for Disabled and Handicapped People*, 5th ed, Cambridge,
    Woodhead-Faulkner, in association with the Royal Associ-
    ation for Disability and Rehabilitation, 1988

J. A. Muir Gray and Heather McKenzie, *Caring for Older
    People*, Penguin Books, 1986

J. P. Wattis, *Confusion in Old Age*, Equation, in association
    with the British Medical Association, 1988

Disability Rights Handbook, from Disability Alliance (ERA),
    1st Floor, East Universal House, 88–94 Wentworth Street,
    London E1 7SA

*British Telecom Action for Disabled Customers: BT's Guide to
    Equipment and Services*, BT, 1991

Education/Training
See Chapter 5, Leisure and Working for Pleasure.

Emergency Alarm Systems and Home Security

Aid-Call plc
Emergency Medical Alarms, 363 Fulham Road, London
SW10 9TN
   Tel. 071–352 2822
This company is highly recommended and provides a service
whereby anyone living alone can call for help simply by press-
ing a button. However, it is just one of a number of firms which
install alarm systems and it is as well to remember that costs
vary as much as reliability. The Disabled Living Foundation
(380–84 Harrow Road, London W9 2HU; tel. 071–289 6111)
has a list of commercial firms supplying alarm systems and will
be able to provide further information.

Community Alarms
The Community Alarms Department, Help the Aged, St
James's Walk, London ECIR OBE
   Tel. 071–253 0253
It may be possible to receive a grant to meet the cost of
installing a system.

Master Locksmiths Association
Units 4–5 Woodford Halse Business Park, Great Central
Way, Woodford Halse, Daventry, Northants NN11 6PZ
   Tel. 0327 62255
Members are approved locksmiths.

The National Supervisory Council for Intruder Alarms
(NSCIA)
Queensgate House, 14 Cookham Road, Maidenhead, Berks
SL6 8AJ
   Tel. 0628 37512
Will send a list free of charge of approved contractors.

Reading

Sue Cook, *The Crimewatch Guide to Home Security*, BBC, 1988

Employment/Voluntary Work
See Chapter 5, Leisure and Working for Pleasure.

Finance
(See also Chapter 4, Finance)

Department of Social Security
Richmond House, 79 Whitehall, London SW1A 2NS
Tel. 071-210 3000
Midlands: Fiveways Tower, Frederick Road, Edgebaston,
Birmingham B15 1SL
Tel. 021-631 4141
Wales: Government Buildings, St Agnes Road, Gabalfu,
Cardiff
Tel. 0222 586000
Scotland and Northern England: 3 Lady Lawson Street,
Edinburgh EH3 9SH
Tel. 031-229 9191
Northern Ireland: Dundonald House, Upper Newtownards
Road, Belfast BT4 3SF
Tel. 0232 650111

Inland Revenue
Somerset House, Strand, London WC2R 1LB
Tel. 071-438 6622

Money Management Council
18 Doughty Street, London WC1N 2PL
Tel. 071-405 1985
Single copies of the following factsheets are available free from
the Money Management Council on receipt of a large (12 x 9
in.) stamped addressed envelope:
'You and Your Money' (outlines the basic principles and the
main possibilities involved in understanding and using your
money)
'All Change for Pensions' (on the 1988 pensions legislation)
'Don't Leave your Money to Chance' (about making a will)
'When Someone Dies' (the practical and money concerns of
bereavement)
'Who Will Give Me "Best Advice"?' (about independent
financial advice and the Financial Services Act)
'What to Do with That Lump Sum' (explains the things you
should consider when investing a lump sum)

IFA Promotion Ltd (Independent Financial Advice)
Head Office, 4th Floor, 28 Greville Street, London ECIN 8SU
 Tel. 071–831 4027
Offers a leaflet 'A Guide to Independent Financial Advice'
and will provide a list of professional advisers in your area who
are authorized to practise under the laws outlined by the
Financial Services Act.

Reading

The following Fact Sheets are available from Age Concern
England:
'Making Your Will' (No. 7), March 1991
'Building Society and Bank Deposit Account Interest' (No.
    14), April 1989
'Your State Pension and Carrying on Working' (No. 19), April
    1991'
'Legal Arrangements for Managing Financial Affairs' (No. 22)
'Raising Income or Capital from Your Home' (No. 12), July
    1991
'Income Tax and Older People' (No. 15), April 1991
'Income Related Benefits: Income and Capital' (No. 16), April
    1990
'National Insurance Contributions and Qualifying for a Pen-
    sion' (No. 20), April 1991
'The Community Charge (Poll Tax) and Older People' (No.
    21), April 1991

Financial Help

The following organizations can offer financial help in times of
need. Most of them are charities or charitable trusts and most
cater specifically for men and women who have had previous
connections with them. Contact the organization and find out
whether you meet their particular criteria, but before setting
out on what might be a disappointing round of telephone calls
and letter-writing, it might be worth contacting The Carers
National Association (29 Chilworth Mews, London W2 3RG;
tel; 071-724 7776) or Counsel and Care for the Elderly (Twyman
House, Lower Ground Floor, 16 Bonny Street, London NW1

9PG; tel. 071-485 1566) for advice and information in the first instance.

Association of Charity Officers
c/o The Royal Institute of Chartered Surveyors' Benevolent Fund, 1st Floor, Tavistock House, Tavistock Square, London WC1H 9RJ
   Tel. 071-387 0578
An association of two hundred benevolent bodies which will find a charity to top up fees for housing costs, provided they are not more than £245 a week.

Actors Benevolent Fund
13 Shorts Gardens, London WC2H 9DT
   Tel. 071-836 6378

Royal General Theatrical Fund
11 Garrick Street, London WC2E 9AR
   Tel. 071-836 3322

Distressed Gentlefolk's Aid Association
Vicarage Gate House, Vicarage Gate, London W8 4AQ
   Tel. 071-229 9341

Guild of Aid for Gentle People
10 St Christopher's Place, London W1M 6HY
   Tel. 071-935 0641

Independent Living Fund
PO Box 183, Nottingham NG8 3RD
   Tel. 0602 290 423

Invalids-at-Home Trust
Mrs Sarah Lomas, 17 Lapstone Gardens, Kenton, Harrow HA3 OEB
   Tel. 081-907 1706

The Officers Association
48 Pall Mall, London SW1Y 5JY
   Tel. 071-930 0125

Royal British Legion
48 Pall Mall, London SW1Y 5JY
  Tel. 071-930 8131

Royal Air Force Benevolent Fund
67 Portland Place, London W1N 4AR
  Tel. 071-580 8343

Soldiers', Sailors' and Airmen's Families Association (SSAFA)
19 Queen Elizabeth Street, London SE1 2LP
  Tel. 071-403 7873

The Royal Naval Benevolent Society (officers)
1 Fleet Street, London EC4Y 1BD
  Tel. 071-353 4080, ext. 471

Royal Naval Benevolent Trust (other ranks)
1 High Street, Brompton, Gillingham, Kent ME7 5QZ
  Tel. 0634 842743

Royal United Kingdom Beneficent Association (RUKBA)
6 Avonmore Road, London W14 8RL
  Tel. 071-602 6274

The Overseas Service Pensioners' Benevolent Society
63 Church Road, Hove, E Sussex BN3 2BD
  Tel. 0273 721630

The Royal Medical Benevolent Fund
24 Kings Road, London SW19 8QN
  Tel. 081-540 9194
This is a fund for medical graduates, their widows, wives, children or other dependants.

People who suffer from specific medical conditions (for example, Alzheimer's disease, Parkinson's disease, rheumatism, deafness, blindness) should contact the specialist organizations involved, preferably with the help of their general practitioner.

Reading

Sally West, *Your Rights: a Guide to Money Benefits for Older People*, Age Concern England, 1989

Luke Fitzherbert and Helene Bellofatto, *A Guide to Grants for Individuals in Need*, 2nd edition ed. by Mike and Nikki Eastwood, Directory of Social Change, 1990

Charities Digest, Family Welfare Association, 1990

Voluntary Organizations – an NCVO Directory (available through the National Council for Voluntary Organizations, 26 Bedford Square, London WC1; Tel. 071-636 4066)

John McQueen, *What to Do When Someone has Debt Problems*, Elliot Right Way (Paperfronts), 1985

Friendships

ARP Devon Companions
Borough Woods House, Shillingford, nr Bampton, Devon
EX16 9BL
    Tel. 03986 485
Social events for single members. (See also under Retirement.)

Saga
Saga Magazine Club, The Saga Building, Middelburg
Square, Freepost, Folkestone CT20 1AZ
    Tel. 0303 857 000
For an annual subscription of £9·90 to the Saga Club, members receive ten copies of the informative *Saga Magazine*, which also features a section for those who wish to advertise through the 'Penfriends and Partnerships' column; for members wanting to trace old friends the notices are free of charge.

Pen-Friends

See Chapter 5, Leisure and Working for Pleasure.

Introduction Agencies

There are now over a thousand introduction agencies operating throughout Britain. A few examples are listed below, together with those taking into account people with special needs.

Association of British Introduction Agencies
23 Abingdon Road, London W8 6AL
  Tel. 071-938 1011
Will provide a list of ABIA members.

Drawing Down the Moon
7-11 Kensington High Street, London W8 5NP
  Tel. 071-938 1721

Heather Jenner Marriage Bureau
124 New Bond Street, London WIY 9AE
  Tel. 071-629 9634

Dateline International Ltd
23 Abingdon Road, London W8 6AL
  Tel. 071-938 1011
Publishes *Singles Magazine*.

Plump Partners
15 Bryn y Foel, Rhosemore, nr Mold, Clwyd, N Wales
CH7 6PW
  Tel. 0352 780919

Helena International VIP Club
17 Hill Street, London WIX 7FB
  Tel. 071-409 2913

Disdate
56 Devizes Avenue, Bedford MK41 8QT
  Tel. 0234 340643
A service for the disabled and those interested in meeting disabled people.

Mammas'n Pappas
PO Box 113, London sw6
    Tel. 081-769 6805
An agency for single parents.

Compassionate Friends
5 Lower Clifton Hill, Clifton, Bristol bs8 1bt
    Tel. 0272 292778
Arranges friendly visits from people with similar problems.

Outsiders Club
PO Box 4ZB, London wia 4zb
    Tel. 071–837 3559
For those who feel that some physical or social handicap makes
it difficult for them to make friends and find someone to love.

Health

Centre for Health and Retirement Education
The Nodus Centre, University Campus, Guildford, Surrey
gu2 5rx
    Tel. 048–339 390

Health Education Authority
Hamilton House, Mabledon Place, London wcih 9tx
    Tel. 071–383 3833

Medical Advisory Service
10 Barley Mow Passage, Chiswick, London w4 4ph
    Tel. 081–994 9874
Telephone service, run by nurses, offering information and
advice on medical and health-care matters, putting people in
touch with the right organization. Hours 7 a.m. – 10 p.m.,
Monday to Friday.

Royal Society of Health
RSH House, 38a St George's Drive, London swiv 4bh
    Tel. 081–630 0121

Reading

Pat Blair and J.A. Muir Gray, *Your Health in Retirement*, Age Concern England, 1990

Pat Blair, *Know Your Medicines*, Age Concern England, 1985

Ruth Lever, *A Guide to Common Illnesses*, Penguin Books, 1990

Harvey and Marilyn Diamond, *Fit for Life – Living Health: The Complete Health Program*, Bantam Books, 1990

Anne Clover, *Homeopathy: A Patient's Guide*, Thorsons, 1984

Arthritis and Rheumatism

Arthritis and Rheumatism Council (ARC)
Copeman House, St Mary's Court, St Mary Gate,
Chesterfield, Derbyshire S41 7TD
  Tel. 0246 558033
ARC is a national charitable organization founded to raise money for research into the cause and cure of arthritis and rheumatism. Their aim is also to promote a better understanding of rheumatic disease. They offer a wide range of help and advice, including information, patient handbooks on specific diseases and information on drugs, exercise and diet.

Arthritis Care
6 Grosvenor Crescent, London SW1X 7ER
  Tel. 071–235 0902
Organizes self-help groups for arthritis sufferers.

Reading

Valerie Sayle and Ian Fraser, *Exercise Beats Arthritis*, Thorsons, 1987

Back Pain

National Back Pain Association
Grundy House, 31–3 Park Road, Teddington, Middlesex
TW11 0AB
  Tel. 081–977 5474

The Back Shop
24 New Cavendish Street, London WIM 7LH
  Tel. 071–935 9120
They sell a variety of products designed to help sufferers. A catalogue is available.

Reading

Sarah Key, *Back in Action*, Century, 1991

Cancer

The Breast Care and Mastectomy Association of Great Britain
15–19 Britten Street, London SW3 3TZ
  Tel. 071–867 8275 (office); 071–867 1103 (help line)
A non-medical information service, complementing medical and nursing care, for people who have undergone or are about to undergo breast surgery.

Cancer Relief Macmillan Fund
(registered as National Society for Cancer Relief)
Anchor House, 15–19 Britten Street, London SW3 3TY
  Tel. 071–351 7811
Provides care and support for cancer patients and their families. In addition to funding Macmillan Nursing Services and building the Macmillan Continuing Care Homes, Cancer Relief also gives financial help to patients in need. Inquiries to the Patient Grants Department at Anchor House.

BACUP (British Association of Cancer United Patients)
121–3 Charterhouse Street, London ECIM 6AA
  Tel. 071–608 1661 (Opening hours: 10 a.m. – 7 p.m.,
    Monday to Thursday, 10 a.m. – 5.30 p.m., Friday.)
A national information service which answers inquiries on all aspects of cancer for patients, relatives, health professionals and the general public.

CancerLink

17 Britannia Street, London WC1X 9JN
  Tel. 071–833 2451

Provides support and information on all aspects of cancer, in response to telephone calls and letters from people with cancer, their families and friends, and from professionals working with them. Acts as a resource to cancer-support and self-help groups, and helps people who are setting up new groups. Details of directories, booklets and other publications sent on request.

Colostomy Welfare Group

15 Station Road, Reading, Berkshire
  Tel. 0734 391537

Advisory and supportive service concerned with the rehabilitation of colostomy patients.

Cosmetic Surgery

Many of the latest techniques in plastic and cosmetic surgery emanate from the United States. There have been recent advances in breast reconstructive surgery but the training takes time and only a handful of surgeons are currently able to perform the the new breast reconstruction technique called flap surgery in which segments of fatty tissue from thighs or buttocks (which closely resembles the normal breast tissue) are transplanted to produce a more natural-looking breast. The American Society of Plastic and Reconstructive Surgeons, Washington DC, can provide useful information on the procedures available. Tel. (from the UK) 0101 202 842 4500

Reading

Joanna Gibbon, *The Independent Guide to Cosmetic Surgery*
  and *How to Find Cosmetic Surgeons in Britain*, The
  Independent (Send £3 cheque, made payable to News-
  paper Publishing plc, to Cosmetic Surgery Booklet Offer,
  Reader Services Dept, The Independent, 40 City Road,
  London EC1Y 2DB.)

Diabetes

British Diabetic Association
10 Queen Anne Street, London WIM OBD
  Tel. 071–323 1531 (Open during office hours.)
A charity offering help, support and advice on every aspect of diabetes. The association's head office will forward a free comprehensive information pack and supply the addresses of local associations.

Disability

See under separate heading.

Eye Care

See also pp. 184 and 277.

Royal National Institute for the Blind
224 Great Portland Street, London WIN 6AA
  Tel. 071–388 1266
The largest organization for blind and partially sighted people in the UK. It aims to improve the quality of life for visually impaired people through the provision of a wide range of services, goods, information and advice. Many of the services are available from: RNIB Customer Services, Royal National Institute for the Blind, Production and Distribution Centre, Bakewell Road, Orton Southgate, Peterborough PE2 OXU (tel. 0733 370777).

The Partially Sighted Society Sight Centre
Dean Clarke House, Southernhay East, Exeter EXI IPE
  Tel. 0392 210 656

British Wireless for the Blind
Gabriel House, 34 New Road, Chatham, Kent ME4 4QR
  Tel. 0634 832 501

In Touch
Broadcasting Support Services, PO Box 7, London W3 6XJ
   Tel. 071–927 4034
BBC Radio 4 programme for visually impaired people. Publishes the *In Touch Handbook* (see p. 277).

Sightline
   Tel. 0287 244442
A telephone counselling service for visually impaired people and their families. Operates between 7·30 p.m. and 10 p.m.

Guide Dogs for the Blind Association
Alexandra House, 9–11 Park Street, Windsor, Berkshire
SL4 1JR
   Tel. 0753 855711
Trains guide dogs and teaches blind people how to use them.

Foot Care

Society of Chiropodists
53 Welbeck Street, London WIM 7HE
   Tel. 071–486 3381
Members of this professional association are state-registered chiropodists. Their list will contain local names and they also offer a number of free leaflets on foot care.

The Podiatry Association
Secretary; Charles Schreiber, Swayes Cottage, Fore Street, Weston, nr Hitchin, Herts
   Tel. 046279 371

Reading

Judith Kemp, *The Footcare Book: An A – Z of Fitter Feet*, Age
   Concern England, 1988

Christopher Cloke, ed., *Voluntary Nailcutting and Footcare Schemes* (available from Age Concern England)

Hair Loss

Hairline International
39 St John's Close, Knowle, Solihull, W Midlands B39 0NN
   Tel. 0564 775281
A lay organization for alopecia sufferers. Elizabeth Steel
founded Hairline International when she suddenly lost her
hair in her thirties through alopecia areata. Hairline provides a
data base of information including new NHS treatments, and
gives a personal assessment of each member's case. The organization also links members with others in the same area and
sets up national meetings in the north and south of the UK. It
helps provide discounts on the purchase of wigs, both at stores
and by mail order; it has been granted a concession by a
leading eyelash manufacturer and can provide lashes at just
over half price.

National Institute of Trichologists
2–8 Stockwell Road, Brixton, London
   Tel. 071–733 2056
Will supply a list of their members nationwide.

Reading

Elizabeth Steel, *Coping with Sudden Hair Loss*, Thorsons

Health Services
See under separate heading.

Hearing

British Association for the Hard of Hearing
7–11 Armstrong Road, London W3 7JL
   Tel. 081–743 1110/1353

Royal National Institute for the Deaf
105 Gower Street, London WC1E 6AH
   Tel. 071–387 8033

The RNID is a voluntary organization concerned with all aspects of deafness. Services include: library, information and publications; residential care, rehabilitation and training for deaf people; telephone exchanges for deaf people; text users' help scheme; hearing tests and advice on hearing aids and other devices; training for professional workers and public service staff; self-help groups for tinnitus sufferers.

The RNID has set up a helpline for victims of tinnitus on 0345 090210 from 10 a.m. to 3 p.m and 6–8 p.m. on weekdays; all calls charged at local rates.

British Tinnitus Association
105 Gower Street, London WCI 6AH
 Tel. 071–387 8033

Reading

Robert M. Youngson, *How to Cope with Tinnitus and Hearing Loss*, Sheldon Press, 1986

Richard Hallam, *Living with Tinnitus*, Thorsons, 1989

Heart and Stroke

Coronary Prevention Group
102 Gloucester Place, London WIH 3DA
 Tel. 071–935 2889

British Heart Foundation
102 Gloucester Place, London WIH 4DH
 Tel. 071–935 0185

Chest, Heart and Stroke Association
123–7 Whitecross Street, London ECIY 8JJ
 Tel. 071–490 7999

Action Heart
Wellesley House, 117 Wellington Road, Dudley,
W Midlands DY1 1UB
  Tel. 0384 230222

Action Heart is a registered charity which provides rehabilitation services following a heart attack. Their rehabilitation exercise programme is held at Russells Hall Hospital, in Dudley.
Individual care and attention is given to each patient and their
family, who receive regular advice and counselling on topics
relating to coronary heart disease.

Reading

'Healthier Eating and Your Heart' (free from the Coronary
    Prevention Group, see above)

Tom Smith, *Heart Attacks – Prevent and Survive*, Sheldon
    Press, 1990

D. J. Thomas, *Strokes and Their Prevention*, British Medical
    Association, 1988

Hormone Replacement Therapy
See under Menopause.

Incontinence

The Incontinence Advisory Service
Disabled Living Foundation, 380–84 Harrow Road, London
W9 2HU
  Tel. 071–289 6111

Disabled Living Centres
Listed in the telephone directory. Advice on managing incontinence.

Reading

'Help with Incontinence' (Fact Sheet No. 23), Age Concern
    England

R. J. Millard, *Overcoming Urinary Incontinence: A Simple Self-help Guide*, Thorsons, 1987

G. Stokes, *Incontinence and Inappropriate Urinating*, Winslow Press, Bicester, Oxon, 1987 (Common Problems with the Elderly Confused Series)

'Incontinence. You Can Do Something about It' (available free from Nicholas Laboratories Ltd, Health Care Division, 225 Bath Road, Slough, Middlesex SL1 4AU)

'Regaining Bladder Control' (available free from Coloplast Foundation, Peterborough Business Park, Cambs PE2 OFX)

'Is Laughing not a Laughing Matter?' (available free from Medical Assist Ltd, Commerce Way, Colchester, Essex CO2 8HH)

R. C. L. Fenely and J. P. Blannin, *Incontinence*, Longman, 1984 (Churchill Livingstone Patient Handbook No. 18)

Dorothy Mandelstam, *Understanding Incontinence*, Chapman & Hall, 1988. An explanation of incontinence and what to do about it.

Penny Mares, *In Control – Help with Incontinence*, Age Concern England, 1990

Keep Fit

Keep Fit Association
16 Upper Woburn Place, London WC1H OQG
    Tel. 071–387 4349
Teachers are specially trained to work with older people.

Reading

Laura Mitchell, *The Magic of Movement*, Age Concern England, 1990. A book for those who are finding everyday activities more difficult. It includes gentle exercises to tone up muscles and ideas to make you more independent and avoid boredom.

Menopause

The following list of menopause clinics, while it provides a useful guide, is not complete. Other sources include, in the first instance, the general practitioner, the gynaecology department of your local hospital and the well-woman clinic or family planning clinics. NHS clinics will require a letter from your GP. Some private insurance schemes – BUPA and PPP – will pay for private treatment but will also require a letter of referral.

National Health Service

Beckenham Hospital
379 Croydon Road
Beckenham Kent BR3 3OL
  Tel. 081–650 0125

Women's Hospital
Queen Elizabeth Medical
  Centre
Birmingham B15 23TG
  Tel. 021–472 1377

Birmingham and Midland
  Hospital for Women
Showall Green Lane
Sparkhill
Birmingham B11
  Tel. 021–772 1101

Family Planning Clinic
Morley Street
Brighton
E Sussex BN2 2RA
  Tel. 0273 693600

Dryburn Hospital
North Road
Durham DH1 5TW
  Tel. 091–386 4911

Gynaecology OPD
Royal Infirmary
Lauriston Place
Edinburgh EH3 9YW
  Tel. 031–229 2477

Queen Elizabeth Hospital
Gateshead
Tyne and Wear
  Tel. 091–487 8989

Glasgow Royal Infirmary
Castle Street
Glasgow G4 0SF
  Tel. 041–552 3535

Stobhill Hospital
Balornock Road
Glasgow G21
  Tel. 041–558 0111

Airedale General Hospital
Streeton
Keighley
W Yorkshire BD20 6TD
  Tel. 0535 52511, ext. 442

Clarendon Wing
Leeds General Infirmary
Belmont Grove
Leeds LS2 9NS
  Tel. 0532 432799, ext.
  3886

Royal Liverpool Hospital
Prescott Street
Liverpool L7 8XP
  Tel. 051-709 0141

St George's Hospital
Blackshaw Road
London SW17
  Tel. 081-672 1255, ext.
  55960/1

PMT and Menopause Clinic
The London Hospital
Whitechapel
London E1 1BB
  Tel. 071-377 7000, ext.
  2030

Dept of Obstetrics and
    Gynaecology
Guy's Hospital
St Thomas Street
London SE1
  Tel. 071-407 7600, ext.
  2690

Gynaecology Outpatient
    Dept
St Thomas' Hospital
Lambeth Palace Road
London SE1
  Tel. 071-928 9292, ext.
  2533

Royal Free Hospital
Pond Street
London NW3 2Q9
  Tel. 071-794 0500, ext.
  3858

Menopause Clinic
Queen Charlotte's Hospital
Goldhawk Road
Chiswick
London W6 0X6
  Tel. 081-748 4666

Samaritan Hospital for
    Women
Marylebone Road
London W1
  Tel. 071-402 4211

Queen Mary's Hospital
Roehampton Lane
Roehampton
London SW15 5PN
  Tel. 081-789 6611

Outpatients Dept
Montagu Hospital
Adwick Road
Mexborough
S Yorkshire
  Tel. 0709 585171, ext. 219

Dept of Medicine
Newcastle General Hospital
Westgate Road
Newcastle upon Tyne NE4
  6BE
  Tel. 091-273 8811, ext.
  22675

Gynaecology Outpatient
Department
George Elliot Hospital
College Street
Nuneaton
Warwickshire
Tel. 0203 384201

Oldham and District General
Hospital
Rochdale Road
Oldham
Lancs
Tel. 061–624 0420

John Radcliffe Hospital
The Anderson Clinic
Headington
Oxford OX2 6HE
Tel. 0865 64711, ext 7795

The Ella Gordon Centre
East Wing
St Mary's Hospital
Portsmouth
Tel. 0705 866301

Northern General Hospital
Gynaecology Department
Herries Road
Sheffield
Tel. 0742 232323

Stafford District General
Hospital
Weston Road
Stafford
Tel. 0786 57731

Charges are made by the following clinics

Fairfield's Clinic
Fairfield Road
Basingstoke
Hants RG21 3DR
Tel. 0256 26980

Richmond Hill Clinic
25 Denmark Street
Bristol BS1 5SQ
Tel. 0272 292183

IFPA
5–7 Cathal Brugha Street
Dublin 1
Tel. 0001 727363/727276

Dublin Well Woman Centre
73 (Lower) Leeson Street
Dublin 2
Tel. 0001 610083/610086

Queensway Health Centre
Hatfield
Herts
Tel. 07072 64577

The Wycombe Clinic
6 Harlow Road
High Wycombe
Bucks HP13 6AA
Tel. 0494 26666

Family Planning Association
13a Western Road
Hove
E Sussex
   Tel. 0273 774075

Marie Stopes Clinic
108 Whitfield Street
London W1
   Tel. 071–388 0662/2585

BUPA Screening Unit for
   Women
BUPA Medical Centre
Battle Bridge House
300 Grays Inn Road
London WC1X 8DU
   Tel. 071–837 6484, ext.
   2304

The Amarant Trust
Churchill Clinic
80 Lambeth Road
London SE1 7PW
   Tel. 071–928 5633

Family Planning Association
17 North Church Street
Sheffield S1 2HH
   Tel. 0742 721191

Slough Family Planning
   Clinic
Osborne Street
Slough
   Tel. 0753 26875

Family Planning Clinic
21 Dudley Road
Tunbridge Wells
Kent TN1 1LE
   Tel. 0892 30002

Health Centre
Bowling Green Road
Ware
Herts
   Tel. 0920 2388

Menopause: Hormone Replacement Therapy

The Amarant Trust
Head Office: 80 Lambeth Road, London SE1 7PW
   Tel. 071–401 3855

Telephone Information Lines: These lines have been devised
and recorded by specialists from King's College Hospital,
London. All proceeds go towards further research into the
menopause and HRT. Calls are charged at 25p a minute off
peak and 38p peak.

Ring 0836 400, plus any of the following:

   190 Introduction and description of other lines
   191 HRT – what is it and is it safe?

192 When should I start and how long should I stay on it?
193 Is it for everyone? (Contraindications)
194 What are the possible side-effects?
195 How do I take it?
196 Where can I get it?
197 What checks and tests do I need before and while taking it?
198 What can it do for me? Short-term benefits
199 Osteoporosis and long-term benefits explained

Reading

Malcolm Whitehead and Teresa Gorman, *The Amarant Book of Hormone Replacement Therapy*, Pan Books, 1989

Barbara Evans, *Life Change*, Pan Books, 1988

Wendy Cooper, *No Change*, Arrow Books, 1983

Lilia Nachtigall, *Oestrogen*, Arlington Books, 1988

Mental Health
See under separate heading.

Osteoporosis

The National Osteoporosis Society
Barton Meade House, PO Box 10, Radstock, Bath BA3 3YB
    Tel. 0761 432472
The society is an independent organization working to raise awareness of the problem of osteoporosis and to persuade government and the medical professions to improve prevention and treatment. Membership is £5 and includes free publications. To non-members, the following publications are available for £1 each:

What Every Woman Needs to Know about Osteoporosis and Hormone Replacement Therapy (HRT)
What Every Sufferer Needs to Know about Osteoporosis: How to Cope!
What Everyone Needs to Know about Osteoporosis
The New Approach to Osteoporosis: A Guide for General Practitioners.

Physical Pain

The addresses below are in the London area but, thanks in great part to the work of the hospice movement, much more research is now being carried out into the cause and relief of severe, intractable pain. Specialist treatment for pain may be available at a hospital or hospice in your area; your GP should be able to give you information on what is available locally.

The Pain Clinic
212 Kilburn High Road, London NW6
   Tel. 071–328 9161
This is a private clinic; the fees are £20 per consultation.

Guy's Hospital
St Thomas's Street, London SE1
   Tel. 071–955 5000
A pain clinic is held once a week (National Health Service).

Sexual Problems
See separate entry.

Teeth

Unless your income is low enough so that you would be entitled to receive income support, dentistry, whether private or on the NHS, is never free – although the latter is still considerably cheaper.

British Dental Health Foundation
Eastlands Court, St Peter's Road, Rugby, Warwickshire CV21 3QP
   Tel. 0788 546 365
Offers advice to personal inquirers and publishes a range of leaflets including: 'Dental Care for Elderly People', 'Diet', 'Oral Hygiene', 'Partial Dentures and Bridges' and 'Dentures and Cosmetic Dentistry'.

Denplan Ltd
Kings Court, The Broadway, Winchester, Hampshire SO23 9BE
    Tel. 0962 866662
The company offers an insurance scheme whereby a sum of
money is paid each month which entitles the insured to check-
ups and treatment when required.

Reading

'Dental Care in Retirement', Age Concern England (Fact Sheet
    No. 5, June 1991)

Health Services

National Health Service

M. Rigge, ed., *College of Health Guide to Hospital Waiting
Lists, 1991*, College of Health Publications, 1991 (available
from the College of Health, St Margaret's House, 21 Old Ford
Road, London E2 9PL). The *Guide* is intended to help patients
find shorter waits for non-urgent operations. It sets out the
number of patients waiting in the four main surgical specialities
in each district and what proportion have been waiting for over
a year. Where delays are long, there is nearly always another
district in the same region where all or most patients are
admitted within a year.

Martin Page, *The Good Doctor Guide*, Sphere, 1989. The
Guide lists five hundred 'Harley Street' specialists, most of
whom work in NHS hospitals, who have been recommended
by colleagues who believe they are the best in their field.

Private Sector

SPS (Medical Insurance Consultants)
Bradley House, 59 Maple Road, Surbiton, Surrey KT6 4AW
    Tel. 081–390 6777
Free service which includes an initial cost comparison and
recommendation, together with an ongoing service which looks
after annual renewals and helps with claims procedures if necessary.

Private Patients Plan Ltd
PPP House, 20 Upperton Road, Eastbourne, E Sussex
BN21 1BR
 Tel. 0323 410505

PPP New Cavendish Medical Centre
99 New Cavendish Street, London WIM 7FQ
 Tel. 071–637 8941
For information concerning annual check-ups and 'Wellness'
programmes. They will supply addresses of other centres
around the country.

The British United Provident Association Ltd (BUPA)
Provident House, Essex Street, London WC2R 3AX
 Tel. 071–353 5212

Budget BUPA Centre
Freepost, Staines TW18 1BR

BUPA Medicall
The association has recently launched a twenty-four-hour telephone helpline operating 365 days a year. It is a comprehensive family health-information service which gives up-to-date
information on seven hundred different topics covering a wide
range of illnesses and problems from AIDS and ulcers to
insect bites and travel preparations. Topical medical issues are
dealt with on the Medicall Hotlines; for example, food poison-
ing, nurofen and kidney damage and embryo research. To get
a copy of the BUPA Medicall Directory call the twenty-four-
hour answerphone service (071–971 0022) or your local BUPA
office. For further information call the BUPA Editor (071–
975 9000 between 9 a.m. and 5.30 p.m.)
(N.B. The addresses given above are the company head offices.
The local telephone directory will indicate whether there is an
office in your area.)

Holidays
See Chapter 5.

Housing

There are now so many housing options designed to suit the needs of older people that the picture can be somewhat confusing. The different headings below are followed by a description of the kind of housing involved, together with names and addresses of contacts. The lists are by no means conclusive and serve the reader only as a starting-point for further investigations. It is absolutely essential that any option is carefully followed up to the minutest detail. Costs, value, comfort, care and personal requirements vary enormously and no new 'home' should be entered into without the closest prior observation, either by the client concerned or, if for reasons of disability that is not possible, then by individual family members or carers. Remember that *private* housing for elderly residents is big business these days. Learn to be at least as cynical as the business men and women behind the ventures!

Residential Care (Residential and Nursing-Home Accommodation)

(a) Local authority residential-care homes (Part III homes)
Part III homes are run by the Social Services Department of the local authority. They are allocated through social workers or the Social Services Department.

(b) Private residential homes
Private residential homes are run for profit by private organizations and individual proprietors.

(c) Voluntary residential homes
These are non-profit-making and run by registered charities and religious organizations, sometimes for groups of people who must meet specific criteria.

National Care Homes Association
5 Bloomsbury Place, London WC1A 2QA
   Tel. 071–436 1871
Offers advice on private and voluntary residential care and nursing homes.

Carematch
286 Camden Road, London N7 0BJ
  Tel. 071–609 9966
Carematch is a computer service for physically disabled people seeking residential care.

Caresearch
162–4 Upper Richmond Road, Putney, London SW15 2SL
  Tel. 081–780 9596
This is a nationwide computer service for mentally handicapped people seeking residential care.

Grace Link
Upper Chambers, 7 Derby Street, Leek, Staffordshire
ST13 6HN
  Tel. 0345 023300
A flat fee of £23 is charged for this comprehensive advisory service for people seeking private residential or nursing-home accommodation.

Registered Nursing Homes Association
Calthorpe House, Hagley Road, Edgbaston, Birmingham
B16 8QY
  Tel. 021–454 2511
Provides information on registered nursing homes in the UK and the Republic of Ireland.

British Federation of Care Home Proprietors
852 Melton Road, Thurmaston, Leicestershire LE4 8BN
  Tel. 0533 640095
An organization of individual care home owners. The federation's qualifying monitoring system is operated in accordance with its own national guidelines.

Reading

Pat Young, *A Home in a Home*, Age Concern England
A practical guide to moving into residential accommodation.

Registered Nursing Home Association Reference Book, annual (available from the Registered Nursing Homes Association, 75 Portland Place, London WIN 4AN; tel. 071–631 1524). Gives details of nursing homes throughout the country.

Registered Nursing Homes, Clinics and Hospitals in the UK, Registered Nursing Homes Association, annual (available c/o Sunbury Nursing Home, Thames Street, Sunbury-on-Thames TW16 6AJ; tel. 0932 765444). Entries in blue indicate members of the association, approved by them and the Department of Health; entries in black indicate non-members which have been approved by the Department of Health. Edmund White, the book's coordinator, says members are of a much higher standard than non-members.

The Which? Guide to Choosing a Residential Care Home (available from the College of Health, Castlemead, Gascoyne Way, Hertford SG14 1LH; tel. 0992 598031). Six checklists to help you come to a decision.

Croner's Care Homes Guide: A Directory of Residential, Nursing and Sheltered Accommodation for the Elderly and Infirm, 2 vols., *North and Midlands* and *South*, Croner, 1987. Does not include Scotland, Wales or Northern Ireland. Recommended by Help the Aged.

Care Guide 88, Laing and Buisson Publications, 1988. Eleven volumes, each covering a different area of the UK.

Age Concern England publishes the following Fact Sheets:
'Finding Residential and Nursing Home Accommodation' (No. 29), April 1991
'Local Authorities and Residential Care' (No. 10), August 1990
'Housing Schemes for Older People Where a Capital Sum is Required' (No. 24), July 1990
'Income Support for Residential and Nursing Homes' (No. 11), December 1990

Sheltered Accommodation

The types of sheltered accommodation vary enormously from fairly independent, self-contained flats to 'very sheltered' or 'extra-care' accommodation. The main feature of this kind of housing is that it is usually overseen by a resident warden whose job it is to take care of the welfare of the residents. There are also built-in emergency alarm systems. The 'very sheltered' accommodation has a higher level of support, which may include meals, twenty-four-hour warden cover and domestic help.

Sheltered Accommodation may be rented or purchased; it may be owned by the council, a housing association or a private developer.

(a) Contacts for Local Authority Sheltered Housing

Social Services Department; Housing Department; Department of Social Security; Citizens Advice Bureau; Community Health Council; Age Concern.

(b) Contacts for Housing Associations

Housing associations operate in different ways (a description of one of the Abbeyfields Society houses, for example, can be found in Chapter 3) but many provide rented accommodation for older people.

The Housing Corporation
Main office: 149 Tottenham Court Road, London WIP OBW
   Tel. 071–387 9466
Has the power to fund, supervise and control registered housing associations. For regional office addresses, contact the main office.

Abbeyfield Society
186–92 Darkes Lanes, Potters Bar, Herts EN6 IAB
   Tel. 0707 44845

Anchor Housing Association
Anchor House, 269a Banbury Road, Oxford OX23 7HU
   Tel. 0865 311511

Baptist Housing Association
1 Merchant Street, Bow, London E3 4LY
   Tel. 071–281 9724

Beth Johnson Housing Association
Three Counties House, Vestible Way, Stoke-on-Trent ST1 5PX
   Tel. 0782 219 200

Bradford and Northern Housing Association
Butterfield House, Otley Road, Baildon, Shipley BD17 7HF
   Tel. 0274 588840

English Churches Housing Group
Central House, 32–66 Stratford High Street, London E15 2PD
   Tel. 081–203 9233 (head office); 081–519 4028

Collingwood Housing Association
1 Outram House, Piccadilly Village, Great Ancoats Street,
Manchester M4 7AA
   Tel. 061–274 4744

Coventry Churches Housing Association
Highfield House, St Nicholas Street, Coventry CV1 4BN
   Tel. 0203 552767

Derwent Housing Society
Phoenix Street, Derby DE1 2ER
   Tel. 0332 46477

Downland Housing Society
Downland House, 51 Fishbourne Road, Chichester,
W Sussex PO19 3HZ
   Tel. 0243 533133

Guinness Trust
4 Corporation Street, High Wycombe, Bucks HP13 6TH
   Tel. 0494 535 823

Hanover Housing Association
18 The Avenue, Egham, Surrey TW20 9AB
  Tel. 0784 438361

Humanist Housing Association
311 Kentish Town Road, London NW5 2TJ
  Tel. 071–485 8776

James Butcher Housing Association
James Butcher House, 39 High Street, Theale, Reading
RG7 5AH
  Tel. 0734 323434

Jephson Housing Association
Jephson House, 1 Blackdown, Leamington Spa CV32 6RE
  Tel. 0926 339311

Manchester and District Housing Association
Apex House, 266 Mosley Road, Levenshulme, Manchester
M19 2LH
  Tel. 061–224 1814

Merseyside Improved Houses
46 Wavertree Road, Liverpool L7 1PH
  Tel. 051–709 9375

North British Housing Association
4 The Pavilion, Portway, Preston
  Tel. 0772 824441

Northern Counties Housing Association
Princes Buildings, 15 Oxford Court, Oxford St, Manchester
M2 3WQ
  Tel. 061–228 3388

North Housing
Ridley House, Regent Centre, Gosforth, Newcastle upon
Tyne NE3 3JE
  Tel. 091–285 0311

Raglan Housing Association
Wright House, 12–14 Castle Street, Poole, Dorset BH15 1BQ
  Tel. 0202 678731

Royal British Legion Housing Association
PO Box 32, Unit 2, St John's Industrial Estate, St John's
Road, Penn, High Wycombe, Bucks HP10 8JF
   Tel. 0494 813771

Servite Houses
125 Old Brompton Road, London SW7 3RP
   Tel. 071–370 5466

Sutton Housing Trust
Sutton Court, Tring, Herts HP23 5BB
   Tel. 0442 891100

WRVS Housing Association
Refuge House, 64–6 Stuart Street, Luton, Beds LU1 2SW
   Tel. 0582 429398

Warden Housing Association
Park House, 69–77 Park Way, Ruislip Manor, Middlesex
HA4 8NS
   Tel. 0895 676161

(c) Contacts for Purchasing Sheltered Accommodation

New Homes Marketing Board
82 New Cavendish Street, London W1M 8AD
   Tel. 071–580 5588
Has a list of developers building sheltered housing.

Sheltered Housing Services Ltd
8–9 Abbey Parade, London W5 1EE
   Tel. 081–997 9313
Estate agents who, for a small fee, can give details of sheltered
housing schemes in areas throughout the country.

(d) Sheltered Housing for Members of the Asian Community

ASRA Greater London Housing Association
155 Kennington Park Road, London SE11 4JJ
   Tel. 071–820 0155

ASRA Leicester
58 Earl Howe Street, Highfield, Leicester LEI ODF
   Tel. 0533 558121

(*e*) *Almshouses*

The Almshouse Association
Billingbear Lodge, Wokingham, Berks RGII 5RU
   Tel. 0344 52922
A charitable organization which offers sheltered accommodation in various parts of the country to people on low incomes. Most residents tend to come from the local catchment area but exceptions are made.

(*f*) *Salvation Army Homes*

The Salvation Army Social Services Headquarters
105–9 Judd Street, King's Cross, London WCIH 9NN
   Tel. 071–383 4230
Provides sheltered accommodation for men and women who can no longer live independently.

Reading

A Buyer's Guide to Sheltered Housing, Age Concern England, 1989

'The NHBC Sheltered Housing Code of Practice' (available from the National House Building Council, 58 Portland Place, London WIN 4BU)

Croner's Care Homes Guide
See under Residential Care above.

Age Concern England publishes the following Fact Sheets:
'Sheltered Housing for Sale' (No. 2), April 1990
'Housing Schemes for Older People Where a Capital Sum is Required' (No. 24), July 1990.

General

The following organizations will be able to help with general inquiries:

Elderly Accommodation Council
46a Chiswick High Road, London W4 1SZ
  Tel. 071–995 8320
This is a charity which provides lists of all forms of private and voluntary accommodation for older people. For a fee of £5 (those on low incomes are exempt), the client will receive a computer printout describing the facilities of all accommodation available in the desired area.

Counsel and Care for the Elderly
Twyman House, 16 Bonny Street, London NW1 9LR
  Tel. 071–485 1566
Provides free general advice but will also give information on private and voluntary accommodation for older people nationwide. This voluntary body also visits every nursing and residential home in the Greater London area once a year and gives a frank opinion on what it finds. Clients are advised on what is available and their rights, and can be put in touch with the right charity in order to top up the cost of the home.

Help the Aged Housing Division.
Head Office, St James' Walk, London EC1R OBE
  Tel. 071–253 0253

Royal Association for Disability and Rehabilitation (RADAR)
25 Mortimer Street, London W1N 8AB
  Tel. 071–637 5400
For advice on housing for the disabled.

Royal Institute of British Architects (RIBA)
66 Portland Place, London W1N 4AD
  Tel. 071–580 5533

Royal Institute of Chartered Surveyors (RICS)
12 Great George Street, London SWIP 3AD
   Tel. 071–222 7000

Royal Society for the Prevention of Accidents (ROSPA)
Cannon House, The Priory Queensway, Birmingham B4 6BS
   Tel. 021–200 2461

*Standing Conference of Ethnic Minority Senior Citizens
(SCEMSC)*
5–5a Westminster Bridge Road, London SE1 7XW
   Tel. 071–928 0095

Special-needs housing in Wales
Contact the Housing Aid Centre through the local authority
Housing Department; telephone number in the local direc-
tory.

Local Social Services Department
The Registration Officer, Residential Care, of the Social Services Department of your local authority will provide a list of
homes in the area and may give unbiased information.

Reading

David Bookbinder, *Housing Options for Older People*, Age
   Concern England, new ed., 1988

Cecil Hinton, *Using Your Home as Capital*, Age Concern
   England, 1991

Christine Orton, *Sharing your Home*, Age Concern England

The College of Health Guide to Homes for Elderly People,
   Victoria Park Publications, 1984 (available from the Col-
   lege of Health, Castlemead, Gascoyne Way, Hertford,
   SG14 1LH; Tel. 0992 598031)
Mentions some commercial home-finding agencies.

Age Concern England also publishes the following Fact
   Sheets:

'Rented Accommodation for Older People' (No. 8), December
    1989
'Finding Help in the Home' (No. 6), June 1990
'Rented Accommodation for Older People in Greater London'
    (No. 9), December 1989

The Law and Legal Aid

Citizens Advice Bureaux
(address in local library or telephone directory)
    CABx will be able to supply the leaflet 'The Legal Aid
Guide', which describes conditions of entitlement.

The Law Society
113 Chancery Lane, London WC2A 1PL
    Tel. 071–242 1222

The Law Society of Scotland
The Law Society's Hall, 26–8 Drumsheugh Gardens,
Edinburgh EH3 7YR
    Tel. 031–226 7411

The Law Society of Northern Ireland
Law Society House, 98 Victoria Street, Belfast BT1 3JZ
    Tel. 0232 231614

Legal Aid Head Office
5th/6th Floor, 29–31 Red Lion Street, London WC1R 4PP
    Tel. 071–831 4209
Advice and information on all aspects of Legal Aid, including
terms of eligibility. Written inquiries should be addressed to
the Chief Executive.

Law Centres Federation
Duchess House, 18–19 Warren Street, London W1P 5DB
    Tel. 071–387 8570
There may be a Neighbourhood or Community Law Centre in
your area; if not the Law Centres Federation will advise you of
your rights and put you in touch with a solicitor.

Lawline
  Tel. 0898 600 600
Recorded tapes give information about the more common legal problems such as divorce and making a will.

For complaints

The Solicitors Complaints Bureau
Portland House, Stag Place, Victoria, London SWIE 5BL
  Tel. 071–834 2288

Legal Services Ombudsman
(can be contacted through the local Citizens Advice Bureau or the Law Society)
  In Scotland and Northern Ireland, complaints should be directed to the respective Law Societies.

Reading

'Legal Arrangements for Managing Financial Affairs' (Fact
    Sheet No. 22), Age Concern England, October 1990
Sally Greengross, ed., 'The Law and Vulnerable Elderly
    People', Age Concern England, 1986
'Probate-Dealing with Someone's Estate' (Fact Sheet No. 14),
    Age Concern England, September 1991

Leisure
See Chapter 5, Leisure and Working for Pleasure.

Mental Health – Peace of Mind

The Samaritans
Head office (also for voluntary work): 10 The Grove, Slough
SLI IQP
  Tel. 0753 532713
Almost all *branches* can be telephoned twenty-four hours a day, every day of the year, and can be visited any day or evening. The local telephone number is in the telephone directory. If no directory is available, dial 100 and ask the operator for the Samaritans. There is also a branch for correspondence only: PO Box 9, Stirling.

Mind (National Association for Mental Health)
22 Harley Street, London WIN 2ED
Tel. 071–637 0741 (advisory service open 2–4 p.m.
weekdays)
Leading mental-health organization in England and Wales,
with comprehensive information service. Telephone advisory
service is not a counselling service but a guide towards finding
the appropriate kind of help. For details of the nearest local
association, contact the regional office. For a list of publications, send s.a.e. to Mind Mail Order (PI) at South-east Mind
office (see below).

Addresses of the regional offices are as follows:

North-west Mind
21 Ribblesdale Place, Preston PRI 3NA
Tel. 0772 21734

Northern Mind
158 Durham Road, Gateshead, Tyne and Wear NE8 4EL
Tel. 091–4900 109

South-east Mind
Fourth Floor, 24–32 Stephenson Way, London NWI 2HD
Tel. 071–380 1253

South-west Mind
9th Floor, Tower House, Fairfax Street, Bristol BSI 3BN
Tel. 0272 250 960

Trent and Yorkshire Mind
First Floor Suite, The White Building, Fitzalan Square,
Sheffield SI 2AY
Tel. 0742 721 742

Wales Mind
23 St Mary Street, Cardiff CFI 2AA
Tel. 0222 395123

West Midlands Mind
Third Floor, Princess Chambers, 52–4 Lichfield Street,
Wolverhampton WVI IDG
Tel. 0902 24404

Mental Health Association of Ireland
6 Adelaide Street, Dun Laoghaire, Co. Dublin
  Tel. 010–3531 2841166

Mental Welfare Commission for Scotland
25 Drumsheugh Gardens, Edinburgh EH3 7BB
  Tel. 031–225 7034
Helps people who because of mental disorder may be unable to
help or protect themselves.

Scottish Association for Mental Health
Atlantic House, 38 Gardiners Crescent, Edinburgh EH3 8DQ
  Tel. 031–229 9687

Link
Glasgow Association for Mental Health, 2 Queen's Crescent,
Glasgow G4 9BW
  Tel. 041–951 2429
The centre offers advice and practical support for sufferers
and relatives through sheltered group living accommodation, a
network of clubs which are run by people who have had
mental illnesses, and a range of specialized self-help groups,
including tranquillizer withdrawal and relaxation classes.

Northern Ireland Association for Mental Health
Beacon House, 84 University Street, Belfast BT7 1HE
  Tel. 0232 439945
The association provides help and support including day care,
residential care, advice and information services, and education
and public awareness programmes. They have thirty-two organizations throughout Northern Ireland and they also arrange
self-help groups for a variety of problems.

Alzheimer's Disease Society
158–60 Balham High Road, London SW12
  Tel. 081–675 6557
The primary aim of the society is to help the families of
dementia sufferers. This is done through a network of local
branches, support groups and contacts, all of whom have

personal or professional experience. The society also helps with legal, social or family matters and any counselling needed. A Caring Fund has been established which can offer financial assistance.

The Richmond Fellowship for Mental Welfare and Rehabilitation
8 Addison Road, Kensington, London W14 8DL
  Tel. 071–603 6373
The fellowship runs 'halfway houses' built on the lines of therapeutic communities for individuals who are emotionally disturbed or who have had a mental breakdown.

The Parkinson's Disease Society
22 Upper Woburn Place, London WC1H 0RA
  Tel. 071–383 3513

Reading

Michael A. Weiner, *Reducing the Risk of Alzheimer's*, Bath, Gateway Books, 1991

Chris Lay and Bob Woods, *Caring for the Person with Dementia: A Guide for Families and Other Carers*, 2nd ed. revised by J. Brown, Alzheimer's Disease Society, 1989 (available from the society – address above)

Harvey Sagar, *Parkinson's Disease*, Optima, 1991

Depressions

Depressives Anonymous
36 Chestnut Avenue, Beverley, North Humberside HU17 9QU
  Tel. 0482 860619
A self-help organization with groups in various parts of the country. It offers a newsletter, a pen-friend scheme and open meetings.

Depressives Associated
PO Box 5, Castletown, Portland, Dorset DT5 1BQ
Supports self-help groups and works to promote a better understanding of depression and the problems associated with it.

The SAD (Seasonal Affective Disorder) Association
51 Bracewell Road, London W10 6AF
A self-help organization for SAD sufferers and their relations.

Phobias

Agoraphobia Information Service
4 Manorbrook, Blackheath, London SE3 9AW
   Tel. 081-318 5026
An information service is provided through a weekly telephone
newsletter and an information pack. S.a.e required.

Phobics Society
4 Chiltenham Road, Chorlton-cum-Hardy, Manchester
M21 1QN
   Tel. 061-881 1937
Provides help, information, advice and social contact for people
with agoraphobia and other phobic conditions.

Action on Phobias Association
6 Grange Street, Kilmarnock, Scotland
   Tel. 0357 22274
The association has a network of twenty-six self-help groups
throughout Scotland. Leaflets and booklets can be supplied
and training can take place at home. Weekend workshops are
also organized.

Sexual Problems
See separate entry.

Stress

Continuing stress unrelieved by comfort and support from
other people can contribute to mental ill health. Listed below
are organizations offering support to those under stress,
whether from a particular crisis such as bereavement or family
problems, or any underlying source of stress.

The Stress Clinic
The University College and Middlesex School of Medicine,
Middlesex Hospital, Mortimer Street, London W1
Offers help to anyone suffering from the effects of stress.
Unlike most hospital departments, the Stress Clinic will take
self-referrals.

Cruse
See under Bereavement and Death.

OPUS (Organizations for Parents under Stress)
Natalie Long, Tinley Garth, Kirbymoorside, N Yorkshire
Umbrella organization for various groups that help parents
under stress. Will advise on help available locally.

Family Network Helpline
c/o National Children's Home, 85 Highbury Park, London
N5 1UD
   Tel: 071–226 2033
A network of helplines throughout the country offering support
for family stress.

Portia Trust
Workspace, Maryport, Cumbria CI5 8NF
   Tel. 090 081 2114
Helps those in trouble with the law through stress and depres-
sion (Midlands and northern England).

Stress – Ways to Relax

Stress Care
7 Park Crescent, London WIN 3HE
   Tel. 071–631 0156
A specialist organization in the field of stress management and
prevention. Offers companies comprehensive, tailor-made programmes to help deal with stress within their work-forces.

The Floatarium
21 Bond Street, Brighton, Sussex BNI IRD
   Tel. 0273 679555.
The Floatarium is run by Emma Read and Anabelle Rankin.
The former is a psychotherapist and hypnotherapist. Some
people have found an almost miraculous answer to their problems of stress floating in a dark enclosed tank of blood tempera-
ture and a dense Epsom salts solution. An hour's float costs £16.

Transcendental Meditation
24 Linhope Street, London NWI 6HT
   Tel. 071–402 3451
or Freepost, London SWIP 4YY
   Tel. (free of charge) 0800 269303
An alternative means of coping with stress, Transcendental
Meditation is a simple technique which is easily learned and is
usually practised daily for about twenty minutes in the morning
and twenty minutes in the evening, sitting comfortably with
the eyes closed. Courses of instruction are held regularly
throughout the UK and Ireland.

Reading

Consumers' Association, *Understanding Mental Health*,
   Hodder & Stoughton, 1986
   Discusses what is known about the causes and treatments
   of a variety of mental illnesses and disorders and emotional
   problems. It offers practical information on living with
   mental illness as a patient or as a relative, and notes the
   different provisions in Scotland and Northern Ireland.

Joy Melville, *First Aid in Mental Health*, Unwin Publications,
   1984
   Written in conjunction with Mind, it looks at the experience of mental illness from the point of view of both
   patients and relatives, and provides details of help available
   and patients' rights. There are chapters on schizophrenia,
   anxiety and stress, depression, postnatal depression, anorexia and the elderly mentally infirm.

Paul Bebbington and Liz Kuipers, *Living with Mental Illness: A Book for Relatives and Friends*, Souvenir Press, 1987 (Human Horizon Series)
Written mainly for the relatives of those who have suffered mental illness, it offers an insight into their experiences and how to cope.

Val Marriott and Terry Timblick, *Loneliness – How to Overcome it*, Age Concern England

Tony Lake, *Defeating Depression*, Penguin Books, 1987

Ellen Mohn Catalano, *Getting to Sleep: Simple Effective Methods for Falling and Staying Asleep, Getting the Rest You Need and Awakening Refreshed and Renewed*, Oakland, CA, New Harbinger Publications Inc., 1990

Claire Weekes, *More Help for Your Nerves*, Angus & Robertson, 1984
Recovery from nervous suffering through understanding nervous fatigue.

Richard G. Abell and Corliss Wilbur, *Own Your Own Life*, Bantam, 1977
Describes the process by which people can change and enhance their lives.

Anthony Storr, *The Integrity of Personality*, Penguin Books, 1960

Tony Lake, *Relationships*, Michael Joseph, 1981

Money
See under Finance.

Relationships

Marriage

Relate – National Marriage Guidance
Hubert Gray College, Little Church Street, Rugby, Warwickshire CV21 3AP
   Tel. 0788 573241

Tavistock Institute of Marital Studies
The Tavistock Centre, 120 Belsize Lane, London NW3 5BA
   Tel. 071-435 7111

Women's Aid Federation
   Tel. 0272 428 368
For women suffering from violence.

Family

Parents Anonymous Helpline
9 Manor Gardens, Holloway Road, London N7 6LA
   Tel. 071-263 8918

The Family Rights Group
6–9 Manor Gardens, Holloway Road, London N7

Grandparents

Grandparents Federation
78 Cook's Spinney, Harlow, Essex CM20 3BC
Information and advice concerning grandchildren and grandchildren in care.

Reading

Jill Manthorpe and Celia Atherton, *Grandparents' Rights*, Age
   Concern England and the Family Rights Group, 1989

Stepfamily

National StepFamily Association
(Elizabeth Hodder), Ross Street Community Centre,
Cambridge CB1 3BS

Retirement

See also Chapter 1, Retirement and the Rewards of Early
Planning; Chapter 4, Finance; and Chapter 5, Leisure and
Working for Pleasure.

Planning

Pre-Retirement Association of Great Britain and Northern Ireland (PRA)
Nodus Centre, University Campus, Guildford, Surrey GU2 5RX
 Tel. 0483 39323
The PRA is the national association for retirement counselling. Its Retirement Preparation Service runs courses for firms and individuals.

Scottish Retirement Council
Alexandra House, 204 Bath Street, Glasgow G2 4HL
 Tel. 041–332 9427
Runs retirement courses in various parts of Scotland.

Centre for Health and Retirement Education
26 Russell Square, London WC1B 5DQ
 Tel. 071–636 8000
Developing health education to combat the impact of retirement and redundancy.

General

The Association of Retired Persons (ARP/050)
Parnell House, Wilton Road, Victoria, London SW1V 1LW
 Tel. 071–895 8880
The ARP, recently merged with the 050 Club, is a membership association for those over the age of fifty 'who believe in improving the opportunities and lifestyle for pre- and post-retired people in the UK'. The American equivalent, AARP, has become a powerful political lobby in the US, working to change society's attitude towards the retired.

Members' benefits: one year's subscription to *Retirement Planning and Living Magazine*; free helplines (see below); free lump sum cover of £1,000 with no upper age limit, if you sustain bodily injury requiring medical treatment following a reported assault or mugging; a free automatic income of £30 per day, to spend as you choose, if you are hospitalized for more than twenty-four hours following an accident – available to you as part of membership, regardless of age, for up to 100 days; free admission to the Retirex Exhibitions and ARP/o50 Centres around Britain. Invitations to local and national ARP/o50 events.

Special services and discounts include:

Age Works – a nationwide employment agency specializing in helping to find temporary, flexible and permanent employment opportunities for the over-fifties;

ARP/o50 Companions Club for single members – a forum for meeting other members with similar interests; friendship centres nationwide

special discounts on Avis Car Rentals;

special discount offers from the ARP/o50 Travel Club;

special discounts on National Breakdown car rescue service;

a 15 percent discount on health care from Private Patients Plan;

a specialized banking service provided exclusively for members by the Bank of Scotland;

individual insurance and investment services developed for members by the Commercial Union.

ARP domestic and legal helplines (available twenty-four hours a day, 365 days a year):

THE DOMESTIC HELPLINE (0206 863123) will locate, agree charges and, with your consent, call out a contractor. Advice is given on a wide range of topics from securing the home before going on holiday to what can be done to prevent burst pipes.

THE LEGAL HELPLINE will give advice which will be confirmed in writing: (English law) 0206 867775; (Scottish law) 041–332 2887.

THE ACTION HELPLINE (0272 253254, office hours): information given on travel, finance, health, support groups and consumer concerns.

Reading

Some recommended general books on the subject of ageing and retirement:

Loving, Living and Ageing, Age Concern England

Keith Hughes, *Making the Most of Your Retirement*, Kogan Page in association with Legal and General, 1989

Rosemary Brown, ed., *The Good Retirement Guide*, Bloomsbury

Helen Franks, ed., *What Every Woman Should Know About Retirement*, Age Concern England

Renee Myers, *A Guide to Good Living in Retirement*, Crowood Press, 1990

Saga publish a series of Retirement Guides, including *Health*, *Money*, *Rights*, *Food*, *Leisure* and *Property*.

Sexual Problems

Albany Trust
24 Chester Square, London SW1W 9HS
    Tel. 071–730 5871
Helps people, especially members of sexual minorities, who have psycho-sexual worries.

Association of Sexual and Marital Therapists
PO Box 62, Sheffield

Sexual and Personal Relationships of the Disabled (SPOD)
286 Camden Road, London N7 0BJ
    Tel. 071–607 8851

Institute of Psycho-sexual Medicine
11 Chandos Street, Cavendish Square, London W1M 9DE

Notes

1. Dr Anthony Clare, 'Blueprint for a Serene Maturity', *Sunday Times*, 22 May 1988.
2. D. B. Bromley, *Human Ageing*, 3rd ed., London, Penguin Books, 1988, p. 30.
3. Gail Sheehy, *Pathfinders*, New York, Bantam Books, 1981.
4. Central Statistical Office, *Social Trends*, 20, London, HMSO, 1990.
5. Bernice Neugarten, ed., *Middle Age and Ageing*, Chicago, Chicago University Press, 1968.
6. Central Statistical Office, *Social Trends*, op. cit.
7. Lawrence M. Brammer, Patricia A. Nolen and Margaret F. Pratt, *Joys and Challenges of Middle Age*, Chicago, Nelson-Hall Inc., 1982, pp. 20–22.
8. Erik Erikson, *Childhood and Society*, New York, W.W. Norton, 1950, p. 232.
9. Joyce Brothers, *What Every Woman Should Know about Men*, New York, Simon & Schuster Inc., 1982; London, Granada, 1982, pp. 55–6.
10. Alex Comfort, *A Good Age*, London, Mitchell Beazley, 1977, p. 183.
11. Joseph and Jean Britton, *Personality Changes in Ageing*, New York, Springer Publishing Co. Inc., 1972, p. 167.
12. Mintel, *The Lifestyle of the Over 50s*, London, Mintel Publications, 1989, p. S. 18.
13. ibid., p. S. 8.
14. Mintel, *Women 2000*, London, Mintel Publications, 1988.
15. Carl Gustav Jung, *The Portable Jung*, ed. Joseph Campbell, New York, Viking, 1971, p. 19.
16. Mintel, *Women 2000*, op. cit.
17. E.L. Kelly and J.J. Conley, 'Personality and Compatibility: a Prospective Analysis of Marital Stability and Marital Satisfaction', *Journal of Personality and Social Psychology*, 52 (1987), pp. 27–40.

18. Brothers, op. cit., p. 56.
19. ibid., p. 94.
20. Jung, op. cit., pp. 19–20 (extract from *The Stages of Life*).
21. Brothers, op. cit., p. 74.
22. Shere Hite, *The Hite Report on Male Sexuality*, London, Macdonald Futura, 1981, p. 142.
23. Central Statistical Office, *Social Trends*, op. cit.
24. Central Statistical Office, *Population Trends*, 55, London, HMSO.
25. David Cole Gordon, *Overcoming the Fear of Death*, New York, Macmillan, 1970, pp. 20, 17.
26. Mintel, *The Lifestyle of the Over 50s*, op. cit., p. S. 9.
27. Gail Sheehy, *Passages*, New York, Dutton, 1976, p. 343.
28. Peter O'Connor, *Understanding the Mid-life Crisis*, South Melbourne, Australia, Sun Books, 1981, pp. 50–51.
29. Mintel, *The Lifestyle of the Over-50s*, op. cit., p. S. 9.
30. ibid., p. S. 19.
31. Gillian Douglas and Nigel Lowe, 'The Grandparent–Grandchild Relationship in English Law', paper presented at the Grandparents' Forum, Divorce Conciliation and Advisory Service, London, 2 March 1989.
32. Mintel, *The Lifestyle of the Over-50s*, op. cit.
33. Erik Erikson, Joan M. Erikson and Helen Q. Kivnick, *Vital Involvement in Old Age*, New York, Norton, 1986.
34. Brian Deer, 'Glad to be Grey', *Sunday Times*, 22 May 1988.
35. Peggy Wakehurst, *In a Lifetime Full*, 1989.
36. Martin Tolchin, *The New York Times*, 19 June 1989.
37. Jung, op. cit., p. 19 (extract from *The Stages of Life*).
38. 'Family Money-go-round', *Daily Telegraph*, 21 September 1986.
39. Department of Health, 'Working for Patients: the Health Service. Caring for the 1990s' (HSR1), HMSO, 1989.
40. *Independent*, 21 February 1989.
41. D.G. Zaridze and R. Peto, eds., *Tobacco: a Major International Health Hazard* (IARC Publications, no. 74), Lyon, International Agency for Research on Cancer, 1986.
42. Richard Peto, 'Influence of Dose and Duration of Smoking on Lung Cancer', in ibid.
43. *Nursing Times*, vol. 84, no. 8 (24 February 1988), p. 52.
44. Brian L. Mishara and Robert Kastenbaum, *Alcohol and Old Age* (Seminars in Psychiatry), New York, Grune & Stratton, 1980, pp. 163–73.
45. Deborah L. Sherouse, *Professional's Handbook on Geriatric Alcoholism*, Springfield, Illinois, Charles C. Thomas, 1983, p. 27.

46. 'Identifying and Measuring Alcohol Abuse among the Elderly: Serious Problems with Existing Instrumentation', *Journal of Studies on Alcohol*, vol. 47 (1986), pp. 322–6.

47. Alcohol Concern, *Alcohol and other People: Safer Drinking for the Over 60s*, p. 5.

48. 'Early Detection of the Problem Drinker', *Psychiatry in Practice*, vol. 8, no. 1 (spring 1989), p. 7.

49. Walter R. Frontera, Carol N. Meredith, Kevin P. O'Reilly, Howard G. Knuttgen and William J. Evans, *Strength Conditioning in Older Men: Skeletal Muscle Hypertrophy and Improved Function*, American Physiological Society, 1988.

50. Dr Michael Hosking *et al.*, *Journal of the American Medical Association*, April 1989.

51. Brian S. Katcher, *Prescription Drugs: An Indispensable Guide for People over Fifty*, New York, Macmillan (Atheneum), 1988.

52. Morris Notelovitz and Marsha Ware, *Stand Tall! The Informed Woman's Guide to Preventing Osteoporosis*, Gainesville, Florida, Triad, 1982; New York, Bantam, 1985, pp. 65–6 (Bantam edition published under the title *Stand Tall! Every Woman's Guide to Preventing Osteoporosis*).

53. *Sunday Times*, 22 May 1988.

54. Peter Laslett, *A Fresh Map of Life: The Emergence of the Third Age*, Weidenfeld & Nicolson, 1989, pp. 19–20, 165.

55. Alex Comfort, 'Course in Psychosexual Medicine', lecture at the RPMS Institute of Obstetrics and Gynaecology, University of London, 16–17 October 1989.

56. ibid.

57. 'The ARP Sex Survey', *Retirement Planning and Living* 6 (spring 1990), p. 12.

58. *The New York Times*, 4 August 1989.

59. K.G. Manton and B.J. Soldo, 'Dynamics of Health Changes in the Oldest Old: New Perspectives and Evidence', *Millbank Memorial Fund Quarterly*, 63 (1985), pp. 206–85.

60. Richard Lamerton, *Care of the Dying*, Penguin Books, 1980, pp. 184–5.

61. ibid., p. 186.

62. Colin Parkes, *Bereavement: Studies of Grief in Adult Life*, 2nd ed., Penguin Books, 1986.

63. Susan O. Mercer, *Elder Suicide: A National Survey of Prevention and Intervention Programs*, Washington DC, American Association of Retired Persons, 1989.

64. Dr Christopher C.H. Cook, in *British Medical Journal*, 88 (1988), pp. 735–48, 796.

Index of Associations and Organizations

FOR THE BEST IN PAPERBACKS, LOOK FOR THE 🐧

In every corner of the world, on every subject under the sun, Penguin represents quality and variety – the very best in publishing today.

For complete information about books available from Penguin – including Puffins, Penguin Classics and Arkana – and how to order them, write to us at the appropriate address below. Please note that for copyright reasons the selection of books varies from country to country.

In the United Kingdom: Please write to *Dept E.P., Penguin Books Ltd, Harmondsworth, Middlesex, UB7 0DA.*

If you have any difficulty in obtaining a title, please send your order with the correct money, plus ten per cent for postage and packaging, to *PO Box No 11, West Drayton, Middlesex*

In the United States: Please write to *Dept BA, Penguin, 299 Murray Hill Parkway, East Rutherford, New Jersey 07073*

In Canada: Please write to *Penguin Books Canada Ltd, 2801 John Street, Markham, Ontario L3R 1B4*

In Australia: Please write to the *Marketing Department, Penguin Books Australia Ltd, P.O. Box 257, Ringwood, Victoria 3134*

In New Zealand: Please write to the *Marketing Department, Penguin Books (NZ) Ltd, Private Bag, Takapuna, Auckland 9*

In India: Please write to *Penguin Overseas Ltd, 706 Eros Apartments, 56 Nehru Place, New Delhi, 110019*

In the Netherlands: Please write to *Penguin Books Netherlands B.V., Postbus 3507, 1001 AH, Amsterdam*

In West Germany: Please write to *Penguin Books Ltd, Friedrichstrasse 10–12, D–6000 Frankfurt/Main 1*

In Spain: Please write to *Alhambra Longman S.A., Fernandez de la Hoz 9, E–28010 Madrid*

In Italy: Please write to *Penguin Italia s.r.l., Via Como 4, I-20096 Pioltello (Milano)*

In France: Please write to *Penguin Books Ltd, 39 Rue de Montmorency, F-75003 Paris*

In Japan: Please write to *Longman Penguin Japan Co Ltd, Yamaguchi Building, 2–12–9 Kanda Jimbocho, Chiyoda-Ku, Tokyo 101*